Energy and the Environment: Interactions

Volume I
Perspectives on Energy and the Environment
Part A

Editors

Louis Theodore, Eng. Sc.D.
Professor
Department of Chemical Engineering
Manhattan College
Bronx, New York

Anthony J. Buonicore, M.Ch.E.
Vice President
York Research Corporation
Stamford, Connecticut

Consulting Editor

Edmund J. Rolinski, Ph.D.
Materials Research Engineer, Group Leader
Electromagnetic Materials Division
Air Force Materials Laboratory
Wright-Patterson Air Force Base
Dayton, Ohio

CRC Press, Inc.
Boca Raton, Florida

Library of Congress Cataloging in Publication Data

Main entry under title:

Perspectives on energy and the environment.

    (Uniscience series on energy and the environment, interactions; v. 1)
    Bibliography: p.
    Includes index.
    1. Energy development—Environmental aspects.
I. Theodore, Louis. II. Buonicore, Anthony J.
III. Rolinski, Edmund J. IV. Series.
TD195.E49P47   333.7   79-14412
ISBN 0-8493-5562-1 (v. 1)
ISBN 0-8493-5563-X (v. 2)

Direct all inquiries to CRC Press, 2000 N.W. 24th Street, Boca Raton, Florida, 33431.

© 1980 by CRC Press, Inc.

International Standard Book Number 0-8493-5562-1 (Part A)
International Standard Book Number 0-8493-5563-X (Part B)

Library of Congress Card Number 79-14412
Printed in the United States

PREFACE TO THE SERIES

Energy is the keystone of American life and prosperity. It is also a vital component of environmental rehabilitation. The problem is whether reasonable energy demands can be met without significantly harming the environment. Adequate energy supplies and a satisfactory living environment are national goals of overriding importance to every American. It is neither fair nor appropriate to describe the energy-environmental conflict as a battle. Who can argue with the major thesis of each side?

There is no question that the environment must be protected and the quality of life improved. At the same time, however, economic stability must be maintained. Conflicts that occur between energy and environmental interests do not stem from differences on these two basic positions. Rather, they spring from a zealous pursuit of change by one group and a normal resistance by the other. Recent developments provide persuasive evidence that these two objectives, in all their many ramifications, will rank high on our list of national priorities and be prime determinants of our domestic and foreign policies for many years to come.

The expenditure of energy in any form must reflect a careful assessment of the total environmental impact. Inevitably the use of energy damages the environment — not only when it is used but also when it is extracted, processed, transported, and distributed to the consumer. The apparent conflict between energy needs and environmental goals poses a problem that can only be solved by understanding the factors that influence energy demands and by developing energy systems that meet these demands with minimal damage to the environment.

It is the intent of this series to provide sufficient information to permit assessment and evaluation of those spheres of interaction between energy systems and environmental concerns.

Louis Theodore
Anthony J. Buonicore

PREFACE TO VOLUME I

The present energy situation is now and will remain a problem of critical magnitude on the national scene. A direct consequence of the continually increasing demands for more energy, the energy situation has caused two issues to become pervasive concerns of the entire nation. One is the adequate, reliable supply of all forms of energy, and the other, the growing public concern with the environmental and socio-economic ramifications of its production and use.

The expenditure of energy in any form must reflect a careful assessment of the total environmental impact. No one can deny that the energy and environmental spheres interact constantly. Any negligence involved in planning for one can seriously affect the other. Energy use does damage the environment — not only when it is used, but also when it is extracted, processed, transported, and distributed. As energy use continues to multiply, so also does the attendant impact on the total environment. The conflict between energy needs and the environment poses a problem that must be solved by understanding the factors that influence the demands for energy and by developing and concentrating on those energy systems that can meet these demands with minimal damage to the environment.

The purpose of this volume, *Perspectives on Energy and the Environment,* is to examine the environmental impact of conventional and nonconventional energy systems.

The editors are indebted to Daniel Duprey for his contribution to this volume.

Louis Theodore
Anthony J. Buonicore

THE EDITORS

Louis Theodore is presently Professor and Director of the Graduate Program in Chemical Engineering at Manhattan College. He received a B.Ch.E. degree from The Cooper Union, New York, New York, in 1955. The degrees of M.Ch.E. and Eng.Sc.D. were obtained from New York University in 1957 and 1964, respectively.

Dr. Theodore joined the faculty at Manhattan College with the rank of Instructor in the fall of 1960. In 1963 he was appointed Director of the Chemical Engineering Laboratory. In 1964 he was appointed Director of Computer Utilization in the Chemical Engineering Department. He has taught courses in Transport Phenomena, Kinetics, Statistics, Mathematics for Chemical Engineers, and Air Pollution and Its Control, served as a lecturer in Transport Phenomena for industry and education here and abroad, and has presented invited lectures and seminars in the air pollution control area. He has consulted for several industrial companies in the field of pollution control and energy related matters, supervised NSF environmental projects, and serves as a consultant to both the DOE and EPA. In addition to his academic and consulting activities, Dr. Theodore has published nearly fifty technical papers and over a dozen text and reference books.

Early in 1967, the Ford Foundation awarded Dr. Theodore a Residency in Engineering Practice for the 1967—68 year. He accepted a position with the Mobile Research & Development Corporation and worked for the Process Simulation Group of the Computer Methods and Control Section, developing and solving mathematical models to simulate and improve the performance of existing refinery process units.

Dr. Theodore received a sabbatical for the 1973—74 academic year. He accepted a position (half-time) with the Air Pollution Training Institute of the Environmental Protection Agency. Part of Dr. Theodore's responsibilities include active participation in the Institute's courses "Control of Gaseous Emissions" and "Control of Particulate Emissions". It was during this period that Dr. Theodore helped organize what is now the National Conference on Energy and the Environment.

Dr. Theodore is a member of Tau Beta Pi, Phi Lambda Upsilon, Sigma Xi, American Chemical Society, American Society for Engineering Education, Royal Hellenic Society, Air Pollution Control Association (APCA), and the New York Academy of Sciences. He is also a member of the IAABO (International Association of Approved Basketball Officials) and is certified to referee scholastic basketball games.

Anthony J. Buonicore received his B.Ch.E. and M.Ch.E. from Manhattan College in New York, specializing in environmental engineering. He is presently Vice President of York Research Corporation, a leading environmental-energy consulting engineering firm headquatered in Stamford, Conneticut. Previously he worked as a Project Manager for Entoleter, Inc., a major environmental control firm specializing in the engineering, design, and fabrication of pollution control equipment. Prior to his work at Entoleter, Mr. Buonicore held the positions of Principal Environmental Engineer in the Office for Environmental Protection of the Civil Engineering Center at Wright-Patterson Air Force Base and Process Design/Environmental Engineer with Stauffer Chemical Company's Eastern Research and Development Center in Dobbs Ferry, New York. Mr. Buonicore is a licensed professional engineer in the states of Ohio and Connecticut and a Diplomate in the American Academy of Environmental Engineers.

Mr. Buonicore has also been a member of the faculty of the Engineering and Science Institute of Dayton and the Department of Chemical Engineering at Manhattan College. He has frequently been an invited guest lecturer on energy and environmental topics for both industrial and governmental institutions, including the Air Force Institute of Technology, the National Science Foundation, the National Bureau of Standards, and the U.S. Environmental Protection Agency.

Mr. Buonicore is listed in *Who's Who of Scientists and Engineers* and is an active member of the American Institute of Chemical Engineers and Air Pollution Control Association, where he chairs the Basic Science and Technology Division. He has also been instrumental in organizing and promoting the AIChE/APCA sponsored annual conference on Energy and the Environment and acted as its first General Chairman. His other affiliations include Tau Beta Pi, Sigma Xi, the American Society for Testing Materials, and the Ad Hoc Committee for Resource Recovery.

DEDICATION

TO

Aunt Pridder
my favorite sister
and Uncle Tony

AND

Margit Carleen
who has helped make life so worth living

CONTRIBUTORS

James Abert, Ph.D.
Vice President for Research and
  Development
National Center for Resource Recovery,
  Inc.
Washington, D.C.

K. P. Ananth, Ph.D.
Associate Director
Environmental and Materials Sciences
  Division
Midwest Research Institute
Kansas City, Missouri

Wilfrid Bach, Ph.D.
Professor, Director of the Center for
  Applied Climatology and
  Environmental Studies and the
  Department of Geography
University of Muenster
Muenster, West Germany

Anthony J. Buonicore, M.Ch.E.
Vice President
York Research Corporation
Stamford, Connecticut

John P. Fanaritis, B.S.
Executive Vice President
Struthers Wells Corporation
Warren, Pennsylvania

Paul S. Farber, P.E.
Energy and Environmental Systems
  Division
Argonne National Laboratory
Argonne, Illinois

Robert E. Hillman, Ph.D.
Research Leader
William F. Clapp Labs, Inc.
Battelle-Columbus Labs
Duxbury, Massachusetts

Julian W. Jones, M.S.
Chemical Engineer
Emissions/Effluent Technology Branch
Utilities & Industrial Power Division
Industrial Environmental Research
  Laboratory-RTP
Research Triangle Park,
North Carolina

Charles L. Kusik, D.Sc.
Senior Staff Member
Arthur D. Little, Inc.
Cambridge, Massachusetts

Edward P. Lynch, B.S.
Chemical Engineer
Special Projects Group
Argonne National Laboratory
Energy and Environmental Systems
  Division
Argonne, Illinois

Raymond P. Morgan, II, Ph.D.
Principal Research Scientist
William F. Clapp Labs, Inc.
Battelle-Columbus Labs
Duxbury, Massachusetts

Michael C. Osborne, M.S.
Environmental Engineer
Emissions/Effluent Technology Branch
Utilities & Industrial Power Division
Industrial Environmental Research
  Laboratory-RTP
Research Triangle Park,
North Carolina

Frank T. Princiotta, B.Ch.E.
Director of Energy Processes Division
ORD/Office of Energy, Minerals and
  Industry
Environmental Protection Agency
Washington, D.C.

Roger K. Raufer, M.S.
Manager
Environmental Studies
ETA Engineering, Inc.
Westmont, Illinois

Edmund J. Rolinski, Ph.D.
Materials Research Engineer, Group
  Leader
Electromagnetic Materials Division
Air Force Materials Laboratory
Wright-Patterson Air Force Base
Dayton, Ohio

Larry J. Shannon, Ph.D.
Division Director, Environmental and
  Materials Sciences Division
Midwest Research Institute
Kansas City, Missouri

Thomas T. Shen, Ph.D.
Senior Research Scientist
New York State Department of
  Environmental Conservation
Albany, New York

James I. Stevens, M.Ch.E.
Management Staff Associate
Arthur D. Little, Inc.
Cambridge, Massachusetts

Louis Theodore, Eng. Sc.D.
Professor
Department of Chemical Engineering
Manhattan College
Bronx, New York

John J. Yates, M.S.
Manager
Energy Systems and Economic Analysis
  Section
ETA Engineering, Inc.
Westmont, Illinois

TABLE OF CONTENTS

Part A

Part B

Chapter 1

ENERGY AND THE ENVIRONMENT IN PERSPECTIVE

A. J. Buonicore and L. Theodore

TABLE OF CONTENTS

I. INTRODUCTION

Energy is the keystone of American life and prosperity as well as a vital component of environmental rehabilitation. The environment must be protected and the quality of life improved but, at the same time, economic stability must also be maintained. These two objectives will be prime factors in determining domestic and foreign policies for years to come.

Energy consumption is a major contributor to environmental pollution; thus, decisions regarding energy policy alternatives require comprehensive environmental analysis. Environmental impact data must be developed for all aspects of an energy system and/or programs and must not be limited to its separate components.

II. ENVIRONMENTAL IMPACTS OF VARIOUS ENERGY SYSTEMS

The major environmental impacts of various energy systems are summarized in Tables 1 through 3.[1-3] Additional details are given below, with more comprehensive analyses presented in subsequent chapters.

A. Coal

The nation's coal reserves are vast and are estimated to range from 500 billion to more than 1 trillion tons.[4] Coal is mined either by surface or underground methods. About 3,200,000 acres of land have been disturbed by surface mining. Of this total, about 41% results from coal production. Although the total land area directly disturbed by surface mining amounts to only a few tenths of 1% nationally, the effects are often severe in local areas. Surface mining often leads to acid drainage and silt runoff which degrade water quality. Strip mining can result in serious erosion if adequate plant cover is not available to hold the soil, especially when water is permitted to run off the site from roads and slopes. Erosion causes deposits of sediment in channels, thus reducing the capacity of lowland streams to carry floodwaters. Surface mining has contributed to landslides and floods, degraded fish and wildlife habitats, impaired scenic values, and counteracted efforts to conserve soil, water, and other natural resources.

Underground mining can also have an adverse impact on the environment. It often results in acid drainage and can cause land subsidence over mined-out areas unless systems are designed to prevent the deterioration and failure of abandoned mine pillars. Some 1,850,000 acres of land in the U.S. have been affected by subsidence due to the underground mining of coal.

About 30% of all coal is transported directly from the mine to the user. The rest is washed to reduce the inorganic and ash content, producing about 90 million tons of waste annually. If not returned to the mine, this residue can accumulate in piles which may ignite and burn for long periods, creating an air pollution problem. Rainwater can leach salts and acid from the piles to contaminate nearby streams.

Most coal is moved to power plants by rail, with a considerable amount of land devoted to railroad rights of way. A typical 1000 MW coal-fired power plant requires about 100 carloads of coal each day. If power projections for the year 2000 were to be met by coal-fired plants alone, it would require the daily movement of 100,000 railroad cars and the daily dumping of coal into billions of cubic feet of storage space.

At the power plant the coal is burned to produce electricity, causing several pollution problems. A 1000 MW power plant emits large quantities of air pollutants — primarily sulfur oxides, nitrogen oxides, and particulates — and thermal discharges to air and water. The solid waste is in the form of ash and slag. About 30 million tons of these

TABLE 1

Environmental Factors Related to Energy

Environmental element affected	Type of impact	Pollutant
Air	Chemical-physical	Carbon dioxide
		Carbon monoxide
		Sulfur oxides
		Nitrogen oxides
		Hydrocarbons
		Photochemical smog
		Particulates
		Organics
		Trace metals
	Radiological	Noble gases
		Particulates
	Resource use	Oxygen
		Helium
	Other	Thermal inputs
		Electromagnetic emissions
		Noise
Water	Chemical-physical	Oil spills
		Acid mine drainage
	Radiological	Tritium
		Other effluents
		Uranium milling wastes
	Thermal	Thermal inputs
Land	Chemical-physical	Acid fallout from the air
		Mineral fallout from cooling towers
		Solid wastes
	Radiological	High-level wastes
	Resource use	Land subsidence
		Strip-mining of coal
		Land use for power production and transmission
		Hydroelectric dams
		Land use for sludge disposal

materials are collected each year. An estimated 8 million tons of solids are discharged into the atmosphere. In the absence of stringent environmental controls, coal can cause extensive damage to the environment.

B. Coal Gasification

Coal is likely to remain the dominant fossil fuel for generating electricity in the immediate future. One means of reducing the extent of the environmental problems arising from coal production and use is the gasification of high-sulfur coal to produce a low-sulfur gas. Because of the inefficiencies of converting coal to a gas, a conventional gas-fired power generator would make this system less efficient than the direct combustion of coal. However, using a combined-cycle power plant, where the gas would first generate electricity through a gas turbine and then be completely burned to produce steam to operate a turbine, the system could increase its electrical output and become more efficient.

A typical plant of 250 million ft³ daily capacity would consume about 6 million tons of bituminous coal annually, with 100,000 gal of water per minute required for circu-

TABLE 2

Major Environmental Impacts of Various Energy Sources

Energy source	Impact on land resource			Impact on water resource			Impact on air resource		
	Production	Processing	Utilization	Production	Processing	Utilization	Production	Processing	Utilization
Coal	Disturbed land, erosion subsidence, solid waste	Solid waste	Ash, slag disposal	Acid mine drainage, silt runoff	Process waste water, contaminant runoff	Increased water temperature			Sulfur oxides, nitrogen oxides, particulates, carbon monoxide
Oil	Brine disposal		Ash disposal	Oil spills, blowouts, brines	Oil spills	Increased water temperatures	Evaporative losses	Evaporative losses	Sulfur oxides, carbon monoxide, nitrogen oxides, particulates
Natural gas	Brine disposal					Increased water temperatures	Leaks	Impurities	Nitrogen oxides
Uranium	Disturbed land, very small amounts radioactive solid waste	Solid Disposal of radioactive waste materials	Very small amounts of radioactivity in effluents	Disposal of radioactive material	Increased water temperatures, release of very small quantities of short-lived radionuclides	Very small amounts of radioactivity in releases		Releases of small quantities of short-lived radionuclides	
Hydro			Destruction of natural scenic values			Silting			

Geothermal	Subsidence, seismic activity			Wastewater discharge, increased water temperatures		Hydrogen sulfide, sulfur oxides
Oil shale	Disturbed land subsidence	Extensive wastes (spent shale disposal)		Large amounts of water required, organic and inorganic pollutants	Increased water temperatures	Hydrogen sulfide	Nitrogen oxides, carbon monoxide, Hydrocarbons
Coal gasification	Disturbed land, erosion, subsidence	Solid waste	Ash, slag disposal	Acid mine drainage, silt runoff	Process waste water, contaminant runoff	Increased water temperatures	Nitrogen oxides, carbon monoxide

TABLE 3

Emission Estimates from Stationary Combustion Systems, 1976

Environmental element affected	Pollutant	Emission rate, 10^3 ton/year
Air	Sulfur oxides	22,100
	Nitrogen oxides	10,950
	Hydrocarbons	353
	Carbon monoxide	1,070
	Particles	7,060
	Organics	
	Benzene soluble	125
	Particulate polycyclic organic material	4.14
	Benzo (*a*) pyrene	0.40
Water	Total solids	5,000
	Dissolved solids	3,700
	Waste heat	7.9×10^{15} BTU/year
Solid waste	Total ash	54,000
	Fly ash	36,000
	Desulfurization solids	3,500

lation, of which 20,000 gal would be consumed. Special precautions would be necessary to prevent discharging water-soluble contaminants such as phenols. Thermal pollution can be significant because the conversion of coal to pipeline gas is only about 65% thermally efficient. The disposal of coal ash from the processed coal is also necessary. The gas produced would be essentially free of sulfur, having only a few parts per billion. The net environmental benefit would be a reduction in sulfur oxides and particulate matter discharged into the air. Although air pollution is reduced, coal use would increase with its mining impacts and waste disposal problems.

C. Oil

Onshore oil production, except for accidental occurrences, does not present any difficult pollution problem although nearly 3 bbl of brine must be disposed of for every barrel of oil produced. Environmental degradation resulting from offshore production, dramatized by the serious oil leak at Santa Barbara, Calif. causes a more difficult pollution problem, although much progress has since been made in preventing and controlling oil pollution from spills and blowouts.

About 42% of each barrel of oil is refined into gasoline for the nation's 100 million vehicles. Including the oil refined into diesel and jet fuels, this figure approaches 54%. The average uncontrolled motorcar consumes 4,500 lb of fuel and 60,000 ib of air annually. It exhausts 1700 lb of carbon monoxide, 500 lb of unburned hydrocarbons, 90 lb of nitrogen oxides, and 5 to 10 lb of particulate matter.

Refined residual oil is usually transported directly to a power plant by barge or tanker. Transfer operations can result in oil spills, and water contamination results if tankers discharge oil during bilge and tank-cleaning operations. At the power plant, the burning of residual oil causes air pollution — primarily sulfur oxides and nitrogen oxides — and results in thermal discharges to water.

D. Natural Gas

Natural gas extraction is in many ways similar to oil production with both fuels often taken from the same well. Gas extraction on land affects some acreage through the use of drilling rigs, and also produces brine posing a disposal problem. Pipelines, having extensive rights of way, then transport the gas to processing facilities where impurities are removed, resulting in some air pollution.

Combustion of natural gas at the power plant causes minor amounts of air pollution in the form of carbon monoxide and nitrogen oxides, and also produces thermal discharges to water. Natural gas is by far the least environmentally damaging of the fossil fuels. There is essentially no water pollution other than thermal discharges, and the amounts of solid wastes produced are not serious. Total air pollution is less than 5% of the emissions from a coal system and is significantly less than that from oil.

E. Nuclear Fission

Nuclear power has already produced some of the strongest environmental actions to date. Public controversy over thermal pollution, radioactivity releases, waste disposal, and nuclear accidents promises to grow more difficult in the coming years with the nuclear industry undergoing much closer scrutiny.

Uranium, mined by either open-pit or underground methods, creates problems similar to those involved in mining coal, only on a much smaller scale. Because of the high potential energy content of nuclear fuels, relatively little land is affected in supplying the annual needs of a 1000 MW power plant. Estimates of the solid wastes from the mining of ore and the subsequent extraction of the desired uranium product are 38 million tons annually. In processing uranium ores, some of the potentially hazardous radioactive elements or isotopes, particularly Ra-226 and Th-230, are partly dissolved during the leaching operation used to recover uranium oxide. While most processing plants are in isolated areas, contamination of water supplies by the radioactive constituents of liquid effluents must be avoided. Disposal of effluent is principally by impoundment and evaporation, controlled seepage into the ground, and injection through deep wells into saline or nonpotable aquifers. Where ore-processing plants are adjacent to rivers or streams, the effluents are frequently released directly to streams at controlled rates where, after dilution, the concentration is within predetermined limits.

At the light-water reactor (LWR) power plant, fission energy is released in the form of heat and is transferred to a conventional steam cycle which generates electricity. Because of coolant temperature limitations in LWRs, their thermal efficiency is lower than those of modern fossil fueled plants. This lower efficiency, as well as the absence of hot, gaseous combustion products released through the stack, means that an LWR power plant discharges over 60% more heat to receiving waters than its fossil fuel counterpart. Extremely small amounts of radioactivity are routinely released to water bodies and to the atmosphere, but only enough to give an annual ionizing radiation exposure in the range of 0.01 to 10.0% of the exposure received from natural background radiation. Tables 4 and 5 provide an indication of the quantities of released radioactivity in gaseous and liquid effluents.[5]

The spent fuel, containing highly radioactive fission products, is stored at the reactor for several months while the radioactivity decreases. It is then transported to a reprocessing plant where the fuel is chemically treated to recover the remaining uranium and some plutonium (produced during the fission process). Other fission products are also removed and concentrated. In the entire fuel cycle, radioactive emissions to the air are greatest from the reprocessing plant. Practical procedures for the control of such gaseous wastes are necessary. The concentrated fission products in the solid and liquid wastes must also be controlled. Because of their biological hazards and long half-lives, they must be kept out of the biosphere indefinitely. Highly radioactive wastes now amounting to about 90 million gal, produced largely in military programs, are temporarily stored in large steel and concrete tanks which require constant surveil-

TABLE 4

Releases of Radioactive Halogens and Particulates from Power Reactors in Gaseous Effluents

| | Curies | | Percentage of |
Location of reactor	Released	Permissible[a]	permissible
Dresden 1, Ill.	0.26	85.	0.3
San Onofre, Calif.	<.0001	0.8	<.001
Humboldt Bay, Calif.	0.65	5.6	12.
Nine Mile Point, N.Y.	<.001	63.	<.001
Big Rock, Mich.	0.2	38.	0.53
Oyster Creek, N.J.	0.003	126.	0.002
Saxton, Pa.	<.0001	10.	<.001
Indian Point 1, N.Y.	0.025	7.6	0.33
Connecticut Yankee, Conn.	0.001	0.27	0.37
Ginna, N.Y.	<.0001	1.7	<.001
La Crosse, Wis.	<.063	1.6	<4.
Yankee, Mass.	<.0001	0.03	0.01
Peach Bottom, Pa.	<.0006	0.12	;1t.5

[a] Maximum permissible releases are based on the most restrictive isotopes found, iodine-131 and strontium-90. The annual limit was reduced by a factor of 700 to account for reconcentration.

TABLE 5

Releases of Radioactivity from Power Reactors in Liquid Effluents

| | Mixed fission and corrosion products | |
Location of reactor	Released (curies)	Percent of limit[a]
Dresden 1, Ill.	9.5	22.
San Onofre, Calif.	8.	14.
Humboldt Bay, Calif.	1.5	8.7
Nine Mile Point, N.Y.	0.9	8.2
Big Rock, Mich.	12.	5.6
Oyster Creek, N.J.	0.48	4.1
Saxton, Pa.	0.01	2.5
Indian Point 1, N.Y.	28.	1.5
Connecticut Yankee, Conn.	12.	1.4
Ginna, N.Y.	0.02	0.4
La Crosse, Wis.	8.5	0.11
Yankee, Mass.	0.019	0.07
Peach Bottom, Pa.	<.001	0.002

[a] The limit refers to the maximum permissible concentration (MPC) of specific isotopes.

lance, and some of which require cooling. A safer and more permanent means of disposal is needed now. If the nuclear industry is to continue to expand and radioactive wastes continue to accumulate, a suitable permanent disposal method must be found. Neither the salt mine concept nor any other radioactive waste disposal plan has as yet received general scientific endorsement.

The proposed development of the fast breeder reactor could severely increase all of these problems. Despite the principal advantage of the fast breeder reactor — its ability to create more nuclear fuel than it burns — this does not come without penalties. The most obvious is the large increase in the amounts of extremely toxic and highly radioactive plutonium which would be produced and shipped about the country. Safety problems would be greater. To the already difficult problem of maintaining cooling under all circumstances in conventional reactors which use water as a cooling medium would be added the difficulty of using liquid sodium, a highly reactive, opaque material.

While some of the problems such as thermal discharges and radioactive releases are on their way to being solved, others will be compounded by planned developments. The problems of waste disposal, serious accident, and the threat of theft or sabotage at nuclear facilities and during transportation cannot be completely solved, and may grow more serious. Thus, the expansion of nuclear power is likely to carry with it some serious and irreducible risks. Whether the economic and social benefits of the industry counterbalance these risks is still a question which has not yet been publicly resolved.

F. Hydroelectric Power

Water power is now used almost exclusively for the generation of electricity and at present it meets only 4% of total energy needs in the U.S. No major expansion of hydroelectric power is anticipated, partly because most of the readily available sites have been developed, and partly because of growing concern for preservation of the remaining natural rivers. Primarily because of silting in the reservoirs behind the dams, hydroelectric plants have an expected lifetime of 100 to 200 years. Although the effect is relatively small, hydroelectric power systems may cause environmental degradation through the destruction of natural scenic values, fish and wildlife habitats, and deterioration of water quality.

G. Geothermal Energy

Geothermal steam or superheated water is naturally produced when the earth's heat energy is transferred to subsurface water from rocks in the earth's crust. Geothermal energy sources are beginning to be exploited on an increasing scale. Recent explorations have revealed that the resource is more extensive than had been supposed, and there is evidence that reservoirs of steam and hot water are widespread in the earth's crust. Where the pressure and temperature are adequate, the steam output may be used in turbines for conversion to electricity. However the temperatures and pressures at which the steam emerges are usually well below those used in traditional electric generating plants, and would result in inefficiencies in power production. In addition to the generation of electricity, geothermal steam or hot water can be applied to desalting sea water; to heating houses, greenhouses, and swimming pools; and to providing nonelectrical energy for refrigeration and air conditioning.

Most of the environmental effects of a geothermal resource are local because it must be used near its source. At the site, up to several thousand acres are used for extraction wells. The sound of the steam issuing from the wellhead is usually rather loud, presenting a noise pollution problem. Geothermal wells also release gaseous pollutants such as hydrogen sulfide, and wastewater discharge may be a problem because the geothermal steam power plant condensate contains trace quantities of harmful chemicals such as boron.

Other problems arise in the disposal because of the mineral content, which can be as high as 30%. These materials can corrode, or solidify, and block the pipes and turbines. Once through the turbine, the condensed water is often too full of contaminants to dump into natural streams or lakes. Trials at several fields have shown that the contaminated effluent can be injected back into the field without reducing production. Problems may be encountered when the saline and siliceous solids precipitate out as water temperature and pressure drop, making this reinjection more difficult. Although the reinjection of water into faulted areas would relieve the stresses and reduce the possibility of land subsidence caused by the removal of large quantities of fluid, induced seismic activity is possible.

H. Oil Shale

Extensive shale deposits are found in Colorado, Utah, and Wyoming, where an estimated 600 billion bbl of oil could be extracted from thick oil shale seams to yield 20 or more gallons of oil per ton of shale. Considerably more oil exists in less economic concentrations.

Oil shale production will require extraction by underground or surface mining, more like mining coal than drilling for petroleum. This is followed by heating or retorting to produce crude oil, or the shale could be heated *in situ* and then withdrawn by drilling as with crude oil.

At the midpoint in the lifetime of a 1000 MW power plant, surface mining of oil shale would disrupt an estimated 1000 acres. If underground mining without backfilling were employed, about 2000 acres would be affected; but if 60% of the spent shale were returned to the mine, the possibility of subsidence would be greatly reduced and less than 300 acres would be affected by the excess spent shale. Use of an *in situ* process would minimize the amount of land disrupted.

The retort process would produce significant amounts of hydrogen sulfide. It would also produce extensive solid waste by-products, the volume of which, before compaction, is 50% more than the in-place shale. After compaction, the volume remains about 15% more than the in-place shale. Because the solid waste is far less dense than the shale and cannot be readily compacted, only 60 to 80% can be returned to the mine.

Retorting, spent shale disposal, and shale oil upgrading would use large amounts of water in a region where water is already scarce. Producing enough oil for a 1000 MW power plant would require almost 1.5 billion gal of water annually — primarily for spent shale disposal. Surface disposal of the spent shale could lead to the leaching of salts which could contaminate surface waters. The retorting also discharges water containing organic and inorganic pollutants, increasing the water pollution problem.

One major benefit of the residual oil that could be produced from shale crude would be its low-sulfur content. Thus, air pollution at a power plant would be reduced.

The development of shale oil holds promise for greatly increasing domestic oil resources, but environmental and water supply problems remain major obstacles. The overall environmental impact will depend on the methods used to extract and process the shale, to dispose of spent shale, and to reclaim mined lands.

III. ENERGY SOURCES OF THE FUTURE

Nuclear fusion, solar energy, wind energy, biomass, energy produced as a result of thermal gradients in the earth or the oceans, tidal energy, and advanced chemical energy systems show promise as potential power sources in the future with minimum environmental damage.

Controlled thermonuclear fusion is receiving increasing research and development funds. It would make use of light-element fuels which are sufficiently abundant to supply power needs almost indefinitely.

Solar energy is also receiving increasing attention as a virtually pollution-free and inexhaustible source of energy. The National Science Foundation puts the nation's goals in solar energy use by the next century at 35% of the energy needed for heating and cooling.

The renewed interest in tidal power systems stems from their environmental advantages. They produce no harmful wastes, cause minor scenic and ecological disturbances, and are inexhaustible. The huge tidal power plant proposed for Passamoquoddy Bay, between Maine and New Brunswick, with its 45-ft tides, would have an electrical generating capacity of 300 MW. Although not economically feasible at this time, tidal energy is another future source which could reduce the environmental consequences of power generation.

IV. ENERGY CONSERVATION

Energy conservation will reduce the environmental damage from the various energy systems. Conservation also will enhance the reliability of future energy supplies. By slowing the rate of growth of energy demand, the longevity of energy supplies may be extended, allowing more flexibility in developing systems for meeting long-term needs. For too long a time, energy has been considered a limitless commodity. Energy was continuously wasted because it was abundant and cheap. This situation is now reversed. No longer will refuse and other solid wastes which are potential sources of energy be discarded. Instead, they will be used to supplement fuel supplies. No longer will reusable items be discarded. Recycling, which inherently will extend the lifetime of many natural resources, in many instances will be found profitable and compatible with environmental goals. The use of public transportation systems and car pools will increase. People will be more conscious of the energy they expend, first, because it will cost more, and second, because they realize that energy sources are not inexhaustible.

There is also tremendous potential for conservation in the energy production and consumption stages. On the average, only 30% of the oil in a reservoir is being extracted from onshore wells; offshore extraction is somewhat more efficient. As the price of crude oil rises, more extensive use of secondary recovery techniques, such as water flooding and thermal stimulation, will become evident. In the deep mining of coal, less than 60% of the resource in place is recovered, and over 10% of the energy in coal can be lost in cleaning. The pillar method of mining coal limits primary coal recovery to 30 to 60%. Secondary coal recovery techniques, such as the "Robbing-the-Pillars" method, will become economical and increase the amount of recoverable coal from the mine.

For electric power systems, a major source of inefficiency is the power plant itself. Thermionic or magnetohydrodynamic topping of electric power plants and the use of combined cycles show promise in increasing power plant efficiency by almost 20%. This will significantly reduce the thermal discharge to the environment and conserve fuel resources, and the constructive use of the waste heat will benefit the environment. Waste heat from power plants is a rich source of energy for plant growth. Already there have been very successful applications of warm-water irrigation to increase yields. There is a great deal to be learned about aquaculture, but it appears that clams, shrimp, and scallops are adaptable to this procedure.

V. CONCLUSION

Energy systems must be evaluated in light of their impact on the total environment in all aspects of their respective production methods and uses. As more and more air and water pollution control devices are employed, air and water emissions will be reduced considerably, but increasing amounts of solid waste will be generated. More land will then be needed for the disposal of this waste and this will reduce the net effects of reclamation of mined-out areas. Although the damages from air and water pollution are much less severe with controls, the need to avoid unintentionally shifting environmental problems from one medium or location to another must be recognized. Finally, much of the environmental damage from the use of energy lies in the systems which provide the energy to the consumer. If these systems were to function more efficiently, then the adverse environmental effects of energy production would be lessened. Similarly, if less energy were to be expended to achieve desired ends, then energy production and environmental damage would be reduced. It is critically necessary that environmental impacts of various energy policies and of new energy technologies be considered to meet reasonable energy demands without significantly harming the environment.

REFERENCES

1. Buonicore, A. J., Energy and the environment, *Mil. Eng.,* 434, 347, 1974.
2. Buonicore, A. J., Theodore, L., and Rolinski, E., Energy source alternatives with environmental considerations perspectives: *Proc. Symp. on Energy, Ecology, and Society,* Michigan State University, East Lansing, 1974, 53.
3. GCA Corporation, Bedford, Mass., GCA/Technology Division, Preliminary Emissions Assessment of Conventional Stationary Combustion Sources: Volume II — Final Report, EPA Report 600/2-76-046 b, March 1976.
4. Root, D. H., Taking stock of future energy sources, *Hydrocarbon Process.,* p. 193, 1978.
5. Dole, S. H. and Papetti, R. A., Environmental Factors in the Production and Use of Energy, Report R-992-RF, Rand Corporation, Santa Monica, Calif.

Chapter 2

THE ENVIRONMENTAL IMPACT OF CONVENTIONAL FOSSIL FUEL SOURCES

T. T. Shen

TABLE OF CONTENTS

I. INTRODUCTION

At present, there are two major energy sources in use: the fossil fuel energy source and the nuclear energy source. The fossil fuel may be subdivided according to the various raw fuels such as coal, oil, natural gas, liquefied petroleum gas, wood, coke, refining gas, blast furnace gas, and by-product fuels. This chapter covers only the three major fossil fuels: coal, oil, and natural gas.

The fossil fuel energy picture has changed drastically since the 1973 oil crisis. The current national energy policy aims toward energy independence and promotes an increased coal utilization, due to increasingly severe shortages of domestic oil and natural gas. An increase of coal consumption would produce more pollutants which are carried through the environment affecting individual organisms and ecosystems. Emphasis is placed on the impacts of fossil fuel cycles on physical environment.

A brief discussion of U.S. energy trends which illustrates a general picture of fossil fuel supply and demand and the different consumers of each fuel is presented in Section II. Section III classifies the three major fossil fuels and the compositions. The major environmental problems of each fuel may be determined by examining its fuel composition.

Environmental impacts on air quality, water quality, land use, and noise are described in Section IV, V, VI and VII, respectively. A summary of the impacts is presented at the end of this chapter in Table 1. In discussing environmental impacts, the entire fuel cycle rather than just the power-generation phase is considered. Since each fuel cycle, whether coal, oil, or natural gas, has its specific environmental problem, consideration is given to all environmental aspects associated with each fuel cycle with emphasis on the coal cycle. The fuel cycle is discussed according to its sequence of activities: extraction, processing, transportation, storage, power generation and transmission, and, finally, use by the consumers. Among these activities, attention is focused upon the electrical power generation which is the most important aspect of the energy picture and affects the environment the most. Some of the activities would produce similar types of pollutants and differ only in quantity. In such cases, common impacts are described collectively to avoid redundant discussion.

Section VIII outlines the essential U.S. environmental legislation relating to energy production and consumption. It is felt that legislation is the first step and the key to minimizing the impacts on the environment. The future environmental impacts from coventional fossil fuel energy sources depend greatly upon the implementation of federal and state environmental regulations which are discussed in Section IX.

Due to lack of adequate data in certain areas, there are some uncertainties in describing the environmental impacts. This chapter provides the essential information and emphasizes the concept of total environment which is needed for the understanding of interdependent effects within the problems of air, water, and land pollution. Such understanding will allow development of future energy sources in an environmentally acceptable manner. For detailed information, the reader is referred to the cited references and the vast body of materials published by the government and private agencies.

II. ENERGY TRENDS

Total U.S. energy supply is projected to increase from an estimated 38 million bbl/day oil equivalent (MB/DOE) in 1978 to 54 MB/DOE in 1990 as shown in Figure 1. Of this, the fossil fuel supply is expected to increase from 34 MB/DOE in 1978 to 47 MB/DOE in 1990. The combined supply of hydro, geothermal, solar, and nuclear

TABLE 1

Summary Sheet of Environmental Impact of Conventional Fossil Fuel Sources

Energy source	Impacts on air quality	Impacts on water quality	Impacts on land	Impacts on noise
Coal	Sulfur oxides Nitrogen oxides Particulates Hydrocarbons Carbon monoxide Carbon dioxide Trace elements Radionuclides Polynuclear organic matter	Chemical mine drainage Combustion products fallout Increased water temperature Leached water from coal storage piles and waste piles; also from ash and sludge disposal sites	Disturbed land Large amounts of solid waste Mine tailings Subsidence	Mining operations Blasting Stationary engines Power plant sites
Oil	Nitrogen oxides Sulfur oxides Particulates Hydrocarbons Carbon monoxide Carbon dioxide Trace elements Radionuclides Polynuclear organic matter	Increased water temperature Oil spills Effluents from refineries Combustion products fallout	Wastes in the form of brine Pipeline construction Oil spills	Mining Stationary engines Refinery operations Power plant sites
Gas	Nitrogen oxides Carbon oxides	Increased water temperature	Pipeline construction	Exposing stationary engines

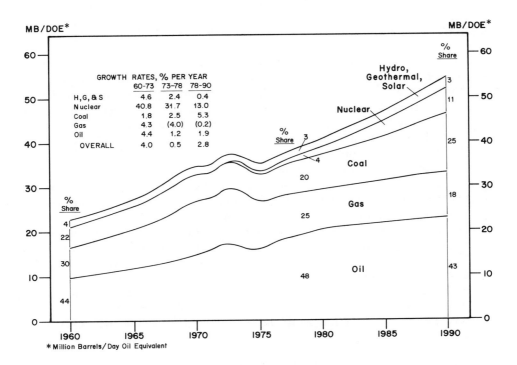

FIGURE 1.   U.S. energy supply.

TABLE 2

U.S. Consumption of Electricity[28]

	1973[a]		1980[a]		1990[a]	
Industrial	706.1	(41%)	1108.7	(39%)	1942.8	(38%)
Residential	555.0	(32%)	930.2	(33%)	1749.3	(34%)
Commercial	390.8	(23%)	634.0	(23%)	876.0	(23%)
Other	68.0	(4%)	122.4	(5%)	234.0	(5%)
Total	1719.9		2795.2		5067.7	

[a] Billions of kWh.

energy is expected to share only 7% of the total supply in 1978 and gradually increase to 14% in 1990.[1]

Approximately 93% of the total thermal energy consumed in the U.S. is currently supplied by coal, oil, and natural gas. Of this, oil and natural gas provide three-fourths of the fossil fuel consumption. Fossil fuel will remain the predominant fuel to be used until renewable and inexhaustible sources of energy are developed and commercialized.

One of the major concerns with the recent U.S. energy supply lies in the fact that domestic petroleum production has been declining rapidly and imports have been increasing even more rapidly. At the height of the oil embargo of 1973 to 1974, imports were reduced by 2 million bbl/day which was about 12% of U.S. total demand at that time. This situation led to the establishment of the present national energy plan, aiming toward energy independency. The energy demand is to be met by utilizing the abundant domestic sources of coal instead of foreign oil. The 1975 Energy Program began mandating that the U.S. Environmental Protection Agency (EPA) issue orders prohibiting the use of oil or gas by any power plants (new or existing) which had the capability of burning coal.

It should be noted that the various energy sources have different qualities and ranges of use. Oil is heavily used by residential, commercial, industrial, and transportation sectors; but is needed most for transportation sectors where no substitute is currently available. Natural gas is heavily used in industry; it is the premium fuel for residential and commercial use because it is an efficient, clean, and convenient source of heat. Coal is used principally by industry and electric utilities. The electric utilities consume about 90% of the coal consumption.[2]

The U.S. energy conservation program has reduced the energy demand somewhat. However, in order to keep up with the socioeconomic growth, the demand for energy is expected to continue increasing about 2.8% annually in industrial, commercial, residential, and transportation use. Electricity consumption in the U.S. has increased rapidly in the past and the increase will be more rapid in the future as shown in Table 2. It appears that the percentages of the total annual consumption of electricity shared by industrial, commercial, residential, and other consumers are rather constant. The quantities of electricity derived from various energy sources between 1973 and 1990 are given in Table 3. It should be noted that as a result of the current national energy plan, the source of electricity will be shifted toward coal utilization. However, it is predicted that by the year 2000, most of the energy that is consumed will probably be in the form of electricity.[3]

III. FOSSIL FUEL CLASSIFICATIONS

The conventional fossil fuel energy described hereafter refers only to the three major

TABLE 3

Source of Electricity[29]

Energy source	1972[a]	1980[a]	1990[a]
Hydro	273 (15.6%)	317 (10.2%)	381 (6.4%)
Coal	771 (44.2%)	1211 (38.9%)	1651 (27.8%)
Oil	272 (15.6%)	421 (13.2%)	521 (8.7%)
Gas	375 (21.4%)	410 (13.2%)	445 (7.5%)
Nuclear	54 (3.1%)	750 (24.1%)	2913 (49.3%)
Other	2 (0.1%)	4 (0.1%)	20 (0.3%)
Total	1747	3113	5922

[a] Billions of kWh.

TABLE 4

Classification of Coals[30]

Class	Moisture (%)	Fixed carbon limits (%)	Volatile matter limits (%)	Calorific value limits (Btu/lb)
Anthracite	<2	86—98	2—14	14,000—16,000
Bituminous	2—15	50—86	14—50	10,500—14,000
Subbituminous	20—30	40—60	—	8,300—10,500
Lignite	30—50	<40	—	6,300—8,300

sources: coal, fuel oil, and natural gas. Other fuels are in relatively small quantities. Thus, the production and use of these fuels are not expected to impose significant environmental impacts, and will not be discussed.

A. Coal

The most common fossil fuel is coal. It contains many compounds in varying amounts, but predominantly carbon. The exact nature and quantity of these compounds are determined by the location of the energy source producing the fuel.

Coals are classified to provide data for predicting the probable performance under given conditions. One classification of coal is by rank or age. Volatile matter, fixed carbon moisture, and oxygen are all indicative of rank. In the American Society for Testing and Materials (ASTM) classification, the basic criteria are the fixed carbon and the calorific values calculated on a mineral matter-free basis.[4]

Bituminous coal (soft) and anthracite coal (hard) are two major classes. The distinct difference between them is believed to depend upon not only the high temperature and pressure to which anthracite coal is subjected, but also upon the differences in the original vegetation. Each class may be further divided into different groups, and even then there is considerable room for variation within each subgroup.

Table 4 shows the analysis of bituminous coals as ranked by ASTM D388 specification for classification of coals.[4] The range of variation is relatively high for compo-

TABLE 5

Bituminous Coal Ash Properties[5]

	Eastern	Western
Fusibility temperature (°F)		
Ignition temperature	2440	2540
Fusing temperature	2700 +	2700 +
Ash composition (%)		
SiO_2	52.2	55.5
Al_2O_3	25.1	28.1
Fe_2O_3	8.7	5.5
CaO	1.9	5.6
MgO	1.3	1.1
Na_2O	0.5	0.2
K_2O	3.3	0.8
TiO_2	1.1	1.3
P_2O_5	0.6	0.1
SO_3	1.5	3.9
Base/acid ratio	0.20	0.16
FeO_3/CaO ratio	4.6	1.0

nents such as moisture content, volatile matter, sulfur content, and oxygen content. Other components such as hydrogen, nitrogen, ash, and heating value vary slightly.

Table 5 lists the typical ash composition and fusibility data for bituminous coals deposited in the eastern and western sections of the U.S.[4] There is not much difference in fusibility temperatures between eastern and western coals. Ash of typical eastern coals (Appalachian and central states) has a higher iron oxide concentration than the combined calcium and magnesium oxides. Conversely, typical ash compositions of western coals (Rocky Mountains and North-Central Plains) have a higher combined calcium and magnesium content than iron oxide. The sulfur content of U.S. coals ranges from 0.2% to 4% with an average sulfur content about 2.5%. The sulfur is present naturally as mineral sulfates, as pyrite (iron sulfide or other metal sulfides), and as organic sulfur compounds. The organic component is chemically bound to the coal and cannot be removed without decomposing the fuel.

B. Fuel Oil

Oil constitutes another form of fossil fuel. Crude petroleum, as it comes from the ground or under the sea, is a mixture of thousands of hydrocarbons and other organic molecules. The composition of crude petroleum, like that of coal, varies considerably with geographic origin. An example of this variability is the organic sulfur content of crude petroleum.

The various grades of fuel oil available today are No. 1, No. 2, No. 4, No. 5, and No. 6. The first two are distillates; the last three, residual oils. These oils are classified according to ASTM standard D396 specifications for physical characteristics. The primary difference is that residual oil has a higher ash and sulfur content and is much more viscous; therefore, it is harder to burn properly.

Distillate fuel oil is primarily a domestic fuel, but it is used in some commercial and industrial applications where a high quality oil is required. Residual fuel oil can be used only in industrial boilers and electric utilities. The range of properties for residual oil found in the U.S. is listed in Table 6. Residual fuel oils have a heating value of approximately 10,000 kcal/ℓ (150,000 Btu/gal); the heating value for distillate oils is about 9,300 kcal/ℓ (140,000 Btu/gal). The composition of the ash in residual oil varies greatly; the presence of a large number of elements has been detected. Normally, sul-

TABLE 6

Properties of Grade 6 Fuel Oil[5]

Property	Minimum	Maximum
Gravity (°API)	−3.33	23.0
Flash point (°F)	15.2	365
Viscosity, furol, at 122°F, (sec)	13.7	415
Sulfur content (wt%)	0.34	4.00
Ramsbottom carbon residue on 100% sample	4.9	23.6
Ash (wt%)	0.002	0.3
Water and sediment (vol%)	0.0	1.0
Pour point (°F)	−10	90

fur, aluminum, calcium, iron, nickel, silicon, sodium, and vanadium are found in complex organic forms in the oil. Other elements have also been found in the ash in very small quantities; barium, chlorine, chromium, copper, gold, lead, molybdenum, silver, strontium, thallium, tin, uranium, and zinc.[5] A general analysis of the ash from oils is shown in Table 7.

C. Natural Gas

Natural gas is a clean fuel; that is, it contains little sulfur or ash relative to those quantities present in coal and oil. The sulfur component is primarily hydrogen sulfide. The primary components of natural gas are methane (80 to 90% by volume) and ethane (5 to 15% by volume), but small quantities of inorganics are also present, ranging up to 10% by volume. The heating value of natural gas is about $9,350 \pm 850$ kcal/Nm^3 ($1,050 \pm 100$ Btu/std ft^3).

Natural gas is used in domestic and commercial space heating, in industrial heating, and in some power plants where air pollution is a problem. It is usually processed before combustion to remove most of the sulfur-bearing compounds. As a result, its contribution to sulfurous pollution is usually negligible.

IV. IMPACT ON AIR QUALITY

The conversion of naturally occurring fossil fuels into usable energy involves various operations and processes such as fuel extraction, processing, transportation, combustion, and waste disposal. The impact on air quality results principally from the emission of particulate and gaseous pollutants into the atmosphere. The main concern for air pollution has been placed on combustion emissions from electrical generating power plants. Figure 2 shows a schematic diagram of a fossil fuel power plant. Other activities contribute relatively less to air pollution.

A. Extraction/Processing/Transportation[6, 7]

Extraction involves the surface or underground mining of coal, the drilling of on-shore or offshore petroleum and natural gas wells, and the recovery of the crude resources. Processing prepares the crude resource for transportation and marketing. Transportation involves the use of special pipelines or carriers such as tankers, ships, trains, or trucks to convey the resource to storage points.

Coal must be recovered from beneath the surface of the earth by either underground or stripping systems which involve the removal of varying thicknesses of overburden to reveal the seam. To mine coal underground requires an input of electric power,

TABLE 7

Uncontrolled Air Pollutant Emission Factors for Fossil Fuel Combustion by Weight[31]

	Particulate		Sulfur oxides		Nitrogen oxides		Hydrocarbons		Carbon monoxide	
Bituminous coal	lb/ton	kg/MT	lb/ton	kg/MT	lb/ton	kg/MT	lb/ton	kg/MT	lb/ton	kg/MT
Pulverized general	16A	8A	38S	19S	18	9	0.3	0.15	1	0.5
Pulverized wet bottom	13A	6.5A	38S	19S	30	15	0.3	0.15	1	0.5
Pulverized dry bottom	17A	8.5A	38S	19S	30	15	0.3	0.15	1	0.5
Pulverized cyclone	2A	1A	38S	19S	55	27.5	0.3	0.15	1	0.5
Spreader stocker	13A	6.5A	38S	19S	15	7.5	1	0.5	2	1
Handfire units	20	10	38S	19S	3	1.5	20	10	90	45
Fuel oil	lb/10³ gal	kg/10³ l	lb/10³ gal	kg/10³ l	lb/10³ gal	kg/10³ l	lb/10³ gal	kg/10³ l	lb/10³ gal	kg/10³ l
Power plant	8	1	159S	19S	105	12.6	2	0.25	3	0.4
Residual	23	2.75	159S	19S	40—80	4.8—9.6	3	0.35	4	0.5
Distillate	15	1.8	144S	17S	40—80	4.8—9.6	3	0.35	4	0.5
Domestic	10	1.2	144S	17S	1	0.12	3	0.35	5	0.6
Natural gas	lb/10⁶ ft³	kg/10³ m³	lb/10⁶ ft³	kg/10³ l	lb/10⁶ ft³	kg/10⁶ m³	lb/10⁶ ft³	kg/10⁶ m³	lb/10³ gal	kg/10³ l
Power plant	15	240	0.6	9.6	600	9600	1	16	17	270
Industrial process	18	290	0.6	9.6	120	1920	3	48	17	270
Domestic & commercial	19	302	0.6	9.6	80—120	1280—1920	8	128	20	320

Note: S = sulfur content; A = ash content.

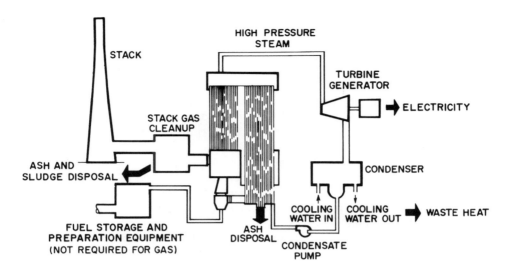

FIGURE 2.   Schematic diagram of fossil fuel power plant.

diesel fuel, water, compressed air, explosives, ventilating air, and other physical components, in addition to men and machines. The product is coal, and the by-products are mineral materials, coal dust, and acid mine drainage. The by-products represent the principal environmental problem of the underground coal mining operation.

Air emissions are not a problem for underground mining since electrically powered equipment is generally used underground. However, surface mining of coal does contribute to local air pollution. Surface mining techniques consist basically of removing the topsoil, rock, and other materials above the coal seam so that the coal can be removed.

A prevalent air pollutant associated with coal mining is dust, particularly in dry climates where high winds are more common. Most of the dust arises from blasting operations, crushing, blending, stocking, and loading, but may also result from abandoned mines as well as spoil erosions.

Coal extraction operations release combustion pollutants from the burning of fuels in mining and hauling equipment, and also in the boiler plant to provide electricity for the colliers. Spontaneous combustion of the coal may occur, releasing smoke containing air pollutants. This is especially serious in underground sites.

Air quality affected by oil shale extraction and processing include construction activities; mining operations; crushing, grinding, and screening operations; burning of off-gases from retorting or refining; and burning of supplemental fuels for power generation. Particulates, sulfur oxides (SO_x), nitrogen oxides (NO_x), and hydrocarbons (HC) are produced from heating and power generation. Carbon monoxide (CO) is present in the oil shale retort gases. Some trace elements that occur in the oil shale may be emitted in the processing of the oil shale. In addition, fugitive dust emissions may result from spent shale disposal. Oil shale disposal sites may also result in the release of highly volatile organics from the spent shale.

The principal activities which cause air pollution in the extraction and production of oil and gas are blowouts and well testing. Blowouts will inject hydrocarbons directly into the atmosphere; additional hydrocarbons are emitted by evaporation of the oil that is dispersed on the water. The extent of the emissions will depend upon the chemical composition of the crude oil and will increase as the fraction of the light ends in the crude oil increases. If a fire occurs in addition to the blowout, combustion products will also be released to the atmosphere.

Oil refining produces various types of air pollution. A summary of air emissions from oil refineries is given below:[7]

1. SO_x emissions result from catalytic cracking, treatment, and combustion. Specific amounts from each source will vary, depending primarily on quality of crude, type of process, and type of control. Total emissions may average 695 lb/1000 bbl processed.
2. NO_x emissions of 130 lb/1000 bbl of crude oil processed.
3.   Particulate emissions are largely from catalytic fires and to a lesser extent from combustion. About 12 lb/1000 bbl of crude oil processed are estimated.
4.   CO emissions result from catalytic cracking. About 15 lb/1000 bbl of crude oil processed are estimated.
5.   HC emissions come from storage tanks, handling and transport facilities, and accidental leaks; estimated emissions are 140 lb/1000 bbl of crude.

Transport of natural gas is normally through underground pipelines, which are relatively safe and have no air pollution problem. The transport of coal and oil is mostly done by carriers such as tankers, ships, trucks, or trains. The carriers involve combustion and, therefore, they may release significant amounts of combustion air pollutants.

Power transmission lines may affect air quality in terms of corona effects associated with the operation of high voltage transmission lines which could generate significant amounts of ozone and nitrogen oxides.

B. Stationary Use of Fuels

Emissions from fossil fuel combustion are dependent on the type and size of combustion units in which the fuel is burned, the composition of the fuel, the method of burning and maintenance, and the type of control equipment used. The major pollutants from combustion sources are SO_x, NO_x, CO, HC_x, and particulates. Emission factors of these major air pollutants from fossil fuel combustion are summarized in Table 7. A comparison of emissions from coal, oil, and natural gas on an equivalent Btu basis is given in Table 8.

In addition to the major air pollutants, significant amounts of waste heat, carbon dioxide, trace elemensts, and carcinogens are also produced from fuel combustion. Most of these are emitted into the atmosphere having significant impacts on the environment since some are highly toxic.

1. Oxides of Sulfur and Nitrogen

The amount of SO_x emitted from fossil fuel combustion in the absence of control is directly proportional to the sulfur content in the fuel burned. Coal and residual oil contain a significant amount of sulfur, which may be inorganically or organically bound. Inorganic sulfur (sulfides, etc.) generally occurs in coal rather than in oil or natural gas. Organic sulfur compounds may be present in oil and natural gas. Some compounds, for example, carbon disulfide (CS_2) and hydrogen sulfide (H_2S) could be used as fuels themselves. Trace sulfur compounds, such as mercaptans, have very powerful and distinct odors.

Whatever the source of sulfur in fuels, when fuel is oxidized, the sulfur does likewise. At high temperatures the stable oxide of sulfur is sulfur dioxide (SO_2). Relatively little sulfur trioxide (SO_3) will be formed. In general, approximately 92% to 98% of the sulfur present in a fuel is converted to SO_2 by combustion, and up to 5% to SO_3. The actual amount of SO_3 emitted depends upon the temperature profile and the

TABLE 8

Comparison of Fossil Fuel Emissions on Equivalent Btu Basis[31]

Fuel burned	Particulate matter		Sulfur oxides		Nitrogen oxides		Hydrocarbons		Carbon monoxide	
	kg Part 10^6 kJ	lb Part 10^6 BTU	kgSO$_2$ 10^6 kJ	lb SO$_2$ 10^6 BTU	kg NO$_2$ 10^6 kJ	lb NO$_2$ 10^6 BTU	kg CH$_4$ 10^6 kJ	lb H$_4$ 10^6 BTU	kg CO 10^6 kJ	lb CO 10^6 BTU
Bituminous coal										
Pulverized general	0.34 (%A)	0.80 (%A)	0.82 (%S)	1.90 (%S)	0.39	0.900	0.0064	0.015	0.021	0.050
Pulverized wet bottom	0.28 (%A)	0.65 (%A)	0.82 (%S)	1.90 (%S)	0.64	1.500	0.0064	0.015	0.021	0.050
Pulverized dry bottom	0.37 (%A)	0.85 (%A)	0.82 (%S)	1.90 (%S)	0.39	0.900	0.0064	0.015	0.021	0.050
Pulverized cyclone	0.04 (%A)	0.10 (%A)	0.82 (%S)	1.90 (%S)	1.17	2.740	0.0064	0.015	0.021	0.050
Spreader stoker	0.28 (%A)	0.65 (%A)	0.82 (%S)	1.90 (%S)	0.32	0.750	0.0064	0.015	0.021	0.050
Fuel oil										
Residual-tangential	0.023	0.053	0.46 (%S)	1.06 (%S)	0.115	0.267	0.0005	0.001	0.0005	0.001
Residual-horizontal	0.023	0.053	0.46 (%S)	1.06 (%S)	0.230	0.535	0.0005	0.001	0.0005	0.001
Distillate-tangential	0.015	0.035	0.41 (%S)	0.96 (%S)	0.123	0.285	0.0005	0.001	0.0005	0.001
Distillate-horizontal	0.015	0.035	0.41 (%S)	0.96 (%S)	0.246	0.570	0.0005	0.001	0.0005	0.001
Natural gas										
Process boilers	0.006	0.014	0.00048	0.001	0.160	0.372	0.016	0.038	0.0005	0.001
Gas turbines	0.006	0.014	0.00048	0.001	0.183	0.425	0.016	0.038	0.0005	0.001

Note: %A = Percent ash in fuel; %S = Percent sulfur in fuel.

amount of excess air in an individual furnace. Overall, SO_x amounts to 19 S lb of SO_2 per 1000 lb of fuel where S is the weight percentage of sulfur in the fuel. The SO_3 reacts rapidly with water vapor to produce sulfuric acid. A small amount of SO_2 is also chemisorbed by fly ash particles to form sulfates.

The current methods for minimizing SO_2 emission from fossil fuel combustion in power plants are the use of low sulfur fuels and the installation of flue gas desulfurization (FGD) systems. Low sulfur fuels are limited in natural resources. Costs for removing sulfur from residual oil by catalytic hydro-desulfurization techniques remain high, and the desulfurized residual oil has a tendency to become "waxy" at low temperatures. To remove sulfur from coal is an even more imposing problem. It is possible to remove pyrites from coal, but this approach is limited by the size of the pyrite particles. Unfortunately, pyrite sulfur makes up only half the sulfur content of the coal, whereas the other half is organically bound. Coal gasification is the only means by which this organic sulfur could be removed.

The FGD systems may be classified as a throwaway system or a by-product recovery system. In the former, the material containing the sulfur removed from the stack gases must be disposed of as waste. In the latter concept, the sulfur removed is recovered and processed into a presumably marketable product, such as elemental sulfur or sulfuric acid. Under ideal conditions the by-product recovery systems would appear to be advantageous from both an environmental and an economic viewpoint.

Nitrogen oxides (NO_x) produced by fossil fuel combustion are derived primarily from fixation of molecular nitrogen when combustion temperatures exceed 1300° C (2400°F), appreciable amounts of NO_x are formed. Of the NO_x known to exit, only nitric oxide (NO) and nitrogen dioxide (NO_2) are formed in significant quantities, but usually less than 1% is NO_2. The NO, once formed at high temperature, can react with excess oxygen to form NO_2. Generally, more NO_2 is formed when atmospheric oxygen reacts with NO.

The rate of NO formation is very highly temperature dependent. The principal factors affecting NO formation are flame temperature, the excess air present in the flame, and the length of time that the combustion gases are maintained at flame temperature.[9] Chemically bound nitrogen in the fuel can also contribute to the overall NO_x emission from combustion processes, since it reacts with oxygen much more readily than the molecular nitrogen supplied with the combustion air.

The amount of NO_x emitted from fuel combustion depends also upon equipment design, combustion conditions, size and type of burner, type of firing (horizontal or tangential), cooling surface area, and operating variables such as fuel consumption rate, and air-fuel ratio. Representative emission factors for NO_x emission from fossil fuel combustion and the comparison of emissions from each fuel type are given in Tables 7 and 8. NO_x indicated in the tables merits a special comment, because it contributes to the formation of photochemical smog. Since large combustion units operate with high temperatures, more NO_x are produced.

The current control techniques for NO_x emission from power plants can be divided into two broad categories: combustion modifications and flue gas cleaning. The former includes two stage combustion, low excess air operation, flue gas recirculation, and changing horizontal firing to tangential firing. All of the modifications involve reduction of peak gas temperatures, operating toward reducing atmosphere, and changes in the time-temperature history of the combustion gases. Field tests of these modification controls of NO_x on industrial boilers demonstrated that reductions of 34 to 45% of NO_x emissions are achievable with no significant impairment of thermal efficiency. The effectiveness of retrofit controls was possible but strongly dependent on the specific design characteristics of the field installation.[27]

2. Carbon Monoxide and Hydrocarbons

Power plants usually operate under careful controls for efficient combustion. Therefore, most of the CO that might be produced in the initial stages of a combustion chamber is oxidized to CO_2 before it leaves the atmosphere. There should be no CO emission if combustion is at maximum efficiency. CO itself is a fuel with a heat value of 4350 Btu/lb, so it should be burned in the furnace. CO emission can be minimized if the combustion system is adjusted, or used, adequately maintained, and correctly operated.

Representative emission factors of CO emissions are 0.001 lb/1 million Btu for gas and oil-fired power plants, and 0.05 lb/1 million Btu for coal-fired plants. However, CO emissions from coal hand-fire units can be as high as 90 times that from coal pulverized units.[6]

The combustion of fossil fuels may result in the emission of hydrocarbons and other organic materials if combustion is not complete. Due to variations in combustion efficiency and type of fuel, hydrocarbon emissions depend on the particular type of combustion equipment. The average hydrocarbon emissions for various types of fuels and furnace sizes are given in Table 7. Considerable variations in these emissions can occur, depending on the operation of an individual unit.

Generally, HCs emissions are proportional to CO emissions for a given power plant. As discussed previously, both emissions of CO and HC result primarily from inefficient combustion of fuels.

3. Particulates

Particulate emissions from fossil fuel combustion are primarily inorganic in nature, being derived from mineral impurities present in the fuel. Oil and natural gas, which contain only small amounts of inorganic impurities, have much lower particulate emission factors than coal.

Particulate emissions from coal combustion generally are greatest from pulverized dry bottom units, lower from chain grate and spreader stoker units, and lowest from cyclone furnaces. The degree of coal grinding before firing and the type of firing employed both influence the particle size distribution in the exhaust gases.

Particulate emissions from residual fuel oil combustion consist of inorganic materials from the ash content of the fuel and organic materials from incomplete combustion. The organic matter consists primarily of unburned carbon soot particles resulting from incomplete combustion of the oil droplets. Approximately 85% by weight of the soot particles are less than 10 μm.

Representative emission factors for particulates from fossil fuel combustion are presented in Table 7. Although the emission factor of particulates is given by weight, characterization of the particles emitted is critical to the assessment of the effect on human health and the atmosphere.

A recent study on characterization of differences between oil-fired and coal-fired power plant emission indicates that about 35.0% of particulates emitted from the coal-fired boiler were less than 3 μm with an average mass median diameter (MMD) of 4.9 μm; while from the oil-fired boiler, about 77.5% were less than 3 μm with an average MMD of 0.38 μm. Particulates from oil-fired emissions have more reactive surface area.[10]

A variety of particulate control devices is commercially available. Table 9 presents the optimum expected performance of various types of particulate emission control systems for stationary combustion sources. More detailed information on the special application and costs of these system can be found elsewhere.[11]

TABLE 9

Optimum Expected Performance of Various Types of Particulate Emission Control Systems for Stationary Combustion Sources[9]

Sources	Removal of uncontrolled particulate emissions, percent systems in operation				
	Settling chambers	Large diameter cyclones	Small diameter cyclones	Electrostatic precipitators	Stack sprays
Coal-fired					
Spreader, chain grate, and vibrating stokers	50	60	85	99.5	60
Other stokers	60	65	90	99.5	80
Cyclone furnaces	10	15	70	99.5	
Other pulverized coal units	20	30	80	99.5	
Oil-fired	5	10	30	75.0	

4. Other Emissions

In addition to the major air pollutants already discussed, fossil fuel combustion also emits a very wide variety of other pollutants including aldehydes, acid mists, trace elements, radionuclides, and organic carcinogens in more or less minor amounts. The actual emissions are not well quantified. Heat and CO_2 are generally not defined as pollutants, but emission in large amounts may introduce significant climate changes.

Sawyer reported that the average aldehyde emissions from power plants burning coal, oil, and natural gas are 0.002, 0.1, and 0.2 lb/1000 lb, respectively.[12] Acid mists are formed near the exit of the power plant stacks where the temperature is sufficiently low to allow formation of liquid water droplets which absorb SO_x and NO_x. Some metal-catalyzed oxidation of sulfite to sulfate almost certainly takes place in these droplets. The amount of sulfate and nitrate emission varies widely from one power plant to another because the sulfate and nitrate formation is a function of concentrations of NO_x, SO_x, H_2O, and catalysts present in the flue gas and also of the temperature profile of the flue gas.

The finely divided sulfates and nitrates can be transported for long distances because these particles are much less readily removed from the atmosphere than SO_2 and NO_2. Sulfates and nitrates, when present as acids, are of particular concern in health effects, visibility degradation, acid precipitation, and corrosion effects.

Numerous trace elements may be present in coal and oil. In some cases these would originally present in the crude oil, while in other cases the presence was artificial insomuch as the trace elements were additives to the fuel. The elements Hg, Zn, Cd, As, Pb, Mn, Mo, Co, Ni, Cr, Se, and Cu occur in association with inorganic material in coal, mainly in the pyrite fraction. Ge, Be, and B show marked organic association. P, Ga, Ti, Sb, and V are associated with both organic and inorganic materials in coal.[13] Trace elements in oil are much lower than in coal with the notable exception of vanadium which is present as organic porphyrin complexes.

Concern about trace element emissions from fossil-fueled power plants has been heightened with the discovery that metals are preferably concentrated in the smallest respirable particles emitted.[14] These particles easily pass through conventional control equipment. Kaakinen and co-workers[15] conducted a study of trace element behavior in coal-fired power plants and concluded that the ability of the type of pollution control equipment to remove trace elements in a flue gas stream depends on the specific equipment design and its operating conditions. Those elements not being volatilized

TABLE 10

Specific Concentrations (µg/gm) and Volume Concentrations (µg/m³) of Trace
Elements in Coal and Oil Fly Ash[15]

	Coal fly ash		Oil fly ash	
Element	µg/gm	µg/m³	µg/gm	µg/m³
As	10—500	60—90	30	5
Ba	100—1,000	30—110	9,000	1,600
Be	1—10	—	—	—
Cd	10—100	—	—	—
Co	10—100	1—5	90	16
Cr	10—1,000	8—20	66	12
Cu	10—1,000	—	—	—
Hg	0.1—1.0	—	—	—
Mn	100—1,000	12—40	45	8
Mo	10—100	—	—	—
Ni	10—1,000	10—25	—	—
Pb	100—5,000	10—15	—	—
Sb	1—100	1—2	5	1
Se	10—100	8—18	5	1
Sn	1—10	—	—	—
V	50—5,000	5—60	100—100,000	1,000—1,200
Zn	1,000—10,000	20—70	3,500	640

in the combustion zone can be removed more efficiently than those elements that are volatilized on combustion. Hg, Se, As, Cd, and Br are emitted as elemental vapor, and thus may not be removed by the conventional control equipment.

The specific concentrations of individual trace elements found in coal and oil fly ashes depend primarily on the trace element content of the original fuel. In general, a fly ash which contains high concentrations of one trace element will also have high concentrations of most others. Table 10 lists some representative specific concentrations (µg/g) and volume concentrations (µg/m³) of particulate trace elements emitted from coal-fired and oil-fired power plants.[16]

There are a number of published reports concerning emission of radioactive substances from coal combustion. Coal-fired power plants discharge radionuclides in the form of fly ash containing trace quantities of uranium, thorium, and their daughter products.[17] The mean values of radium-226, radium-228, and therium-228 from coal combustion emission are 3.8, 2.4, and 2.6 pCi/g of fly ash, respectively. The coal fly ash contains about 10 times more radium-226 than the oil fly ash does.[18] Of interest is the release of radon-222 from the decay of radium-226 in coal. Not only is the radon-222 released during mining and combustion, but it will continue to emanate from fly ash for many many years after the coal has been burned. Radon emission from ash piles may have significant effects on the environment. Another potential long-term problem is the contamination of ground water through leaching of the ash piles which contain radioactive elements.

Combustion of any fossil fuel leads to the formation of a large number of species containing two or more aromatic rings. The actual mechanism of polycyclic organic matter (POM) formation is not fully understood, although the current knowledge suggests that high temperature vapor phase formation of carbon-carbon bond takes place, probably via a free radical mechanism.[19]

Comparison of POM emissions with other products of incomplete combustion indicates that POM emission rates are high when concentrations of carbon monoxide and total gaseous hydrocarbons in the flue gas are high. Much of the published information on organic carcinogens concentrates on the compound benzo(*a*)pyrene (BaP) which is the prime constituent of POM, because BaP is known to have high carcinogenicity and is relatively easy to identify among other species of POM. Quantitative information concerning total potential carcinogen emission is lacking because techniques for sampling and analyzing individual organic carcinogens have not been adequately developed.

The reported BaP emissions from coal-fired power plants range from 20 to 400 $\mu g/$ 10^6 Btu; from oil-fired power plants, 100 to 900 $\mu g/10^6$ Btu; and from gas-fired power plants, 20 to 200 $\mu g/10^6$ Btu.[20] It is believed that new fossil fuel power plants will release much less organic carcinogens simply because of improved design and better combustion performance.

Heat is not normally thought of as waste, but it is put into the environment in large amounts by fossil-fueled power plants. Since the average thermal efficiency of most fossil-fueled power plants is about 33% (modern plants may attain up to 40%), almost 67% of the available energy is not used and must be discarded into the environment as waste heat. Of this, about 15% of the waste heat is released directly into the atmosphere with the stack gas, and 85% of the waste heat must be removed by the water.[3] The release of heated water into the receiving body of water causes thermal pollution which will be discussed further in Section V.

Up to 90% of the heat carried from cooling towers is in the form of water vapor. When it is condensed into clouds, the sun's rays can be shaded by visible plumes. The average visible plume length ranges from about 250 to 500 m in the summer and from 500 to 1000 m in the winter. However, during very humid environmental conditions, stratus clouds have been observed up to 50 km downwind of a power plant.[3]

The emission of carbon dioxide (CO_2) is strongly related to fossil fuel consumption and has been increasing rapidly at an exponential rate for the last 50 years. For identical energy outputs, coal generates 1.8 times as much CO_2 as does natural gas and 1.2 times as much as fuel oil. Large increases of atmospheric CO_2 could produce significant climate changes such as seasonal rainfall and the earth's reflective power primarily through the greenhouse effect. Although the exact amount of CO_2 concentration increase is still uncertain, it is the change in the global circulation pattern associated with the warming which is of greatest concern.[21]

V. IMPACT ON WATER QUALITY

The impact of fossil fuel sources on water quality involves activities such as coal extraction, processing, transportation, storage, oil spills, combustion sources, and thermal pollution. These activities may cause serious water pollution problems which are discussed below.

A. Extraction/Processing[3,6,8]

The mining of coal requires water. Water is used to spray underground mines, surface coal areas, and access roads to reduce dust pollution in the air. Once extracted, coal is washed with water. The process requires large amounts of water and discharges the polluted water that contains mostly inert dust, silt, and dissolved chemicals (including cyanides, hydrochloric acid, and sulfur acids). Coal washing requires up to 2000 gal of water per ton of coal processed.

Coal mining could have impacts on the hydrology of the region. Deterioration of stream quality could also result from acid and alkaline mine drainage, trace elements in mine drainage water, high dissolved solids in mine drainage water, and increased sediment loads.

Acid drainage is typically found in the eastern coals while alkaline drainage is most frequently found in the western coals. The acid drainage from underground mines is more difficulty to control than that from surface mines. But acid drainage pollution can be reduced by preventing the water from entering the mine and by rapid removal of water which does get into the mine. The effects of acid mine drainage can be minimized by neutralizing of the mine water before it is discharged to the streams. The neutralization technique, although highly effective, is more costly. In addition, exposed spoil banks from coal mining may interfere with the flow of surface water. Siltation may reduce the carrying capacity of streams and increase the possibility of flooding. Floods are also occasionally caused by accidental releases of water impounded behind waste piles or silt dams.

Impacts on water quality by surface and underground mining of oil shale are considered negligible, but mine water with high salinity may contaminate ground water supplies.

Oil shale development could affect water quality in several ways depending, in part, on the mining and processing methods and on the area in which the mining occurs. The development requires water for mining and crushing, retorting, shale oil upgrading, spent oil disposal, cooling systems for the power plant, and miscellaneous uses.

Water pollutants from extraction of offshore petroleum and natural gas are primarily nondegradable organics (oils) and dissolved solids (brine). Estimates of the oil content in the discharged brine formation water range from 1 to 4 tons of oil per 1 million bbl of oil production.[22] The amounts of oil discharged into the offshore waters are small relative to the contributions from natural seepages, ship and tanker operations, and urban and industrial runoff.

In offshore operations, the major sources of water pollution are the hydrocarbons released during blowouts and spills, and the hydrocarbons discharged with treated waste water. Sources of water pollution in onshore operations include the construction of roads and canal dredging. The former could affect the quality of area waters when drainage patterns are disturbed or when erosion is possible; the latter can result in temporarily increased turbidity and sediment suspension.

The major environmental impacts occur through the entry of oil, chemicals, brine, and waste materials into the water cycle. Spills and leaks allowing such substances to enter the surface and ground water systems can result from human error and neglect, mechanical failures, burning pits, and from blowouts. During production, large amounts of saltwater are produced daily from the oil wells.

High salinity levels resulting from oil shale processing could impose municipal and industrial water users the need for additional treatment. Saline waters could result from disturbance of the groundwater due to reinjection of excess water, leaching of shale disposal piles, or accidental release of saline mine waters. Other impacts could occur from accidental release of industrial wastes such as oil, from by-product storage pile leaching, from offsite construction, and from the release of organic materials to aquifiers.

Liquid effluents from refineries contain water pollutants including BOD, COD, oil, phenols, and suspended and dissolved solids. BOD for refinery effluents is due primarily to gas treatment; COD is due primarily to alkaylation. Whether the BOD and COD have a serious impact on water quality depends on the rate of discharge. An oxygen demand of 200 ppm in discharge water would be serious. Oil is found in oily cooling and process water, while the principal source of phenols is the catalytic cracking process. The principal dissolved solid is salt from electrostatic desalting prior to fractioning. Suspended solids consist of small amounts of oil sludge not removed in oil/water separators and the dirt from runoff water and solids from biological treatment not removed by settling or flotation.

B. Transportation/Storage[6,8]

Railroads, trucks, tankers, barges, and pipelines are considered as alternative transportation modes to bring fossil fuels to the consumers. The impact on water quality from fuel transportation alternatives depends upon present and future developments in transportation systems. Operational impacts of existing facilities are small, but new construction or upgrading of present facilities could create significant problems in aquatic systems.

Oil, gas, and coal slurry pipelines, by themselves, have little effect on area waters, once they are in place. The major impacts from these pipelines would occur during their construction. Construction activities may disrupt or alter drainage patterns and stream channels, or may degrade the stream quality. However, coal slurry pipelines could have a significant impact on both the quantity and quality of area waters. Such impacts could result from the relatively large amounts of water that may be needed to form slurry and from the disposal of the slurry water at either the receiving facility or the emergency dumping basins.

Coal storage piles and waste piles could yield sediment and organics to streams, and leached water from the piles could be acidic and contain potentially carcinogenic polycyclic aromatic hydrocarbons and toxic trace metals such as cadmium, lead, mercury, molybdenum, and selenium.

C. Oil Spills

Contamination of inland and ocean waters from oil is a major environmental problem. Accidental oil spills are inevitable from time to time. Major oil spills from tanker accidents covering hundreds of square miles may have devastating short-term effects on beaches, inshore waters, and marine life.[8]

In comparison, the amount of oil spills from pipeline shipments is much less than that from barge shipments. Frequency and severity of accidents in pipeline operations are similar to those in marine and inland waterways.

Spill accidents can be minimized by improvement of river and ocean traffic, and in the design of barges and tankers. Spilled oil can be contained by the use of oil booms and by surface-active agent applied around a spill to enclose the oil and keep it from spreading until it can be collected and dealt with by mechanical skimmers.

D. Combustion Sources[23,24]

The impact on water quality from combustion emissions results primarily from acidification of the receiving water by acid precipitation formed from SO_x and NO_x. The potential for acidification of surface water is greatest in areas where the natural buffering capacity of the water is low. Also, airborne combustion emissions are associated with the concentration and distribution of trace elements in the emissions. The trace element contamination of water systems can be from precipitation, soil leaching, surface water drainage, and ground water discharge. Increased input of trace elements from power plant stack emissions may exceed the water quality criteria of certain specific trace elements in the drainage basin where the power plant is located. Among the U.S. average values, Mn is the only element reported to exceed the federal water quality criteria. Other elements of regional concern are As, Cd, Cr, Pb, Hg, and Se.

Another impact of combustion sources on water quality comes from waste disposal of ash and sludge on land. The potential impact is the contamination of ground water by leachate from the ash/sludge disposal areas.

E. Thermal Pollution[3,6]

Regardless of the type of fossil fuel, the production of electricity by combustion

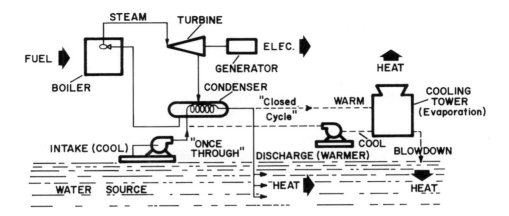

FIGURE 3.   Typical water circulation systems.

releases waste heat. Typical water circulation systems are shown in Figure 3. Significant thermal discharges occur when a power plant utilizes a once-through circulating water system to reject heat not converted into electric energy. The heat energy discharged is directly related to the efficiency of the plant. About 85% of the waste heat is released to the cooling water, and 15% to the atmosphere. For a given amount of heat transfer, the temperature rise of the cooling water is inversely proportional to its flow. On the average, temperature rises of about 9°C (16°F) are encountered for economic and process considerations.

With increasing temperature, the density, viscosity, surface tension, and oxygen solubility of the receiving water are decreased; the vapor pressure, oxygen diffusivity, stream reaeration, and biological oxygen coefficients are increased. As a result, the waste assimilation capacity of the stream is reduced. The receiving waters, where there are rapid temperature changes, are particularly stressful to fish and other aquatic life. The effects may be severe but are generally site specific.

The amount of heat rejected to cooling water represents 45% of the heating value of the fuel used in the most efficient fossil fuel plants. About 40% of all the water used in the U.S. is estimated for cooling electric power plants. Although the same water may be used for cooling many times, it is clear that an upper limit of cooling water availability may be reached. This suggests that the solution is not in treating the heat as a waste product. Rather, the heat must be viewed as a resource that can be used. For example, the waste heat may be used for aquaculture, agriculture, and power for energy intensive industries.

VI. IMPACT ON LAND[6,8]

Land use is affected primarily by mining, fuel processing, power generation facilities, the right of way of roads and transmission lines, and waste disposal. It has been estimated that a 1000 MW power plant requires about 12,300 acres for coal mining, processing, and waste storage and about 3,000 acres for structures and roads.[21] Land requirements for transmission lines vary with the number of lines and the height of towers. Right of way for major transmission lines varies from 100 to 400 ft.[22] The land required for disposal of combustion wastes ranges from 0.4 to 0.7 acres/MW of installed boiler capacity.[21]

A. Extraction/Processing/Transportation/Storage

Effects of mining on land use vary widely and depend upon such factors as the type of mining, characteristics of overburden, steepness of the terrain and amount of precipitation.

Land use for coal extraction by area strip mining varies from 0.8 to 5.9 acres/10^{12} Btu. Augering and contour mining have more severe land impacts than does area mining. Contour mining requires 12.0 acres/10^{12} Btu; augering requires 3.9 acres/10^{12} Btu.

Land impacts of underground mining include subsidence and refuse storage sites and a site for a water treatment facility. Estimates of land disruptions by underground mining range from 9.6 to 23 acres/10^{12} Btu. Underground fires may weaken or destroy coal pillars that support the surface, causing subsidence with consequent damage to surface structures.

The land affected by coal mines can be revegetated. The success of revegetation with native flora depends on climate, topography, and soil. Under certain conditions, for instance, in the arid West or on the steep, eroding slopes in Appalachia, the land damage is very difficult to restore.

A potential source of land pollution from oil extraction is a blowout during drilling. A well blowout may occur at any time during exploratory or development drilling. During a blowout, oil, gas, drilling mud, and brines may be sprayed into the air. Wind-blown pollutants can damage surrounding vegetation and other resources.

A modern petroleum refinery requires a large area for tank farms to store crude oil and products, and for process facilities including setting ponds, water treatment plants, disposal sites for oily sludge, etc. The average minimum land requirements would be 12.5 acres/1000 bbl/day.

Transportation of oil and gas, which is largely by underground pipelines, does not normally produce land problems. However, the special case of transporting oil from Alaska by pipeline raises numerous land-use problems. Coal may be transported by pipeline, waterway, highway, or railway. Land use is affected by the presence of the transportation systems, including their rights of ways. Land is also required for fuel storage.

B. Combustion Waste Disposal[8,26]

Burning coal produces large amounts of solid waste in the form of ash and FGD sludges. The quantities of these depend on several factors: ash and sulfur content of the coal, the emission regulations, the types of ash collection devices and FGD systems, and operating conditions of the systems and boiler. A typical utility operating at 70% load produces 100 to 500 tons of dry sludge annually per megawatt of capacity under New Source Performance Standards.[26]

Some of the ash (about 15%) is being used for the production of cement and building products, in roads, as a filler, and as a soil amendment, but other uses are to be found. At present, coal ash and FGD sludges are disposed of exclusively on land although ocean and mine disposal under careful control conditions may offer alternative disposal options.

Disposal of scrubber sludges on land without pretreatment may create problems. The FGD sludges contain a high concentration of calcium sulfite, which is difficult for dewatering and has poor compaction characteristics. The sludges disposed must be stabilized in order to permit reclamation of the landfill sites.

VII. IMPACT ON NOISE POLLUTION[3,6,8]

There is a certain amount of noise associated with stationary engines used in drilling and production operations, with transportation, with normal refinery operations, and at the power plant sites. Since these sources are located far from populated areas, such noise generally creates only local problems.

The major sources of noise associated with both underground and surface mining operations are from the crusher and from other mining and transportation equipment. The blasting carried out at strip mines produces an intermittent source of intense noise.

No significant problem is expected from oil shale processing plants, refineries, and power generating plants.

A transmission line may generate electromagnetic noise which could interfere with radio and television reception in weak signal areas. Such interference would be confined to a distance of several hundred feet from the line.

VIII. LEGAL ASPECTS

Energy production and use from fossil fuel sources is one of the most important determinants of environmental quality. Current environmental laws and regulations were established mainly on the basis of adverse impact on public health and the environment. In the process of developing laws and regulations, a threshold level of stress is generally assumed below which no harmful impact will occur. This also provides a thrust to develop new control technologies and to achieve better performance. But one of the key problems is the uncertainty associated with predicting how the environment will respond to energy sources, how human health and ecosystems will be affected by the pollution generated, and how measures taken to prevent damage will work. As more is learned about the impact of fossil fuel energy sources on the quality of our air, water, and land, new laws and regulations can be expected and current laws and regulations may be amended.

The severity of environmental impacts resulting from the production and use of fossil fuel energy sources depends critically upon effectiveness of governmental law and regulations, and the technological developments necessary to implement the regulations. Environmental regulations can change the pattern of energy consumption, encourage energy saving through recycling of materials, delay in production and supply, mandate installation of pollution control devices, and push for the best available pollution control technology.

Clean Air Act requires each state to develop an implementation plan (SIP) for regulating air pollution, with federal backup enforcement by the EPA. The Act empowers EPA to establish national new-source performance standards for certain categories of industrial sources, including electricity generating power plants. The current state of affairs is that a new power plant may be constructed in "dirty air" areas only if an equivalent amount of pollution is reduced as an offset in the same area. New sources in clean air areas may only "use up" defined increments of the area's margin above the secondary ambient air quality standards. The Clean Air Act further empowers EPA to set national emission standards for hazardous air pollutants (NESHAP).

The Federal Water Pollution Control Act (FWPCA) divides sources of water pollution into three categories and subjects each to a different method of regulation. The categories are existing sources, new or modified sources, and sources of toxic pollutants, whether existing or new.

The FWPCA requires the achievement of "best practicable control technology" (BPCT) by July 1, 1977. There are three methods of translating the statutory requirements of BPCT into numerical limitations on existing sources of pollution:

1.   EPA sets effluent limits that are binding on the entire industrial category.

TABLE 11

**Federal Environmental Legislation Applicable to Fossil
Fuel Energy Sources**

Energy Supply and Environmental Control Act
The Clean Air Act
The Clean Water Act
The Water Pollution Control Act
The National Environmental Policy Act
The Environmental Quality Improvement Act
The Marine Protection, Research, and Sanctuaries Act
The Solid Waste Disposal Act
The Federal Land Policy and Management Act
The Tanker and Vessel Safety Act
The Alaska Natural Gas Transportation Act
The Surface Mining Control and Reclamation Act

2.   EPA sets guidelines for effluents that will generally be applied to the entire industrial category, but will leave some room for flexibility by the enforcement agencies.
3.   Each source negotiates with the enforcement agency on individual definition of BPCT.

The FWPCA requires EPA to set new-source performance standards (NSPS). These standards apply uniformly to all new sources throughout the U.S., with little left to the discretion of enforcement agencies. The FWPCA also gives EPA authority to set effluent standards for toxic water pollutants. Unlike other regulatory provisions in this Act, enforcement authority is not delegated to the states; but the states may set and enforce their own toxic standards, which may be even stricter than EPA's.

Although air and water pollution controls are by far the most commonly encountered environmental problems for energy production and use, there are other legal issues that may arise and unexpectedly cause severe problems. The most common of these issues are land use, noise, solid waste, occupational safety and health, and nuisance laws. The federal environmental laws and regulations that appear to have the greatest impacts on fossil fuel energy sources are listed in Table 11.

Certainly, successful implementation of the federal laws and regulations require responsible and resourceful state and local environmental control policies and actions. Each state is responsible for establishing its own environmental control rules and regulations for the implementation of both federal and state laws and regulations. As an example, the provisions of the New York State Department of Environmental Conservation's Rules and Regulations and the Environmental Conservation Law applicable to the production and use of fossil fuel energy sources are compiled in Table 12. To implement these regulations is a lot tougher task than one thought it would be. The problems of controlling air, water, and land pollution are interdependent and, therefore, must be solved with the awareness of total environment. For example, the quantities of solid wastes will be greatly influenced by the degree of enforcement of air and water pollution regulations. As the air and water regulations become more restrictive, the solid waste disposal problem due to increased treatment will increase. It is important for the environmental manager to apply the total environmental concept and to minimize the conflict involving the problems of air, water, and land pollution.

TABLE 12

New York State Environmental Law and Regulations Applicable to Electric Generating Power Plants

New York State Environmental Conservation Law (Section)	Title, description
11-0109	General — Jurisdiction of Water Resources Law
11-0503	Nets: License Required; Power of Department
11-1505	General Provision
11-1515	Nets: Hauling and Tagging
11-1749	Previous Grantees not to Divert Waters without a License
17-0823	Power Plant Siting
19-0309	Certificates of Compliance for Purposes of the Tax Law
27-0511	Local Laws, Ordinances and Regulations
49	Protection of Natural and Man-made Beauty
New York Code, Rules & Regulations (Part)	
200	General Provisions — Prevention and Control of Air Contamination and Air Pollution
203	Indirect Sources
207	Control Measures for Air Pollution Episodes
211	General Prohibition
212	Process and Exhaust and/or Ventilation Systems
215	Open Fires
217	Emissions from Motor Vehicles Propelled by Gasoline Engines
218	Emissions from Vehicles Propelled by Diesel Engines
225	Fuel Composition and Use
227	Stationary Combustion Installations
257	Air Quality Standards
360	Requirements for Solid Waste Disposal Facilities
420	General — Mineral Resources (Mined Land Reclamation)
450	Noise from Heavy Motor Vehicles
452	Measurement of Noise Emission, Highway Operation
453	Measurement of Noise Emission, Stationary Test
608	Use and Protection of Waters
615	Environmental Impact Assessment
618	Implementation of State Environmental Quality Review Act (SPDES)
621	Uniform Procedures
750	General — State Pollution Discharge Elimination System
751	Required Permits
752	Applications
753	Notice and Public Participation
754	Provisions of the SPDES Permits
755	Duration and Issuance of SPDES Permits
756	Monitoring, Recording and Reporting
757	Modification, Suspension and Revocations of SPDES Permits and Schedules of Compliance Hearing after Permit Issuance

IX. FUTURE OUTLOOK

Advances in living standards have rested upon the availability and exploitation of energy sources — renewable and nonrenewable. Total energy demand has been and will still be a major factor influencing environmental consequences of energy systems in the future. Energy conservation helps to slow the growth of energy demand, but is not an ultimate solution.

As domestic supplies of oil and natural gas are being depleted, attention has shifted to coal. There will be a strong need to increase coal production if electricity energy grows at the anticipated rate of about twice as fast as the total of all energy sources in the last 20 years. But coal production is contingent on the price of oil and natural gas, environmental regulations, availability of coal transportation, surface mining regulations and other factors.

The application of improved technology in the area of fuel conversion and pollution control can be expected to achieve substantial reduction in the overall environmental impacts. Efforts are underway to replace dwindling supplies of oil and natural gas by converting coal to gaseous and liquid fuels. Synthetic fuels may offer major air quality advantages for currently regulated pollutants, but the fuels present uncertain, potentially serious hazards for pollutants that are not yet regulated. Thus, an increase in coal utilization would add to the risks of environmental damages. However, the damages can be expected to increase at a slower rate because of the dramatic increases in the use of pollution control devices mandated by federal and state regulations now being implemented, and also because of the current trend toward cleaner fuels and renewable energy sources.

REFERENCES

1. *U.S.A.'s Energy Outlook, 1977—1990,* published by Exxon Company, 1977.
2. **McRae, A., Dudas, J., and Rowland, H.,** Eds., *The Energy Source Book,* The Center for Compliance Information, Aspen Publication, Germantown, Md., 1977.
3. U.S. ERDA, The Environmental Impact of Electric Power Generation: Nuclear and Fossil, prepared by Pennsylvania Department of Education, 1975, 121.
4. **Hensel, R. P.,** *ASTM Standardization News,* p. 10, 1978.
5. **Blade, O. C.,** Burner Fuel Oils, Mineral Industry Surveys, U.S. Bureau of Mines, Washington, D.C., 1961.
6. **Dvorak, A. J., et al.,** The Environmental Effects of Using Coal for Generating Electricity, Argonne National Laboratory NUREG-0252, available from NTIS, 1977.
7. **Pikul, R. P. and Rabin, R. ,** Program Plan for Environmental Effects of Energy, Section V Oil and Gas, Report MTR-6726, The Mitre Corporation, McLean, Va., 1974.
8. **Morris, S. C.,** Environmental Effects of Fossil Fuels, BNL-20294, Brookhaven National Laboratory, Upton, N.Y., 1975.
9. **MacKinnon, D. J.,** Nitric oxide formation at high temperatures, *J. APCA,* 24, 237, 1974.
10. **Shen, T. T., Cheng, R. J., Mohnen, V. A., Current, M., and Hudson, J. B.,** Characterization of Differences Between Oil-Fired and Coal-Fired Power Plant Emissions, Proceedings 4th Int. Clean Air Congress, Tokyo, May 1977, 386.
11. U.S. Public Health Service, Control Techniques for Particulate Air Pollutants, National Air Pollution Control Administration, Publication No. AP-51, January 1969, 9.
12. **Sawyer, R. F.,** *Combustion Generated Air Pollution,* Starkman, E. S., Ed., Plenum Press, New York, 1971, 275.
13. **Ruch, R. R., Gluskoter, H. J., and Shimp, N. F.,** Occurrence and Distribution of Potentially Volatile Trace Elements in Coal, Illinois State Geological Survey Report No. 72, Springfield, Ill., 1974.
14. **Natusch, D. F. S., Wallace, J. R., and Evans, C. A., Jr.,** Toxic trace elements: preferential concentration in respirable particles, *Science,* 183, 202, 1974.

15. **Kaakinen, J. W., Jorden, R. M., Lawasani, M. H., and West, R. E.,** Trace element behavior in coal-fired power plant, *Environ. Sci. Technol.,* 9, 962, 1975.
16. **Natusch, D. F. S.,** Characterization of Atmospheric Pollutants from Power Plants, Proc. and Conf. on the Great Lakes, Windsor, Ontario, 1976, 114.
17. **Hull, A. P.,** Radiation in perspective: some comparison of environmental risks from nuclear and fossil-fired power plants, *Nucl. Saf.,* 12, 185, 1971.
18. **Martin, J. E.,** Comparative Population Radiation Dose Commitments of Nuclear and Fossil Fuel Electric Cycles, Proc. 8th Midyear Tropical Symp. Health Physics Society, Knoxville, Tenn., October 1974, 319.
19. Particulate Polycyclic Organic Matter, Report of the Committee on Biological Effects of Atmospheric Pollutants, National Academy of Sciences, Washington, D.C., 1972.
20. Preferred Standards Path Report for Polycyclic Organic Matter, Office of Air Quality Planning & Standards, U.S. Environmental Protection Agency, Durham, N.C., 1974.
21. Federal Register, Vol. 43, No. 10, January 16, 1978, 2235.
22. **Kash, D. E., et al.,** *Energy Under Ocean: A Technology Assessment of Outer Continental Shelf Oil and Gas Operations,* University of Oklahoma Press, Norman, 1973.
23. **Likens, G. E. and Bormann, F. H.,** Acid rain: a serious regional environmental problem, *Science,* 184, 1176, 1974.
24. **Gatz, D. F.,** Comment on "Acid Precipitation in the Northeastern United States" by Charles V. Cogbill and Gene E. Likens, *Water Resour. Res.,* 12(3), 569, 1976.
25. Energy Alternatives: A Comparative Analysis, University of Oklahoma Publication, Norman, Oklahoma, p. 52-56 of Section I, available at the U.S. Government Printing Office, Stock No. 041-011-00025-4, Washington, D.C., 1975.
26. Health and Environmental Impacts of Increased Generation of Coal Ash and FGD Sludges. EPA Report to the Committee on Health and Ecological Effects of Increased Coal Utilization, Environmental Protection Agency, Washington, D.C., November 1977, 1.
27. EPA/IERL No. Control Review, Vol. 1, No. 3, 1977.
28. *Electron. World,* McGraw-Hill, New York, September 1973.
29. Federal Power Commission, Dept. of Energy, Washington, D.C., July 1973.
30. **Simon, J. A. and Hopkins, H. E.,** Geology of coal, in *Elements of Practical Coal Mining,* 111. State Geol. Surv. Reprint, 1973; and Hammond, Metz, and Maugh, *Energy and the Future,* AAAS, 1973.
31. EPA Publication AP-42, Compilation of Air Pollution Emission Factors, 1973.

Chapter 3

THE ENVIRONMENTAL IMPACT OF NUCLEAR ENERGY SOURCES

E. J. Rolinski

TABLE OF CONTENTS

I. INTRODUCTION

The expenditure of energy in any form must reflect a careful assessment of the total environmental impact. This is particularly true for the case of nuclear energy sources since there must be a concern for the extraction of the fuel, its processing, transportation, fuel utilization, and finally its disposal. However, along with these come the attendant problems of power plant siting, licensing, transportation, and ultimate disposal of the fuel and its by-products. Nuclear fission fuels have little utility for producing other chemicals. The only purpose of reactor grade fission fuels is to produce power in power plants. Coal, natural gas, and oil have other uses, either as petrochemicals, raw materials for chemical processes, or coal derivatives. Once these conventional fuels are used up, their usefulness to other industries is gone forever. Nuclear fuels on the other hand provide an effective means of producing the vast amounts of power required, or projected into the 1990s even with a high coal use, expanded natural gas capacity, and oil imports. The critical need for more energy can be supplied in part by nuclear energy sources, but the environmental factors must be weighed very carefully. The apparent conflict between energy needs and the clean environment poses a tremendous problem that must be solved with a clear understanding of the potential risks involved.

This chapter will consider the environmental impact of nuclear energy sources in detail. In order to understand the complex nature of nuclear energy and its implications we will discuss the following:

1.   The fission process
2.   Nuclear fuel and fuel cycles
3.   Nuclear reactors
4.   Types of reactors
5.   Safety systems
6.   Radioactive pollution
7.   Current attitude of public to nuclear power plants

II. THE FISSION PROCESS

The fundamental building block for all matter is the atom. An atom can be considered to be a dense core of particles consisting of neutrons and protons which form a positively charged nucleus, which is surrounded by negatively charged particles of electrons.

A nuclide characterizes an atom by the number of neutrons and protons in the nucleus and by their energy levels. There are more than 1300 known nuclides. As an example, an atom of chlorine has 18 neutrons in its nucleus and is a nuclide, but an atom of chlorine with 20 neutrons is another nuclide.

There are two main distinguishing features of nuclides, i.e., they can be stable or radioactive. Radioactive nuclides which are sometimes called radionuclides, undergo spontaneous nuclear changes which transform them into other nuclides. The process by which this transformation takes place is called radioactive decay. The radioactive decay process transforms the radioactive nuclide eventually into a stable nuclide.

There are about 265 stable nuclides and 66 radionuclides found to occur naturally. The remainder of the 1300 known nuclides are man-made radionuclides, and over 80% of all known nuclides are radioactive.

When the radioactive decay process takes place, the nucleus of a radioactive atom emits radiation. The radiation may be in the form of charged or uncharged particles and/or in the form of electromagnetic rays (photons). Some radionuclides decay by the emission of alpha particles, which are high energy helium nuclei. Other radionuclides decay by the emission of beta particles which can be either high energy negatively charged electrons (negatrons) or positively charged electrons (positrons). Radioactive decay by the emission of these particles is usually followed by the emission of photons of two kinds:

1.   Gamma rays that are produced in the nucleus of the radioactive decaying atom
2.   X-rays that are produced as a result of the rearrangement of orbital electrons

The difference between gamma rays and X-rays are the source of their origin and the fact that X-rays are usually of lower energy and hence are less penetrating than gamma rays.

The radioactive decay process continues until a stable or nonradioactive nuclide is formed. Uranium, for example, is radioactive and it slowly decays into elements of radium, radon, and polonium, and finally when lead is formed, the radioactive decay process stops. The time required for one half of the radioactive atoms of a nuclide to decay to its daughter nuclide is known as the half-life of that nuclide. An atom with a short half-life quickly decays, while an atom with a long half-life decays slowly. A mathematical equation for this radioactive decay is known as an exponential decay law. The half-life of uranium is 4.4×10^9 years, whereas that of UX_1 the first product in the uranium series is 24.5 days. Because of the long life of uranium compared to UX_1 the number of U atoms present in a sample is effectively constant over measurable periods, and the recovery of U activity reaches effectively the same initial activity after repeated separations of daughter UX_1 from parent U. In case the radioactive atom yields a daughter atom which itself is radioactive, and so on in a radioactive series, the kinetics of radioactive decays is treated as consecutive first-order reactions. Thus, the radioactive decay from Uranium 238 to Radium G or Lead 206 requires 15 radioactive decays, where the particles emitted are either alpha, beta, and/or gamma radiation.

When an atom emits an alpha particle, its atomic number decreases by two and mass number decreases by four. The emission of a beta particle increases the atomic number by one. There is no marked change in atomic weight associated with beta emission.

Thus in the Uranium series, five alpha particles each of mass four are lost between radium with an atomic weight of 226 and lead 206. When atoms of certain binary nuclides are bombarded by neutrons, the nuclei of some of these atoms will capture a neutron and become unstable so that they fission or split into two or more smaller atoms. Together the fission products weigh slightly less than the original atom and the bombarding neutron combined. The missing mass is converted into energy. The fission process can be visualized by considering the nucleus as a drop of liquid. When a neutron hits it, oscillations are set up. The positive charges of the protons acquire an unsymmetrical distribution, and the resulting repulsion can lead to splitting of the nuclear drop. Since U-235 contains an odd number of neutrons, considerable energy is set free when it gains a neutron. This kinetic energy starts the disturbance within the nucleus that leads to fission.

As the fission fragments fly apart, most of this energy appears almost instantaneously as heat as the fragments lose their energy of motion to the surrounding material. When an atom fissions, several free neutrons are released. These are available to strike other atoms and cause them to fission. In the case of U-235, it will form Ba-129 as one of its products and two neutrons. The other product is Kr-94. This kind of chain reaction is depicted in Figure 1. If a chain reaction is to continue, there must be

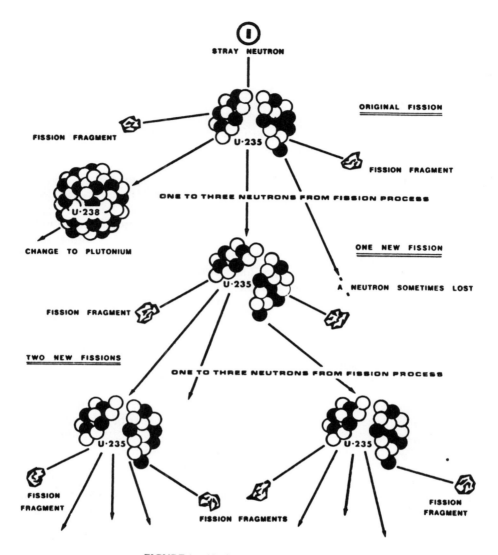

FIGURE 1.   Nuclear fission chain reaction.

enough fissionable atoms packed closely enough to insure the capture of enough neutrons to sustain the fission process. The amount of material required to sustain the fission process is called the critical mass.

Usually the smaller atoms produced by fission are radioactive. These fission fragments decay by negatron emission followed by gamma ray emission as depicted in Figure 2 which shows 1 of the more than 30 possible decay chains which follow the fissioning of an atom of U-235. The fission fragments are atoms of radioactive bromine and xenon and they each in turn decay through many steps by emitting beta particles. The half-life for each part of the decay chain is shown in Figure 2 which must be considered in the operation and design of nuclear fueled power plants.

The heat from the fission process is used to produce hot water and steam or to heat a gas such as helium which can in turn be used to spin turbines and thus generate electricity. Various types of nuclear reactor designs for extracting heat from the fission process will be discussed in Section IV.

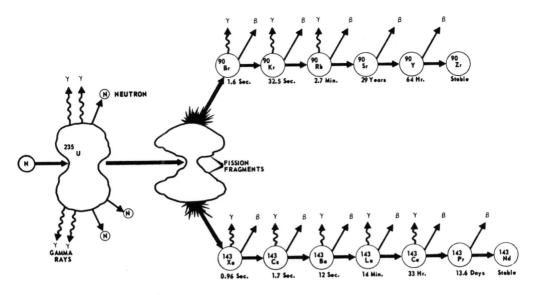

FIGURE 2.   Uranium fission and beta decay chains.

III. NUCLEAR FUEL AND FUEL CYCLES

Uranium is the basic nuclear fuel because it contains U-235, the only nuclide found in nature that readily undergoes fission. The natural concentration of U-235 in uranium is 0.7%, the balance being U-238, which does not readily undergo fission. The fission of a pound of U-235 would produce the same amount of energy as burning 3 million tons of coal, or enough coal to fill about 42 32-ton railroad cars.

The deposits of commercial-grade uranium found in the U.S. are in the western part of the country. Some shallow deposits are mined by open pit techniques but most are taken from underground mines. Uranium mining disturbs land since it takes about 30,000 tons of uranium ore to produce the required 30 tons of uranium needed to fuel a nuclear reactor for a year. The potential environmental damage from nuclear fuel cycle power generation is indicated in Table 1 for air, water, land, solid waste, and radiation, all of which must be considered in detail.

Although only U-235 is fissioned by slow neutrons, some artificial nuclides, notably plutonium-239 and uranium-233, can also be fissioned by slow neutrons. Such nuclides are said to be fissile and must be separated from the fertile material when considering the nuclear fuel cycle (see Figure 3).

The major steps in a nuclear fuel cycle are presented schematically in Figure 3. Since each reactor concept uses its own fuel cycle, the figure is generalized to include the following six steps:

1.   Natural sources and isotopic separations of fissile and fertile material
2.   Fuel fabrication
3.   Reactor operations, steady state and transient modeling of fuel performance
4.   Fuel processing
5.   Fission product and actinide waste management and storage
6.   Recycled fissile and fertile fuel

Another generalized nuclear fuel cycle is shown in Figure 4. The uranium is mined by conventional methods and is shipped to mills where the uranium is separated from

TABLE 1

Potential Environmental Damage from Nuclear Fuel Cycle Power Generation

	Exploration and extraction	Ore concentration and processing	Transportation	Utilization
Air		Particulate emissions		Radiation fallout
Water	Waste banks leaching, uranium mine water	Waste banks leaching		Thermal discharge
Land	Strip mining effects		Transmission lines	
Solid waste	Underground mining wastes	Ore dressing waste		Waste disposal from fuel processing plants
Radiation	Exposure to miners	Exposure to plant workers	Possible accidents	Exposure during generation and disposal of wastes, possible accidents

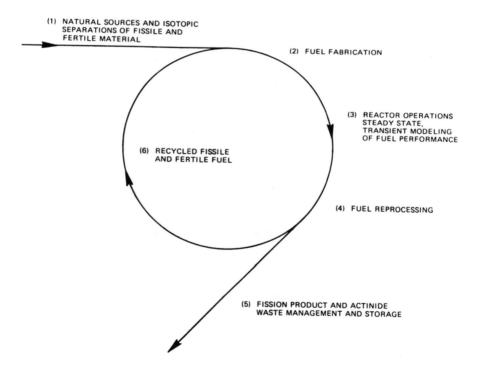

FIGURE 3.   Nuclear fuel cycle.

the extraneous bulk material and concentrated. The uranium compound is refined and converted to gaseous uranium hexaflouride UF_6 and sent to a government owned gaseous diffusion plant for enrichment.

Enrichment is the process by which the concentration of fissionable uranium is in-

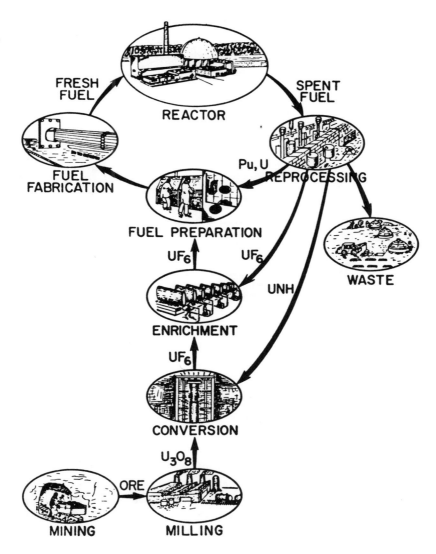

FIGURE 4.   Major steps in nuclear fuel cycle.

creased to a desirable level. At present the method used is the gaseous diffusion process, although the feasibility of gas centrifugation or ultracentrifuge enrichment is being actively developed in several other countries and is on the verge of commercialization in some of them. The process of ultracentrifuge enrichment requires less power than gaseous diffusion plants and has other advantages.[3]

Other enrichment technologies that are also gaining in importance include the aerodynamic, or nozzle mass separation approach which is being developed in West Germany and South Africa. A pilot aerodynamic enrichment plant has been built in South Africa.[3]

The laser technique for isotopic enrichment has also been investigated in the laboratory and may become an important enrichment technique in the future.

The next step in the nuclear fuel cycle is the fuel preparation stage in which the output of the enrichment stage is converted to UO_2 and shaped into pellets.

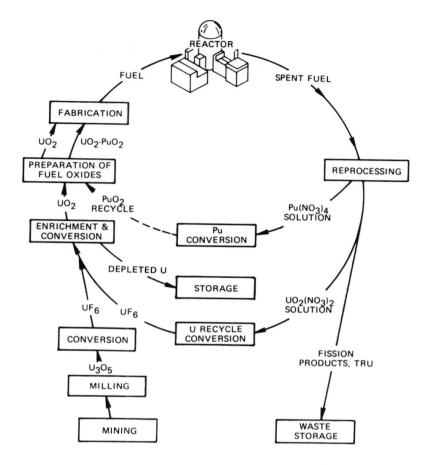

FIGURE 5.   The LWR fuel cycle.

The fuel fabrication step is one of the most expensive and represents almost 35% of the fuel cycle cost. The cost is high because of fuel cladding which represents the primary containment for the fuel in the reactor and later for the fission products which build up as the fuel is used (see Section II). More will be discussed about the exotic cladding required when various reactor designs are presented in Section IV.

The heart of the nuclear fuel cycle is the reactor itself, and although reactor designs will vary, a typical light water reactor fuel cycle is shown in Figure 5. The spent fuel is reprocessed, and its plutonium is recycled through thermal reactors which improves the percentage of the burned-up fuel which usually is only a few percent.[4]

The fuel elements that are withdrawn from the reactor are now highly radioactive as the result of fission product generation and must be cooled (requiring water) and may cause possible contamination problems. The function of the reprocessing step is to separate the unfissioned uranium and plutonium from the fission products.

After reprocessing, the unusable fission products will have to be treated and further allowed to decay and sent to the waste management area (see Section VIII). The fissionable uranium and plutonium are then sent to the conversion enrichment and fuel preparation steps of the fuel cycle, depending on the nature of the material and the demands of the fuel cycle. In considering the reactor operations step, elemental transport and chemical modeling of fuel performance are relatively newly adapted methods which are important when considering dry corrosion mechanisms in fuel elements.

Transient accident modeling is also a high significant aspect to the overall problem of reactor operations. These will be discussed in Section VIII.

IV. NUCLEAR REACTORS

The heart of the nuclear fuel cycle, as well as the heat production source, is in the design of the nuclear reactor. The nuclear reactor serves to provide the environment in which fission reactions can be initiated, sustained, and controlled. They also have to be designed to allow the possible removal of heat for power production. Their design has to allow for the control of runaway situations and transient heat removal problems.

Certain components are common to all nuclear reactors and are:

1. The core where the fuel is fissioning
2. The control system consisting of control rods and other controls
3. The coolant that transfers heat to a fluid for the power cycle
4. Shielding that does not allow fission products into the working area
5. Moderator that slows down neutrons without absorbing them

A neutron freshly produced in a fission reaction travels at 10,000 miles a second. If it collides with U-235 atom it causes fission. However, since in natural uranium there is only one U-235 atom for every 140 U-238 atoms, the possibility of a fast neutron hitting a U-235 atom and producing another fission is small. A neutron is more likely to produce fission if it travels about 1 mile/sec. Therefore, there are two ways of making a reactor to operate, either by slowing down fast neutrons or by increasing the proportion of fissile atoms. The slow neutrons are called thermal neutrons, and the nuclear reactors that use moderators are called thermal reactors. Most current types of power reactors are thermal reactors.

Reactors relying on fast neutrons to maintain the chain reaction are called fast reactors. The fast reactors are fuel in which the proportion of fissile material has been considerably enriched by the addition of either plutonium 239 or more uranium-235.

The reactor core itself is generally made up of bundles of fuel rods which contain uranium oxide pellets. When a number of bundles of rods are assembled, a critical mass is attained and the chain reaction starts. Individual fuel rods do not contain sufficient fuel for a critical mass. The population of neutrons which maintain the chain reaction is controlled with neutron absorbing material such as cadmium, hafnium, and boron usually in the form of rods. These rods, when lowered into the reactor, absorb neutrons, slow down the nuclear reaction, and thereby reduce the reactor output. Raising the rods allows the reaction to build up again. This makes it possible to produce heat at a desired or steady reaction rate, or to shut down the reactor if required.

The coolant, either liquid or gas, flows over the fuel rods and removes heat from the fuel. Normally the coolant is passed through the reactor core, transferring heat to a boiler to produce steam. Immense quantities of heat are generated so that the cooling system must be efficient to avoid overheating and melting of the reactor core. The coolant does not come into contact with the actual fuel, since the radioactive material itself is sealed within the fuel rods. The coolant must be cheap and noncorrosive and must not absorb neutrons. Coolants used include gases such as helium, liquids such as ordinary water, light water, or heavy water, and liquid metals such as sodium. Sometimes the functions of coolant and moderator are combined in a single material, such as ordinary water, since the hydrogen atom in water is a good moderator.

Shielding is necessary to protect the public and reactor operators from neutrons and gamma radiation given off by the fission products. Shielding consists of special materials such as concrete many feet thick, frequently with an inner steel shield to reduce the speed of the fast neutrons before they enter the concrete. Some shielding components are designed to reflect strong neutrons back into the reactor. Other materials are used to absorb radiation to protect structural parts from radiation damage while other shielding components prevent biological damage from escaping radiation from the reactor.

V. TYPES OF REACTORS FOR POWER PLANTS

The types of reactors in use today include the light water reactor which uses boiling water and pressurized water systems, the gas cooled reactor, and a fast breeder reactor. The fast breeder reactor research was slowed down recently. Fast breeder reactors require a vast amount of reprocessing. In April 1977, President Carter announced a deemphasis of fast breeder reactor development. Specifically, the Clinch River breeder reactor project was cancelled.[3] At the same time, the Carter Administration announced plans to streamline the regulatory requirements for installing light water reactors. Thus, the following will emphasize the major reactor developments in light of current trends.

In the fall of 1974, there were 52 nuclear power reactors operating in the U.S. which supplied about 8% of the total electrical power generated. Another 59 nuclear power reactors were under construction and 118 were being planned. At the close of 1973, about 65% of all nuclear power reactors sold were of the pressurized water type, 31% were of the boiling water type, and 3% were of the gas cooled reactor type. During the latter part of 1974, the construction of some 80 nuclear power reactors was stopped or slowed down, because of problems involving capital expenditures and high interest rates, labor problems or material shortages, and licensing requirements. The action of the Carter Administration to streamline the regulatory requirements for light water reactors in April 1977 was intended to boost the installation of nuclear reactors and to enhance the expansion or the continuation of nuclear reactor projects into the 1980s.

Considering that nuclear power stations take about 10 years or more to build, the Carter Administration further took steps to help the sagging nuclear industry indefinitely by deferring the reprocessing of spent nuclear fuel from domestic nuclear power plants and thereby allowing the "once through" fuel cycle to become competitive. This action by the Carter Administration was prompted by the concern for nuclear proliferation and the balance of payments problem aggravated by increasing oil prices and inflation. Current and domestic nuclear reactor fuel supplies are estimated to be adequate for about 700 nuclear reactors for their full life span or an even longer number if a full lifetime commitment of fuel were not made for each nuclear power plant when it began operation.

A. Boiling Water Reactors (BWR)

The boiling water reactor is depicted in Figure 6 in which the fuel is enriched uranium oxide and the moderator and coolant is water. In the boiling water reactor, water is brought into the reactor, allowed to boil, and is expelled from the reactor vessel as saturated steam, which is sent to drive a turbine that in turn rotates at high speed to generate electrical power.

A typical boiling water reactor core is approximated by a right cylinder having a diameter of about 11 ft and a height of about 13 ft (see Figure 7). The reactor core is made up of many fuel assemblies such as the one shown in Figure 8. The fuel assem-

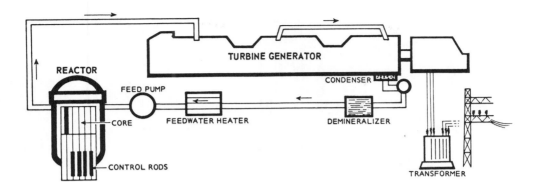

FIGURE 6.   Boiling water reactor.

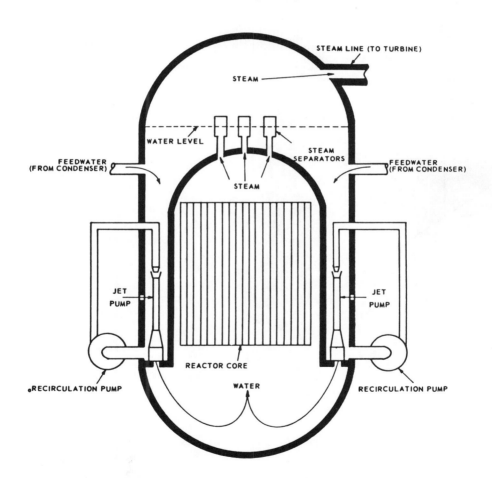

FIGURE 7.   Schematic arrangement of boiling water reactor.

blies contain the fuel rods which are zirconium alloy tubes. Within each zirconium alloy tube, which is the cladding, there is a vertical stack of uranium oxide fuel pellets which contain slightly enriched uranium. Enriched uranium contains more fissionable U-235 than natural uranium, for example 2 to 3% instead of the normal 0.7%.

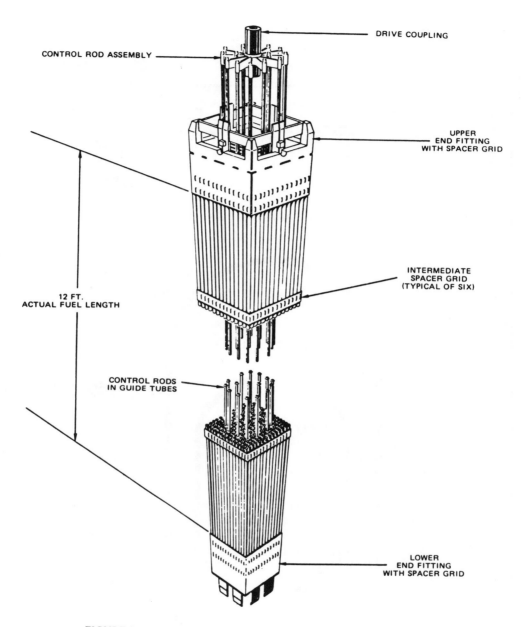

FIGURE 8.   Fuel assembly showing partially inserted control rod assembly.

A BWR is a relatively simple reactor. It has no heat exchanger and the reactor pressure vessel has to withstand smaller pressures than a pressurized water reactor. The main problem with the BWR is that as the water boils in the core, bubbles form that change the moderating and neutron absorbing properties of the coolant/moderator and also affect the transfer of heat from the fuel. To overcome this, the main body of the water is pumped out from the core and returned at a lower point.

Typically, a BWR operates at a pressure of around 1000 psi and produces saturated steam at 550°F. The BWR has the advantage of simplicity and the disadvantage of requiring a large core for cooling. Some of the materials in the water may become

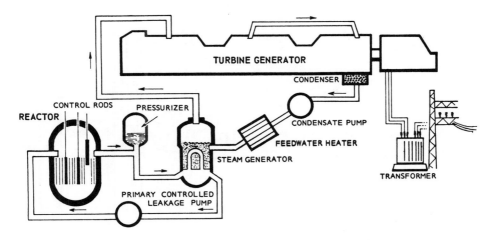

FIGURE 9.   Pressurized water reactor (PWR).

radioactive and can be carried through to the turbine section, increasing the size of the area where radiation exists and must be shielded. Early versions of the BWR had high emissions of radioactive gases as compared with other reactors. The first economic breakthrough in electricity generation in the U.S. was made with the 515 MW(e) plant at Oyster Creek, N.J. that generates electricity more cheaply than a coal station in that area. Large (up to 1000 MW) BWR have been designed and built such as the Dresden nuclear power station in Illinois. The Creek plant introduced a new safety feature "pressure suppression" which allowed any steam escaping from the reactor to be condensed in cool water instead of being given a large volume of space to expand into. Safety features such as these are discussed in Section VIII.

B. Pressurized Water Reactors (PWR)

The coolant in these reactors is ordinary water under very high pressure of about 2000 psia and 590°F, where the high pressure helps keep the water from boiling. A schematic diagram of the PWR is shown in Figure 9. Water is pumped through the core and removed at the top as a heated liquid. The water is then circulated through a heat exchanger where steam is produced from water in a secondary loop which drives the turbine. The cooled water in the primary loop is returned to the reactor to again cool the core. The fuel in a PWR is enriched uranium oxide pellets, large numbers of which are fitted into zirconium alloy tubes to form rods running the length of the reactor core (see Figures 10 and 11). The fuel rods are arranged in groups of fuel assemblies, and the gaps between must be kept small because water is a good moderator.

Because of the high pressure of the coolant, the pressure vessel must be made of very thick steel. The PWR is a very compact reactor, smaller than a boiling water reactor of equivalent power. The PWR is housed in a biological shield, as are the heat exchangers, since the water from the core is radioactive. The coolant in the PWR core does not directly contact the turbine, so the turbine area remains uncontaminated with radioactive materials. The higher pressure allows more efficient heat transfer and requires smaller surface area for the core. An additional heat exchanger lowers the overall efficiency of the PWR and the high temperatures increase the corrosion of the fuel rods, the cladding, and the pressure vessel.

An interesting aspect of the PWR is the use of "chemical shim" that is a way of compensating for long-term reactivity changes associated with fuel depletion and fis-

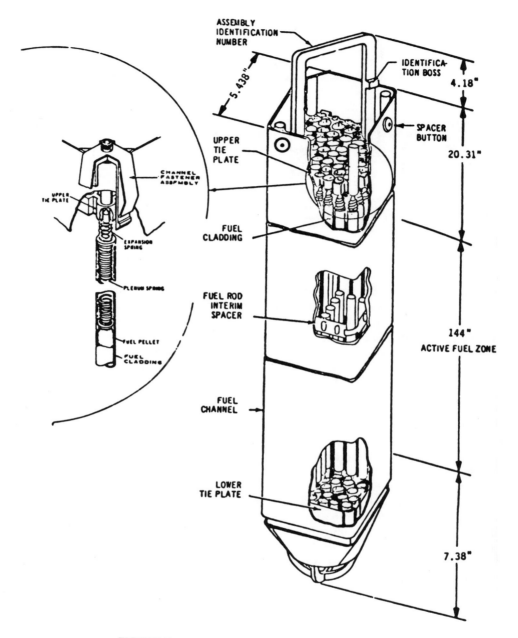

FIGURE 10.   Fuel assembly for pressurized water reactor.

sion product build up. The method consists of mixing a soluble neutron absorber (boron as boric acid) with the coolant. However, control rods are still used and they are clusters of silver-indium-cadmium alloy rods moving in the fuel assemblies in spaces where fuel rods are omitted. Fuel rods are used to control the power output at a steady rate and "chemical shim" takes care of long-term variations in reactivity and decreases the number of control rods needed from 100 to 60 in a typical 1000 MW pressurized water reactor.

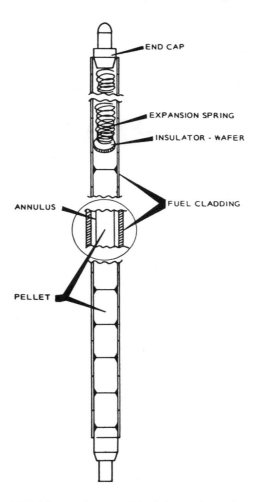

FIGURE 11.   Cutaway of fuel element for nuclear reactor core.

C. High-Temperature Gas-Cooled Reactors (HTGCR)

In the high-temperature, gas-cooled reactor as shown in Figures 12 and 13, the core is cooled by certain gases, usually carbon dioxide or helium. The designs most commonly used employ helium. The central idea is that helium may be used to transfer heat from fission heat sources to systems utilizing the heat at temperatures up to at least 1300 K and potentially higher. This concept allows a number of attractive options for electric power generation. This type of reactor has a low fuel consumption rate since very few neutrons are captured by the coolant. However, since gases are not efficient heat transfer agents, a large volume of gas must be circulated, and the circulation system requires very large blowers, and the core has to be large to present large surface area for heat transfer. The cooling system is extensively enclosed in a steel-lined, prestressed concrete reactor vessel. System pressures may range to 100 atm.

Since gases are poor moderators, a separate moderator system is installed in HTGCR. This moderaor system usually consists of graphite blocks pierced to contain the fuel. The reactor core for a high-temperature, graphite-moderated reactor is usually around 10 m in diameter. Graphite is used in the reactor core because of its strength at high temperatures and it does not react with helium or carbon dioxide.

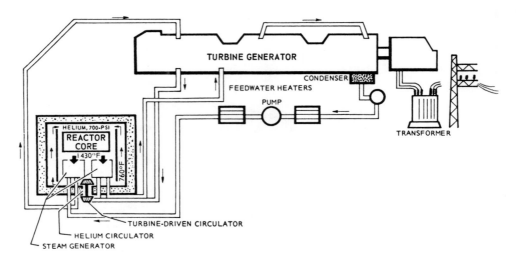

FIGURE 12.   High-temperature, gas-cooled reactor.

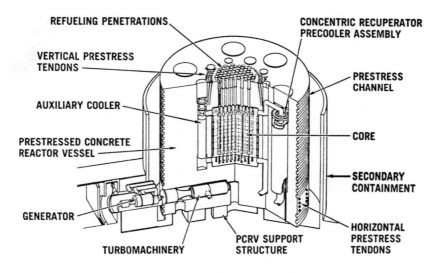

FIGURE 13.   Gas turbine HTGR.

The gas coolant transfers its heat to water circulating through a steam generator. Since the gas coolant can be heated to much higher temperatures than the water coolant, it can produce steam at much higher temperatures than water-cooled reactors—-usually in the range of 1500°F for saturated steam.

The high temperature operation of HTGCR allows the use of the best turbine technology and reduces the release of waste heat. These factors give the HTGCR system the potential for higher thermal efficiencies, equal to the best fossil-fueled power plants. Predicted power plant efficiencies for the HTGCR binary cycle where combined primary cycle steps are merged with the expansion and condensation steps for steam in which yields of an overall efficiency in the range of about 50% are possible.[2]

Problems with HTGCR involve the metallic surfaces in contact with helium at temperatures ranging from 450 K to 1100 K and may absorb species carried in the helium. The temperature of the hotter surfaces is in the range of rapid surface and grain boundary transport of many species. Bulk diffusion in materials of construction is rapid for only hydrogen, carbon, nitrogen, and possibly oxygen. Therefore there is usually a side loop in the system to remove minor constituents in the helium at a fractional rate of from 0.1 to 0.3 per hour. Coolant composition is thus a major consideration during reactor operation.

There are also other problems such as the corrosion and diffusion of hydrogen from water on the process side through heat exchanger tubing to the helium side and thus corrosion of iron. Also, transport of chromium, titanium, and probably other constituents of steels may be appreciable at the high temperatures involved. The transport of fission products from a HTGCR during normal and accidental conditions enters the analysis of reactor safety and will be discussed in Section VI.

D. Fast Breeder Reactors (FBR)

The use of fast breeder reactors was prompted primarily because once-through uranium ore technology was looked upon as being inefficient. The breeder reactor is a method of extending the supply of uranium many times because it produces more fissionable material than it consumes. However, in April 1977, the Carter Administration announced a policy to try to limit the expansion of efforts on the breeder reactor concept primarily because of nuclear proliferation trends which it might accelerate.[3] This is because more reprocessing is required in the case of the breeder reactors and thus there are possibilities that FBR could be used to produce nuclear fuels for nuclear weapons. The Carter Administration jointly announced a plan to defer indefinitely the reprocessing of spent nuclear fuel from domestic nuclear power plants to recover and recycle plutonium and unused fissionable uranium, and that it would try to persuade other nations to do the same. Therefore the nuclear breeder reactors, now in the process scale up stage, are being terminated and will be deemphasized for power plants in the future. In the fast breeder reactor, although the U-238 is not readily fissionable, it converts to plutonium-239 under neutron irridation. Plutonium-239 is fissionable and thus U-238 which make up more than 99% of all uranium is called a fertile material. Also, thorium 232 is another fertile material that converts to U-233 which is also fissionable. U-233 and plutonium 239 can be removed for use in other reactors, or reprocessed for other nuclear uses, and the nuclear proliferation possibilities with the breeder reactor are enhanced.

In a breeder reactor, for each atom of fissionable material consumed, more than one atom of fertile material becomes fissionable material. This can be achieved by increasing the number of free neutrons released in fission and by decreasing the number of neutrons wasted, and hence a larger number of neutrons are available for absorption in fertile material. Thus fuel can be produced economically from lower grade ores.

A fast breeder reactor is depicted schematically in Figure 14. It is called a fast reactor because it contains no moderator material to cause rapid slowdown of fission neutrons. Thus the average neutron velocity in the core is higher than in conventional reactor cores. The coolant used is liquid sodium, and an inert cover gas is used to blanket the sodium. The fuel in such an FBR is a mixture of oxides of plutonium and uranium. Since sodium is an efficient heat transfer fluid, the potential for efficient heat transfer coupled with higher operating temperatures makes the FBR potentially capable of reaching 40% thermal efficiency compared with 31 to 33% for LWRs. However, the disadvantages of FBRs are the use of liquid sodium, a highly chemically reactive element when being exposed to air or water. Also the sodium coolant becomes intensely radioactive with a 15 hr half-life emitting high energy gamma rays, requiring remote control equipment and complex safety systems. Thus, the cost of building FBRs is

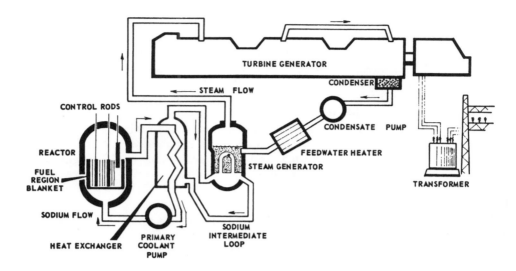

FIGURE 14.   Liquid metal fast breeder reactor.

higher, the operation is more complex, and with greater possibilities for nuclear proliferation due to reprocessing requirements, the FBRs for nuclear power plants at this
time in history seem to be little beyond the reactor development stage.

The cancellation of the Clinch River breeder reactor project in the U.S. in April
1977 indicated the concern for nuclear proliferation. However, the attendant problems
with breeder reactors are still major ones. Several countries are continuing the development of breeder reactors and thus there is even more concern for the quality of life
and environmental problems which could become international in nature. Thus, the
FBR although potentially important will require careful research and continued technological tracking if future nuclear power plants will need to be built which may utilize
FBRs instead of the conventional LWR.

VI. NUCLEAR POWER REACTOR SAFETY SYSTEMS

No accident affecting public health and safety has occurred in a commercial nuclear
power plant nor has a radiation injury ever occurred to a worker in such a plant.*
However, there have been instances of very near-tragic dimension which have been
recently uncovered, one in March 1975 at the Browns Ferry Nuclear Power Plant in
Decatur, Ala., and another near-disaster at the Enrico Fermi breeder reactor near De-
troit, Mich. in October 1966.[5,6] However, there has been no meltdown of reactors and
this is due to stringent safety precautions taken by the builders of nuclear plants which
cannot be built or operated without a license from the Nuclear Regulatory Commission.

Although the nuclear reactor concept is itself simple, the reactor device is very complex. A power reactor contains many thousands of fuel rods, miles of pipes and electrical wiring, and countless valves and other mechanical devices. Thus, with the millions of welds and other fasteners the problem of evaluating the safety of the overall
nuclear power reactor is extremely difficult.

A. Normal Operation of Nuclear Power Plants

Nuclear power plants form small quantities (about several pounds per day) of radio-

* See Note Added in Proof.

active substances and more than 99.99% of these substances stay with the fuel assemblies in normal operation. The small amount that escapes from the fuel enters the reactor coolant system where almost all of it is removed by purification equipment. A miniscule amount of radiation is released to the environment under strict control, subject to enforced health and safety regulations that require the radioactive releases be kept as low as practicable. The question was posed with respect to reactor effluents, i.e., as low as practicable or as low as reasonable[7] and, in 1971, the Atomic Energy Commission established 1 millirem as the maximum acceptable large population exposure. This is based on the assumption that all exposures to radiation, no matter how small, have some element of risk. Some workers on nuclear reactors, exposed to low level radiation for prolonged periods of time, have had higher incidents of leukemia.

This is an area of grave concern for health physicists.[8] In the waste management area it has also been found that because some low level radiation was disposed of in certain concrete, there are again larger probabilities of leukemia among the populace of certain Colorado towns.[8] This area is of enormous concern to the Department of Energy at present.

B. Accident Prevention of Nuclear Power Plants

Water moderated power reactors are uranium dioxide fuel which is enriched to about 3 to 4 times its natural level, about 2 to 3% of the total. In the reactor core, if the rate of fissions increases significantly, more heat is produced. The heat in turn increases the energy of the neutrons in the fuel, and thus increases the proportion of neutrons escaping from the core and captured by nonfissioning atoms. The rate of fission would therefore slow down. This effect is a natural phenomenon and occurs instantaneously and is one reason a nuclear reactor cannot become a bomb. In a bomb, more pure fissionable material is required, and it must be rapidly compressed and held together so that the chain reaction can increase to intensity of a nuclear explosion.

The use of water as a coolant and moderator provides another safety feature. Thus, if the reactor were to exceed its designed power level, it would raise the temperature of the water which would in turn decrease the power level of the reactor.

Other engineered safeguards against the release of radioactive materials are the design variables that include:

1. Ceramic fuel
2. Fuel cladding
3. Primary coolant systems
4. Safeguard systems
5. Containment system for the whole reactor

There are also constant monitoring of reactor neutron intensity to safe limits, reactor control systems designed to insert control rods, reactor safety circuit instrumentation, emergency electronic power systems requirements for the control rods coolant systems after shutdown, and emergency core cooling network.

The emergency core cooling system for a PWR is shown in Figure 15. The reactor consists of a core that is in the heavy wall vessel so that the pressure can be maintained at the high level to suppress boiling and water is circulated through the core by the pump at the left in Figure 15. The water flows along the pipe, through the downcomer, up through the core, up through a steam generator, and back to the pump. The secondary system takes the steam away from the turbine. In the course of licensing a water reactor, the regulations require that a design basis accident be analyzed, and that the design basis accident shall consist of the instantaneous double ended rupture

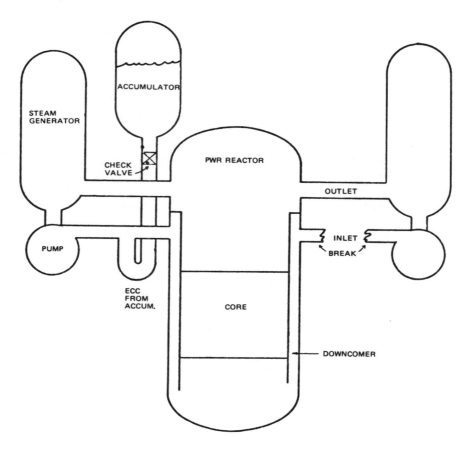

FIGURE 15.   PWR-ECOS schematic.

of the largest pipe in the system, a very unlikely event. The licensing criteria states that the calculated maximum fuel element cladding temperature shall not exceed 2200°F and other requirements are oxidation of cladding thickness, and include a requirement for long term cooling. To meet these criteria, emergency core cooling (ECC) systems are provided, including a low pressure injection system, a high pressure injection system, and a coolant accumulator that consists of a reservoir of water under pressure and separated from the primary system by a check valve (see Figure 15).

The pressure in the accumulator is about 500 psia while the system pressure is about 2200 psia. When the pipe ruptures, the blowdown occurs, and the pressurized water in the vessel starts to escape from the break as does the water that is being supplied by the pumping. As the pressure below the reactor drops there will be liquid supplied from above the reactor. The flow through the reactor will then reverse and the water will continue to blow out the break until the pressure drops down to a low enough level to allow the check valve to operate, at which point the fluid that is in the accumulator will be injected into the vessel and will cool the core. The process of blowdown is fairly rapid.

Figure 16 shows the temperature history at the hot spot in the reactor versus time, according to calculational models applied. The temperature starts out at the hot spot of the reactor, at around 600°F and in equilibrium with the driving fluid with the reactor, and at time zero the rupture in the line occurs. First of all, decompression or depressurization occurs and the fluid tends to flash and boil. The subsequent forma-

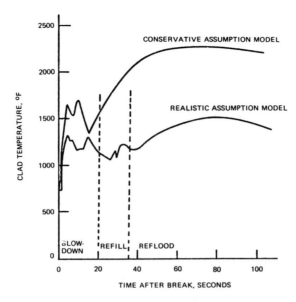

FIGURE 16. PWR fuel clad temperatures during a postulated loss-of-coolant event.

tion of voids shuts the reactor down so that it is producing only decay heat after this time. At the same time as heat production stops, water is still flowing through the core under momentum and the temperature of the cladding drops. At this point water ceases to flow since most of it escapes and stagnant water is left in the core. The core starts to heat, reverse flow occurs, and thus the temperature consequently drops. Once the upper volume of the vessel is voided the heat generation takes over again and the core heat up once more. As long as the temperature remains below 2200°F it is considered to be a controllable situation. Figure 16 shows the temperature history of the hottest spot on the fuel cladding in a PWR for the first 100 sec of a postulated loss of coolant accident (LOCA). The top curve represents the temperature changes when calculated using overall conservative assumptions. The lower curve represents the situation when more realistic assumptions are utilized.

The use of these models has however not been tested experimentally and thus is subject to verification. Limited experimentation of the ECCS has been carried out but the models used are somewhat ambiguous with regard to whether the system would work in a real emergency. Therefore, the proponents of nuclear safety seem justified in requiring a verification or partial experimentation to improve the models since a meltdown situation in the reactor core could quickly melt its way through the bottom of the containment vessel and subsequent amounts of radioactive materials would be immediately released into the atmosphere. Some have coined the term the "China Syndrome" because the super hot mass of material would continue to melt into the earth for a considerable distance. Still, the use of better models which could be experimentally verified need to be investigated.

There are also multiple physical barriers in reactor systems to guard against radioactive substances escaping into the atmosphere. The fuel itself retains most of the fission products even when overheated. The fuel cladding further protects the fission products from entering the reactor coolant system. Then there are the walls of the reactor vessel, and finally a containment system which stops the release of radioactive material that gets past the other barriers. Finally, the reactor building itself may be sealed off as a secondary containment system.

The use of certain models for loss of coolant accidents (LOCA) are not the only accidental events which are considered in the design of safety systems for nuclear power plants. The Atomic Commission has tried to obtain better estimates of the risks from potential accidents.[9] This study resulted in a report entitled "An Assessment of Accident Risks in U.S. Commercial Nuclear Power Plants", the famous W SH-1400 document.[10] In this report, predictive techniques for probability and consequences of nuclear power plant accidents are considered in detail and consisted of seven areas.

Accident sequence — Event trees borrowed from decision theory to define accident sequences may be used.

Probability of failure — Failure rates based on experience data on components, human error, and testing and maintenance contributions combined to fault tree methodology may be used.

Releases of radioactivity — Supplementary analysis to define how much radioactivity would be released from fuel and how it would be transported to various parts of the reactor containment area and the atmosphere may be used.

Environmental distribution — Meteorological dispersion models calculations on the distribution of radioactivity in the environment may be used.

Health effects, property, and other risks — Using calculated probability distributions, this risk provides factors to translate radioactive concentrations into health effects such as acute fatalities and injuries and delayed health effects and into property damage estimates.

Analysis of other risks — Certain other potential risks such as core melting due to internal failure within the power plant, external forces such as earthquakes, tornadoes, or floods and failures due to deliberate acts of sabotage may be used.

Overall risk assessment — This can be compared with other overall risks which can be obtained from actuarial data (automobile and aircraft fatalities and injuries, for example) and other low probability, potentially high consequence accidents such as dam failures and toxic chemical releases.

Perhaps the most important insight gained in the WASH-1400 study is that typical power plant reactors accident sequences are determined by five factors:

1. The probability of some initiating event
2. The probability of single safety system failure
3. The probability of the containment failure mode
4. The probability of particular weather conditions
5. The probability of particular population density will be exposed

From these analyses, it is evident that no one probability factor can dominate the risk, since if the probability of one event is high, there are still four other elements that affect the consequences and the overall risk significantly. Thus, an overall risk of 10^{-9} per reactor year prediction as an overall risk, for the largest accident can be obtained from 10^{-3} probability for pipe failure data (a single event), 10^{-3} probability from measured values of meteorological and demographic data applicable to 100 reactor sites, and 10^{-3} probability estimated by fault tree analysis and engineering studies of emergency cooling core systems and containment mode failures.

Faced with the possibility of nuclear accidents, however remote, the U.S. Government passed the Price-Anderson Act in 1957. It requires a utility which operates a nuclear power plant to purchase the maximum amount of liability insurance it can obtain, currently $110 million. The federal government provides additional insurance, up to a total of $560 million, to pay the public for damages from a nuclear accident. Thus, the government currently provides $450 million in insurance and each utility pays a premium to the government for Price-Anderson insurance coverage. The Price-Anderson Act relieves all parties of liabilities, in the event that damage from a nuclear accident should exceed the $560 million maximum. However, even when the law was passed in 1957, the esimate for a 200 MW nuclear power plant occurrence located about 30 miles from a large city estimated 3,000 to 4,000 immediate deaths and 50,000 delayed deaths from cancer, and $7 billion in property damage. Thus, the $560 million is only about 8% of the total estimate of $7 billion in damages, and thus critics of nuclear power are quick to point out that the maximum amount is hardly enough. Furthermore, the constitutionality of the Price-Anderson Act is now being challenged in court. Therefore, the liability of nuclear reactor occurrences is still an open question. A private insurance pool provides insurance on nuclear facilities. There is no government backed-coverage on nuclear facility property.

VII. RADIATION POLLUTION

Radiation pollution can take the form of effluents from water and effluents from gases. Their concentrations will be small and they must be monitored continously. The radiation activity must be considered with respect to factors that are dilutive and dispersive in nature, and in what form the radiation eventually becomes absorbed in the body and can cause health problems. In considering nuclides the following are vital considerations:

1. Initial body retention
2. Fraction of radioactivity transfer from blood to critical body tissue
3. Radiosensitivity of tissue in active material concentrates
4. Size of critical organ
5. Essentialness of organ to body functions
6. Biological half-life, i.e., time required to eliminate absorbed material
7. Radioactive half-life
8. Energy and type of radiation emitted

These factors are translated to maximum permissible concentrations and are the standards of the industry. They are implemented by the Nuclear Regulatory Agency and published as Standards for Protection Against Radiation as Federal Radiation Commission Standards such as 10CFR20.

A. Radiation Pollution in Mining Operations

Uranium mined by either open pit or underground methods creates problems similar to those involved in mining coal, only on a much smaller scale. Because of the high potential energy content of nuclear fuels, relatively little land is affected in supplying the annual needs of a 1000 MW power plant. Estimates of the solid wastes from the mining of ore and the subsequent extraction of the desired uranium product are 38 million tons annually. In processing uranium ores, some of the potentially hazardous radioactive elements or isotopes, particularly Ra-226 and Th-230, are partly dissolved during the leaching operation used to recover uranium oxide. While most processing plants are located in very isolated areas, steps must be taken to avoid contamination of water supplies by the radioactive constituents of liquid effluents. Disposal of effluent is accomplished principally by impoundment and evaporation, controlled seepage into the ground, and injection through deep walls into saline or nonpotable aqui-

TABLE 2

Releases of Radioactive Halogens and Particulates from Power Reactors
in Gaseous Effluents, 1969

| | Curies | | Percentage of |
Location of reactor	Released	Permissible[a]	permissible
Dresden 1, Ill.	0.26	85.	0.3
San Onofre, Calif.	<.0001	0.8	<.001
Humboldt Bay, Calif.	0.65	5.6	12.
Nine Mile Point, N.Y.	<.001	63.	<.001
Big Rock, Mich.	0.2	38.	0.53
Oyster Creek, N.J.	0.003	126.	0.002
Saxton, Pa.	<.0001	10.	<.001
Indian Point 1, N.Y.	0.025	7.6	0.33
Connecticut Yankee, Conn.	0.001	0.27	0.37
Ginna, N.Y.	<.0001	1.7	<.001
La Crosse, Wis.	<.063	1.6	<4.
Yankee, Mass.	<.0001	0.03	0.01
Peach Bottom, Pa.	<.0006	0.12	<.5

[a]   Maximum permissible releases are based on the most restrictive isotopes found, iodine-131 and strontium-90. The annual limit was reduced by a factor of 700 to account for reconcentration.

fiers. Where ore processing plants are adjacent to rivers or streams, the effluents are
frequently released directly to streams at controlled rates if, after dilution, the concentration is within predetermined limits.

B. Radiation Pollution In Normal Nuclear Power Plant Operation

At the light water reactor (LWR) power plant, fission energy is released in the form
of heat and is transferred to a conventional steam cycle which generates electricity.
Because of coolant temperature limitations in LWRs, their thermal efficiency is lower
than modern fossil-fueled plants. This lower efficiency, as well as the absence of hot
gaseous combustion products released through the stack, means that a LWR power
plant discharges over 60% more heat to receiving waters than its fossil fuel counterpart. Extremely small amounts of radioactivity are routinely released to water bodies
and to the atmosphere, only enough to give an annual ionizing radiation exposure in
the range of 0.01 to 10.0% of the exposure received from natural background radiation.

Tables 2 and 3 show the quantities of released radioactivity released in gaseous effluents in two successive years 1969 and 1970. Tables 4 and 5 show the quantities of
released radioactivity released in liquid effluents in two successive years 1969 and 1970.
Thus, the data indicate that in most cases, reactive designers and operators have been
limiting the amounts and concentrations of releases to levels which are comparable to
long accepted standards However, the whole question as to the practicality of meeting
some of the new guidelines which establish maximum permissible concentrations
(MPC) in terms of annual average boundary or off-site concentrations is also open
question and has to be considered in the overall risk assessments of nuclear power
plant siting and the relative cost of what is reasonable. In an analysis of the comparative public health aspects of oil-fired and nuclear power plants,[13] it has been shown
that public risks are low for the continuous operation of these plants at regulatory
limits. Thus, for a typical oil-fired plant the expected annual average of deaths per 10
million population per 1000 MW plant per year was 60, whereas the nuclear plant was

TABLE 3

Releases of Radioactivity from Power Reactors in Gaseous Effluents 1970[16]

Facility	Noble and activation gases			Halogens and particulates		
	Curies		Percentage of permissible	Curies		Percentage of permissible
	Released	Permissible		Released	Permissible	
Oyster Creek, N.J.	110,000	9.4×10^6	1.2	0.32	130	0.25
Dresden-1,ª Ill.	910,000	1.8×10^7	5.2	3.3	75	4.3
Nine Mile Point, N.Y.	9,500	2.7×10^7	0.037	< .06	63	<0.1
Dresden-2ª Ill.	250,000	2.2×10^7	1.1	1.6	110	1.4
Humboldt Bay, Calif.	540,000	1.6×10^6	34	0.35	5.6	6.2
San Onofre, Calif.	4,200	5.7×10^5	0.75	<0.0001	0.8	<0.001
Ginna, N.Y.	10,000	3.6×10^5	2.8	0.05	1.7	3
Big Rock Point, Mich.	280,000	3×10^7	0.88	0.13	37	0.35
Connecticut Yankee, Conn.	700	2.8×10^5	0.24	0.0015	0.2	0.7
Saxton, Pa.	2,200	3.7×10^3	59	0.15	10	1.5
Indian Point-1, N.Y.	1,800	5.3×10^6	0.03	0.075	7.6	1
Peach Bottom, Pa.	5.7	1.9×10^5	0.003	<0.0006	0.1	<0.6
Yankee Rowe, Mass.	17	6.6×10^3	0.26	Not measured	Not measured	
La Crosse, Wis.	950	3.2×10^5	0.3	<0.063	1.6	<4

ª   The Dresden-1 and -2 percentages are based on their individual limits. The percentage of the site limit is the sum of the individual percentages.

TABLE 4

Releases of Radioactivity from Power Reactors in Liquid Effluents, 1969

Location of reactor	Mixed fission and corrosion products	
	Released (curies)	Percent of limit[a]
Dresden 1, Ill.	9.5	22.
San Onofre, Calif.	8.	14.
Humboldt Bay, Calif.	1.5	8.7
Nine Mile Point, N.Y.	0.9	8.2
Big Rock, Mich.	12.	5.6
Oyster Creek, N.J.	0.48	4.1
Saxton, Pa.	0.01	2.5
Indian Point 1, N.Y.	28.	1.5
Connecticut Yankee, Conn.	12.	1.4
Ginna, N.Y.	0.02	0.4
La Crosse, Wis.	8.5	0.11
Yankee, Mass.	0.019	0.07
Peach Bottom, Pa.	<.001	0.002

[a]   The limit refers to the maximum permissible concentration (MPC) of specific isotopes.

TABLE 5

Releases of Radioactivity from Power Reactors in Liquid Effluents,[a] 1970[16]

Facility	Mixed fission and corrosion products			Tritium	
	Released (Ci)	Concentration Limit (10^7 μCi/ ml)	Percent of Limit	Released (Ci)	Percent of MPC
Oyster Creek, N.J.	18.5	1	71[b]	22	0.0028
Dresden 1, Ill.	8.	1	25	5	0.0005
Nine Mile Point, N.Y.	28	1	21[c]	20	0.0015
Dresden-2, Ill.	13	1	15	31	0.0012
Humboldt Bay, Calif.	2.4	1	15	<7	<0.0014
San Onofre, Calif.	7.6	1	12	4800	0.26
Ginna, N.Y.	10	3	5	110	0.005
Big Rock Point, Mich.	4.7	15	3.1	54	0.018
Connecticut Yankee, Conn.	6.7	3.6	2.8	7400	0.38
Sexton, Pa.	0.012	1	0.33	10	0.01
Indian Point 1, N.Y.	7.8	70	0.28	410	0.03
Peach Bottom, Pa.	0.006	1	0.15	<50	<0.05
Yankee Rowe, Mass.	0.034	1	0.14	1500	0.21
La Crosse, Wis.	6.4	300	0.067	20	0.002

[a]   In addition to the activity listed on this page, quantities of dissolved noble gases have been detected in liquid effluents at some facilities. Estimated curie quantities of these gases are as follows: San Onofre, 56; Connecticut Yankee, 16; Oyster Creek, 2; and the others, less than 1 curie.

[b]   Percent of limit has been increased by a factor of 3.76 to account for possible recirculation in Barnegat Bay.

[c]   In accordance with the Nine Mile Point license the percent of limit is based only on the curies of activity identified by gross beta analysis (9.44 Ci).

1. Both total risk from accidents were negligible. In the case of nuclear reactions the cause of death was cancer and the risk was 6×10^{-5}, whereas in the oil-fired plants the cause of death was respiratory and the risk was 2×10^{-4}. In addition, both power plants usually operate at levels much less than regulated limits.

C. Nuclear Waste Management

The spent fuel containing highly radioactive fission products is stored at the reactor for several months while the radioactivity dies down. It is then transported to a reprocessing plant where the fuel is chemically treated to recover the remaining uranium and some plutonium that is produced during the fission process. Other fission products are also removed and concentrated. In the entire fuel cycle, radioactive emissions to the air are greatest from the reprocessing plant. For example, a single fuel reprocessing facility planned in South Carolina may release as much as 12 million Ci/year of krypton-85 and 500,000 Ci/year of tritium from its stack. Practical procedures for the control of such gaseous wastes are most assuredly necessary. The concentrated fission products in the solid and liquid wastes must also be controlled. Because of their biological hazards and long half-lives, they must somehow be kept out of the biosphere indefinitely. Highly radioactive wastes presently amounting to about 90 million gal, produced largely in military programs, are now temporarily stored in large steel and concrete tanks that require constant surveillance, and some of which require cooling. Tanks have developed leaks, and, for this and other reasons, a more permanent means of disposal is needed. It was just less than a few years ago that nationwide attention was focused on this critically important problem by the leaking of more than 115,000 gal of highly radioactive waste from a storage tank at the AECs Hanford, Wash. facility. The leak was not even discovered for 51 days as it dribbled a daily average of 2500 gal of the boiling liquid into the soil. The crux of the problem lies in that as the nuclear industry continues to expand and radioactive wastes continue to accumulate, there is yet no suitable permanent disposal method available. Neither the salt mine concept nor any other radioactive waste disposal plan has as yet received general endorsement from the scientific community. In fact, it is not even clear than an entirely satisfactory solution can even be found, as this would require complete security for the wastes over thousands of years. The difficulty is that anywhere the wastes can be placed is, by definition, accessible, and it is difficult to imagine a spot which would remain undisturbed for hundreds of thousands of years. No human institution is likely to be able to provide surveillance, or even records of waste disposal, for times extending over geologic eras.

1. Shipping of Nuclear Wastes

Nuclear wastes are shipped to various processing, storage, or burial sites, and are classified as: low level wastes, high level wastes, alpha wastes, and other wastes.

a. Low Level Wastes

Low level wastes are those with such small quantities of radioactivity that they do not present any significant environmental hazards in transportation. Even if they were released from their packages in a truck or rail accident, they would not be a hazard to the public. They would have to be cleaned up like any other freight spilled at the scene of an accident. Under U.S. and international regulations, low level wastes require no special railcars or other transport vehicles or special packaging. These wastes may include such things as residues or solutions from chemical processing; building rubble, metal, wood, and fabric scrap; glassware, paper, and plastic; solid or liquid plant waste, sludges, and acids, and slightly contaminated equipment or objects.

b. High Level Wastes

High level wastes are produced in the reprocessing of highly radioactive fuels that were used in nuclear reactors. These wastes contain so much highly radioactive, long-lived material that they require long-term storage and essentially perpetual surveillance of the storage sites, which are isolated from population centers. The storage sites would be owned and operated by Department of Energy (DOE). The radiation level is so high that heavy, massive shielding is required in the packages (called casks). The high radiation levels also produce considerable heat. The material must therefore be kept in "accident-proof" packages that "contain" the nuclear material but allow the heat to escape. The wastes would be shipped only in solid form because DOE will not handle or process liquid high level wastes at any of its Federal waste repositories.

c. Alpha Wastes

Alpha wastes usually consist of materials contaminated with alpha radiation emitters such as plutonium. They have very low levels of penetrating gamma radiation and so do not require heavy shielding. Alpha emitters can cause contamination if released from their packages. If the amount of radioactive material to be shipped exceeds certain levels, the alpha wastes must also be contained in accident-proof packages, but of a different type than the very heavy high level waste casks. In packaging for transportation the emphasis is on containment, and several containment barriers (boxes within boxes) are provided in the packaging system.

d. Other Wastes

Other wastes, predominantly of the beta-gamma type (e.g., fission products, industrial isotopes, etc.), usually require some shielding material as a part of the package. These wastes may also be a combination of low level, alpha, and other beta-gamma types. Beta-gamma wastes include such things as irradiated structural components, heavily contaminated objects, concentrated solidified sludges or evaporator bottoms, and nonrecoverable radioactive fuel scrap.

Alpha wastes, high level wastes, and some other wastes contain radioactivity in amounts large enough to cause injury to living things or property damage if released to the environment during a transportation accident. For that reason Department of Transportation (DOT) and DOE regulations require that they be packaged so that, even in the event of a severe transportation accident, there would be no significant release of nuclear wastes from the packages. Such accident-proof containers must be strong enough to withstand the types of impact, puncture forces, and fire effects that are often encountered in severe accidents.

Each package type must have its own safety analysis report, which is evaluated by DOE before that kind of packaging is used. Before any package is approved by DOE for high level radioactive waste shipment, it must be able to withstand, without leakage, a series of accident damage tests that are comparable to the actual damage of a severe transportation accident. These "torture" tests include high-speed impact, puncture, fire, and water immersion. Only if the packaging can successfully pass such rigorous tests may it be used. Federal inspectors check the packages during construction to be sure they are properly built. The regulations therefore offer a very high degree of assurance that a package will not break open under severe accident conditions.

At present, there are several hundred different types of radioactive material package designs that have been authorized, ranging in size from small packages weighing a few pounds to massive casks weighing over 100 tons. (See Figure 17.)

Shipping containers for high level wastes will be very similar in their basic design to the shielded casks now routinely used to ship spent fuel assemblies from a nuclear

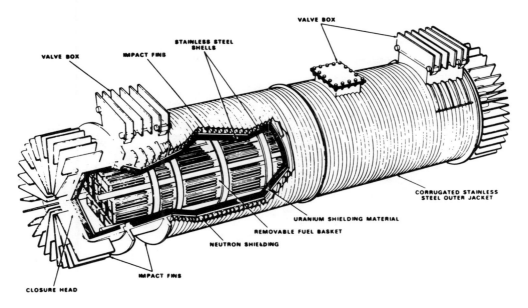

FIGURE 17.   Shipping casks for spent fuel.

power plant to a fuel reprocessing site. Spent fuel is very similar in its overall shipping characteristics to high level wastes in that it is solid, highly radioactive, and generates considerable heat. In both cases, the casks would be essentially the same type — massive, double-walled steel containers, filled with lead, steel, or uranium shielding material. The high level wastes will be in a canister inside the cask. These wastes are inert, immobile, solid material that are nonexplosive, noncombustible, and cannot turn to gaseous form and become airborne. These high level waste casks would be transported mostly by rail or conventional heavy-duty flatcars. Highway load limits, rather than safety reasons, will restrict highway shipments. (See Figure 18.)

D. Waste Management

Wastes, other than high level wastes, are shipped to commercially operated burial grounds. These are now located in Illinois, Kentucky, Nevada, New York, South Carolina, and Washington. At the present time, DOE is planning on long-term storage of all high level wastes at Federal waste repositories, and the ultimate question of where spent nuclear fuel will ultimately be reprocessed or even be reprocessed is still pending. The Carter Administration decision to defer the reprocessing of spent nuclear fuel from domestic resources has caused a reevaluation of the once through uranium cycle and other breeder reprocessing technology.

1. Fuel Reprocessing

Nevertheless, nuclear fuel reprocessing studies have been performed by DOE. Figure 19 shows an artist's concept of a possible pilot plant to confirm the concept of using underground bedded salt to dispose of solidified high level radioactive waste. The waste would be placed in salt beds about 1000 to 3000 ft underground, and would always be retrievable during the pilot plant operation. Nuclear reprocessing is a chemical process that removes the uranium and plutonium from the spent fuel so that they could be reused as nuclear power plant fuel. The remaining materials, which include about ½ of 1% of the plutonium that was in the fuel, are the ''high level'' wastes, meaning high levels of radioactivity. It is important to understand that these wastes,

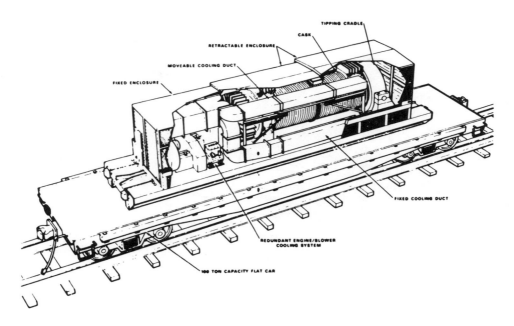

FIGURE 18.   Cask on a railway flatcar.

which are potentially very hazardous and expensive to handle, result only from the chemical reprocessing of used power plant fuel and also that this operation will be carried out at only a few central reprocessing facilities away from the power plants. After the wastes are extracted at the reprocessing plants, they may remain in storage at these plants for up to 10 years before they are turned over to the Department of Energy in solid form for ultimate storage in dry, stable, underground formations. The Department of Energy's plans are currently to:

1. Locate and develop a site in a geological formation for the first pilot demonstration plant. This plant will have a system for retrieving solidified high level waste from storage. If the site proves acceptable, it would be converted to a permanent storage facility. The only specific site presently being considered as a pilot demonstration storage facility for ERDA-generated wastes is about 30 mi east of Carlsbad, N.M. The wastes would be stored in vaults carved out of a massive bedded salt formation (which is not the same geologic structure that contains the Carlsbad Caverns). The cost of such a facility is estimated to be $325 million.
2. Develop methods for large-scale reduction and conversion of liquid high level waste into insoluble glass, ceramic, or other solid form. Solidifying the waste and reducing its volume makes it safer to transport, handle, and store. Also, solidification reduces the chance of the waste ever getting back into man's environment.

With the wastes in underground formations free from circulating water, DOE will effectively prevent these wastes from entering food chains or water supplies.

One ton of slightly enriched nuclear fuel will provide about 200 million kWhr of electricity.

Reprocessing this amount of burned-out fuel and solidifying the wastes will produce about 2 ft³ of solid high level wastes.

Examples of the amounts of wastes to be generated are as follows:

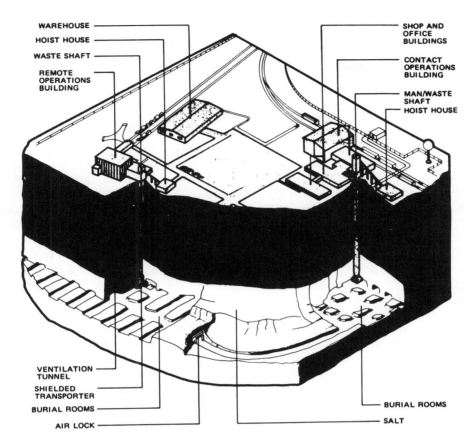

FIGURE 19.   Pilot plant cutaway.

1. The highest projected U.S. cumulative inventory of high level solid wastes for the year 2000 is about 80,000 canisters, 1 ft in diameter by 10 ft long. They would cover an area about the size of a football field if they were placed end to end and stacked 10 ft high.
2. The amount of solidified wastes produced by the amount of electricity used by a person in his lifetime would fit easily into a 12-oz soft drink can.

The 0.5% plutonium-239 that will remain in the wastes has a high radiotoxicity per unit weight and a 24,000 year half-life. Other long-lived radioactive waste products include strontium and cesium, which have half-lives of about 30 years. In typical high level wastes, the strontium and cesium would decay to innocuous levels in about 1000 years, but several hundred thousand years would be required for the plutonium.

Low level wastes consist of a variety of materials containing radioactivity. They are generated from many types of private and government operations: hospitals, laboratories, universities, nuclear power reactors, fuel fabrication plants, scrap recovery plants, and chemical reprocessing plants.

DOE is currently planning an in-depth evaluation of current operational practices at its own land burial sites, including development of criteria for selecting future burial grounds and for correcting undesirable conditions should they appear at existing grounds.

DOE is cooperating with the U.S. Geological Survey and various regulatory groups in this study, since the results may be applicable to commercial burial grounds.

Previous plans for the development of nuclear fission power — both "burner" and breeder — involved reprocessing and reuse of uranium (U) and plutonium (Pu). Partly to resolve some of the uncertainties engendered by any swing away from reprocessing, DOE devised a spent-fuel policy by which the Department would take title to the fuel after a 5-year advance notice and "cooling" time. There could be emergency exceptions to that lead time. Interim 5-year storage might be at-reactor or away-from-reactor at water pool facilities, for example.

When DOE takes title to the spent fuel, the owner-discharger might pay a one-time $150 to 250/kg fee — 60% for interim pool storage, and 40% for geologic storage/disposal. Transfer of the fuel rods would be at the owner's expense. The owner would not be paid for any sacrificed U or Pu values. But if reprocessing is approved in the future, the owner could have fuel retrieved, and receive any appropriate fee refund. There are now 68 nuclear power plants. There may be 75 more by 1985. About 5000 tons of spent fuel have accumulated and 2000 could be generated a few years from now. Even more might come if the additional plants all do indeed start up. The plants' discharged material must be racked in pools at reactor sites, or shipped in casks to away-from-reactor sites, such as GE Morris (Ill.). Still later, after largely cooling down, the fuel must be either reprocessed, or permanently sequestered.

But if storage/disposal sites, reprocessing, or some combination of these options, and necessary transportation for spent fuel are largely unavailable, nuclear reactor shutdown would almost have to occur. Further complicating the transportation/disposal picture are Sections 108 and 122 of the Clean Air Act Amendments of 1977. Section 108 permits regulation of "mobile sources", and could cover spent fuel transportation. Section 122 forces EPA, by August 1979, to determine what if any health hazard in air exists as a result of nuclear materials and spent fuels. Also, that section opens the way to severe federal regulation, but some states may now be even more stringent.

2. Nonproliferation

Proliferation denotes additional countries producing nuclear weapons materials and explosives. This production can be done by military means independent of civilian power, or by diversion (stealing or seizing) of these materials from the civilian power sector. Diversion is only one of eight technical options available to the would-be nuclear weapons nations. It is a difficult one, because of the extreme intricacies of obtaining, purifying, and handling weapons-grade plutonium.

The goal of nonproliferation has motivated the Administration to defer nonmilitary reprocessing and the breeder. One aspect is also preventing transfer, between other nations, of spent fuels for reprocessed fuels. However, the effect may be to accelerate the development and deployment of independent enrichment and reprocessing capabilities overseas. This would increase the chances for both proliferation and diversion.

Recently, the French government's Compagnie Generale des Matieres Nucleaires has contracted to reprocess 1705 tons of spent fuel for 15 West German power companies during 1985 to 1990. That company has parallel contracts with Belgium, Japan, and Sweden and is negotiating with power concerns in Austria, Finland, and Switzerland. Also, the French and British governments have announced that they will expand their reprocessing plants. And, while the present Administration is trying to defer the breeder indefinitely, the U.S.S.R. is going in the opposite direction. That country now operates one at 350 MW on the Caspian Sea; hopes to complete a 600 MW breeder by 1980; and is designing one for 1600 MW. Thus, the final effect of the policies of the U.S. may become one of nuclear proliferation rather than nonproliferation.

VIII. CURRENT ATTITUDE OF PUBLIC TO NUCLEAR POWER PLANTS

There is a growing concern on the part of the public toward nuclear power plants, with demonstrations and cries of "NO NUKES". Several coalitions for nonnuclear construction at certain sites is now commonplace in New Hampshire and Utah. Recently at a conference on spent fuel policy and its implications, Rep. James Jeffords (R., Vt.) indicated that there is a general uneasiness on the part of the public about hearing about the spent fuel problem without any good solutions in sight. He indicated that the nuclear industry's main problem, and that of government regulators as well, is a lack of credibility and one of distrust. Cited as an example was the fact that in Rutland, Vt. nuclear power was rejected by a two-to-one margin. This means that the citizens want more control over plant and waste disposal siting.

The current irresolution over domestic energy policy and the role of nuclear power prompted the Carter Administration to formulate its' no fuel reprocessing policy and the streamlining of regulations for LWRs. The nuclear energy and nuclear nonproliferation goals of the Carter Administration were based on the following:

1. Need to reduce growing outflow of U.S. funds for oil
2. Presence of vast coal deposits and expanding energy needs
3. Energy conservation measures pushing to efficient operations
4. Nuclear industry capacity for LWR
5. Uranium resources
6. Expanding reprocessing technologies

The final response of the world to the goals of nonproliferation will be recorded in history.

Technology for handling and disposing of high level wastes has been developed and partially demonstrated over the past 20 years. Several types of processes have been developed for solidifying high level radioactive wastes. These processes include:

1. Fluidized bed calcination as practiced at the Idaho National Engineering Laboratory
2. Spray calcination and boro silicate glass preparation as developed at Battelle Northwest Laboratory
3. Wide variety of processes developed at Argonne National Laboratory, Oak Ridge National Laboratory, and Lawrence Livermore Laboratory

Each of the processes would be able to perform its intended function in the nuclear waste disposal problem arena without causing harm to the public or to the environment. Therefore, there are some alternatives to waste disposal that are acceptable. The next step, which is the demonstration of these processes on a commercial scale, has never been taken. Therefore, what is needed is the full-scale demonstration of one or more of the disposal methods. Until such demonstration takes place, the American people will not be convinced that nuclear wastes are not a menace and this fear will remain a deterrent to the full and effective utilization of nuclear energy to solve a significant part of our energy dilemma.

The magnitude of nuclear waste disposal and its impact on the role of nuclear power as an energy source must be evaluated and aired before the public. The problem of nuclear waste exists at two levels. One is the technological level. Techniques, as discussed above and elsewhere, are known and must be demonstrated commercially. The second level is the larger difficulty — public opinion and public fear. Currently many people are of the opinion that an evil catastrophe will occur when we begin to process nuclear waste. Although the public knows that nuclear power plants will not blow up like atom bombs, the public does not see the real need for nuclear power and is not convinced that it is safe, and an answer to the dilemma which the U.S. and other nations face in solving energy demands in an ecologically safe manner. However, the energy demands and usage patterns will emerge in the future, but waste disposal is perceived as a threat.

Two basic facts on nuclear waste must be faced. First, the waste can be handled and the long-term radiation hazard minimized. Second, the waste issue will not go away, therefore, it must be addressed now. Nuclear power plants which are operating now create wastes. Military wastes have been accumulating since the Manhattan project in World War II. By not dealing with the problem intelligently and in a reasonable time frame, large volumes of spent fuel elements will be accumulated. This can only add to the cost and magnitude of eventually responding to the problem.

The public is well aware of nuclear waste problems. The public knows that tanks at Hanford have leaked; yet they are not aware of the minimal impact these leaks have had on the environment. The impression that handling nuclear wastes is without risk is also not true. There is nothing without risk. But cataclysmic hazards must not be involved, the risks must be manageable and low. Handling nuclear wastes is a complicated technical task, but it is far from a menacing threat to the human race.

There is another point that should be brought out in considering the magnitude of the nuclear waste disposal problem — its impact on the role of nuclear power as an energy source. By refusing to consider a breeder reactor and by failing to reprocess spent fuel rods from both military and civilian power sources, the U.S. is making the ultimate disposal problem many times worse than it could be. Currently spent fuel elements are being held in cooling basins. This practice seems to be imprudent for two reasons: it squanders our energy resources and it is poor waste management. To dispose of fuel rods permanently without reprocessing to recover nuclear materials capable of heat release and to continue the timid approach to nuclear power seems to be a great disservice to future generations. Not only is there a waste of energy, but if fuel rods are disposed as waste without first removing plutonium, the long term radiation hazard is about 100-fold greater than if 99% of the plutonium is chemically removed and used as fuel in nuclear reactors. It seems ludicrous to extend significantly the period of active radiation by failing to remove and recycle plutonium and other nuclides from spent fuel rods. By reprocessing not only would there be a decrease of the period over which the waste would remain at a hazardous level, but the volume of high level waste in storage would be cut to as little as 10%. At the same time, it should be emphasized that either form of waste has to be handled — the unprocessed fuel rods, or the waste which would result after chemical extraction and reuse of energetic materials. Thus, the Electric Power Research Institute has proposed an international nuclear power sequence which would involve the development of a civilian experimental breeder fuel technology which would make the production of weapons grade material nearly impossible. Before any major decisions regarding the next step in nuclear power sources, the safe disposal of nuclear wastes must be dealt with. Nuclear wastes can be utilized to their fullest extent, if proper safeguards and policy are carried out. It is a waste of energy and resources to continue the policy which does not seem to deal with the problems, only delays final decisions. Processing plants are being built in other countries and will pose other problems into the future.

The problems of waste disposal, serious accident, and the threat of theft or sabotage at nuclear facilities and during transportation will always be risks. The expansion of nuclear power will carry with it some serious and irreducible risks. Whether the economic and social benefits of the industry counterbalance these risks is a question which will have to be publicly resolved. Therefore, nuclear uncertainties abound. They are institutional, technological, and regulatory, and workable policies and procedures must be found if nuclear power plants are to be built and utilized. The environmental implications are tremendous.

NOTE ADDED IN PROOF

The cry of "HELL NO. WE WON'T GLOW" and "NO NUKES" became even more visible during 1979. The main reason for this was the Three Mile Island, Pa. accident in March 1979. An estimated 60,000 people voluntarily evacuated their homes in central Pennsylvania in March-April 1979. The Three Mile Island nuclear power plant near Harrisburg, Pa. was the center of attention around the world. The nuclear accident at Three Mile Island and its subsequent immediate "fix" caused many new outbursts, protests, and signs of awareness with the public. There were NRC violations, equipment failures, design flaws, and human errors, all of which caused a partial meltdown of the reactor and loss of coolant. Some clever engineering "fixes" and response on the part of the NRC have allowed the plant to exist, however, the scars of the incident and the increased vigilence on the part of the Government and the public are now the result of this incident.

Although the average dose of radiation absorbed by people within five miles of the Three Mile Island power plant had been 80 millirems, well below the 1000 millirems considered an immediate threat to health (equivalent to two chest X-rays), the long term implications of such an incident will be felt forever. The Three Mile Island accident painfully pointed out the millieu of government and local red tape, public misinformation, and inadequate information at all levels of government which have to be rectified. The Three Mile Island accident paved the way for greater vigilance on the part of Congress and the government in nuclear safety matters and suspended liscensing at nuclear power plants indefinitely.

Although it is generally recognized that 12.5% of the total U.S. electrical power is generated by nuclear power plants, (it is as high as 35% in New England area) protests from Massachusetts to California have become more intense. Thus, of the 71 nuclear power plants in the U.S., all will have a resident NRC inspector on-site in the future. Of the 92 nuclear power plants in construction, more inspection and operational training will be required. Of the 30 remaining nuclear power plant projects some will probably be delayed or cancelled.

The response of the government has been an increased awareness of potential problems and an openness of potential difficulties, along with dozens of changes in procedure, equipment and safety standards mandated by NRC since the Three Mile Island accident. These changes and training since the Three Mile Island accident has resulted in increased system safety, as evidenced by a similar incident at Crystal River, Florida in March 1980, where the fail safe system worked properly.

The response on the part of the public and the press media toward nuclear power is guarded and confused. The response on the part of the rest of the world is mixed and watchful. The eventual fate of nuclear power is that it be considered an important element of our energy plans. Zero-based reanalysis of nuclear safety may eventually become a reality and replace the Rasmussen report.[10] The problem of storage of spent fuels and their environmental impact will require continuing analysis.

REFERENCES

1. **Moore, W. J.,** *Physical Chemistry,* 3rd ed., Prentice-Hall, Engelwood Cliffs, N.J., 1962.
2. **Anon.,** *Conference on Thermodynamics and National Energy Problems,* National Academy of Sciences, Washington, D.C., June 1974, 150.
3. **Rose, D. J. and Lester, R. K.,** *Sci. Am.,* 238, 45, 1978.
4. **Gaines, M.,** *Atomic Energy,* Bantam Books, Grosset and Dunlap, New York, 1970.
5. **Hull, A. P.,** Reactor effluents: as low as practicable or as low as reasonable?, *Nuclear News, (Hinsdale, Ill.),* p. 53, 1972.
6. **Liverman, J. L.,** Television Appearance, PBS, July 1978.
7. **Ehrlich, A. and Ehrlich, P.,** Is it safe to live near a nuclear power plant?, Part I, *Mother Earth News,* p. 154, 1978.
8. **Ehrlich, A. and Ehrlich, P.,** Is it safe to live near a nuclear power plant? Part II, *Mother Earth News,* p. 116, 1978.
9. **Levine, S.,** Nuclear Reactor Safety, in Proc. Fourth Natl. Conf. Energy and the Environment, Dayton Section, AIChE, 1976, 466.
10. WASH-1400, Department of Energy, Washington, D.C., 1976.
11. **Mills, G., Johnson, H. R., and Perry, H.,** Fuels management in an environmental age, *Environ. Sci. Technol.,* 5, 31, 1971.
12. **Dole, S. H. and Papetti, R. A.,** R-992-RF January 1975, The Rand Corporation, Santa Monica, Calif.
13. **Starr, C., Greenfield, M. A., and Hausknecht, D. F.,** *Nuclear News (Hinsdale, ILL.),* P. 37, 1972.
14. **Anon.,** ERDA Pamphlet, EDM 529, Washington, D.C., 1976.
15. **Anon.,** ERDA Pamphlet, EDM 534, Washington, D.C., 1976.
16. Report on Releases of Radioactivity from Power Reactors and Effluents During 1970, Division of Compliance, U.S. Atomic Energy Commission, October 1971.

Chapter 4

THE ENVIRONMENTAL IMPACT OF NONCONVENTIONAL ENERGY SOURCES

R. K. Raufer and J. J. Yates

TABLE OF CONTENTS

I. INTRODUCTION

There are a number of potential energy sources which are usually referred to as "alternate" or "nonconventional" energy sources. They could have this designation for one of several reasons: economics might currently prohibit further development, the energy conversion methodology might still be in the experimental stage, or the engineering concepts might still be on the drawing boards. Similarly, wide-scale use of certain systems might require considerable societal changes (e.g., toward decentralized energy supply).

As energy supply conditions change, more and more attention is being focused on these alternate sources. This chapter outlines the environmental impacts which can be expected when several of the more prominent alternate technologies are developed. Included are oil shale, geothermal, solar, wind, tar sands, ocean thermal, and hydrogen-fuel systems. These alternate technologies are not necessarily "clean" sources of energy. Some, such as oil shale, have substantial environmental impacts. Others, such as wind power, have relatively few.

The exact role these alternate sources will have in the future is currently the topic of considerable debate. Attempts to develop a national energy policy have not yet been successful, and the expected role of alternate sources ranges from insignificant to well over half of our total energy needs within 50 years. The environmental impacts outlined below are crucial in determining what their ultimate significance will be.

II. OIL SHALE

In addition to its vast coal resources, the U.S. has a considerable fraction of the world's oil shale deposits (approximately 73% according to the 1974 World Energy Conference). Oil shale therefore represents a considerable energy resource which has remained virtually untapped, primarily for economic reasons.

Oil shale resources are present throughout the central and eastern U.S. and Alaska, but virtually all of the commercial development plans have focused on an area in Colorado, Wyoming, and Utah called the Green River Formation. Almost all of the high grade oil shale in the U.S. (i.e., a 25 to 100 gal oil yield per ton of shale) which is recoverable using present technology is in this area. Furthermore, a large fraction of the high grade shale is concentrated within a small area of the formation — in Colorado's Piceance Basin (see Figure 1). Approximately 85% of the 80 billion bbl of oil potentially available from high grade shale is in this one basin.

The environment in the Green River area will be significantly impacted by the development of an oil shale industry. The exact impacts, however, will depend upon the technology used to get the oil from the shale.

FIGURE 1.   Oil shale country. Cottonwood Point near Rifle, Colo. in the Piceance Basin area. (From U.S. Bureau of Mines, Pittsburgh, Pa.)

A. Oil Shale Technology

Oil shale is a sedimentary rock containing an organic material known as kerogen. When the oil shale is heated to approximately 900°F the kerogen is broken down into a liquid hydrocarbon mixture, some combustible gases, and a coke-like residue.[1] The crude shale oil is then treated for impurities (e.g., sulfur and nitrogen) before being used as refinery feedstock.

There are two approaches for obtaining oil from oil shale: conventional surface retorting processes and *in situ* processes. Conventional retorting "is the traditional approach that has been used in various parts of the world for over 100 years and will probably be used for the first development of the Green River Formation."[2] In conventional retorting, the shale is mined using underground or open-pit techniques, and then crushed to the required size for the retorting process. There are four types of retorting processes, distinguished by the method each uses to supply the heat needed to retort the oil shale.[3] Heat is transferred to the shale:

1. Through a wall
2. From hot gases generated in the retort
3. From gases heated outside of the retort
4. From hot solids introduced into the retort

In situ processing is a much more recent approach, having been studied for approximately 25 years. It usually requires a fracturing of the shale seam to enable adequate heat transfer. The shale is then ignited, and is retorted in place. Certain problems are inherent in this technique, however, including "(1) obtaining uniform fracturing, (2) obtaining uniform heating as the flame zone moves through the fracture zone, and (3) self-healing of the fractures."[4] Recent progress indicates that the method is quite promising, however.

It is anticipated that both processes will ultimately be used in developing the Green River resource. Conventional retorting gives higher oil yields for a given amount of

TABLE 1

The Sources and Nature of Atmospheric Emissions from Oil Shale Extraction and Processing[s]

Subprocess	Emission generating activity	Potential criteria pollutants[a]	Potential noncriteria pollutants
Oil shale extraction	Blasting	PM(1) dust (1), CO, NO$_x$, HC	Hg, Pb salts, silica
	Mine equipment use		
	Fuel use	PM(2), CO, NO$_x$, SO$_2$, HC	silica
	Fugitives	dust (1)	
Raw shale transport	Equipment use		
	Fuel use	PM (2), CO, NO$_x$, SO$_2$, HC	silica
	Fugitives	dust (1)	
Preparation	Crushing	PH (1)	silica
	Screening		
	Ore storage		
Retorting operations	Shale preheat		
	Fuel use	PM (1,2), CO, NO$_x$, SO$_2$, HC	trace elements
	Shale dusts	HCs	
	Heat carrier reheating		
	Fuel use	PM(2), CO, NO$_x$, SO$_2$, HC	trace elements, trace organics
	Combustion of shale organic material	PM (2), CO, NO$_x$, SO$_2$, HC	trace elements, trace organics
	Spent shale discharge		
	Moisturizing or dry exit	PM (3), HCs	H$_2$S, NH$_3$, volatile and trace organics
Upgrading and utility operations	Process heaters/furnaces		
	Fuel use	PM (1), CO, NO$_x$, SO$_2$, HC	
Gas cleaning systems	Sulfur recovery and tail gas cleanup	SO$_2$	CS$_2$, COS
	Hydrogen production		
	CO$_2$ removal	SO$_2$	COS
	Fuel use	PM (2), CO, NO$_x$, HC, SO$_2$	
Product storage	Tank evaporation	HCs	
Solid waste disposal	Equipment use	PM (2), CO, NO$_x$, SO$_2$, HC	trace organics
	Fugitives		
	Spent shale transport and spreading		
	Coke, spent catalyst, other wastes — transport, and spreading	PM (3) PM (1)	metals (Ni, Cr, Fe, Mo), trace organics

Suspended particulate matter is the defined criteria pollutants. PM is broken down into 3 general categories in this table: (1) Raw shale and natural soil dusts, (2) Fuel combustion ash and sooty material, and (3) Spent shale dust (including dust from other solid wastes).

shale, but the *in situ* process may have a cost advantage in certain situations.[1] There is quite a significant difference environmentally as well, as outlined below.

B. Air Quality Impacts

Oil shale development is likely to cause a considerable amount of air pollution. Table 1 outlines the types of sources and pollutants which will be generated. Blasting, mining, crushing, and transporting the oil shale all contribute to air quality particulate levels,

TABLE 2

Predicted Emission Rates from Oil Shale Retorting Operations Producing 50,000 bbl/day (tons/year)[1]

Pollutant	*In situ* retorting	Surface retorting
Particulates	1600	300—3250
Sulfur dioxide	8500	960—5800
Nitrogen oxides	2300	600—6400
Carbon monoxide	70	300—3600
Hydrocarbons	1000	1400—4000

and the transportation and storage of spent shale will contribute even more. The *in situ* process will minimize these types of emissions, but both processes will emit substantial amounts of pollutants from the retort operations themselves. Estimated emission rates for the retort operations are given in Table 2.

Despite the fact that there are very few anthropogenic emission sources located in the oil shale region, air quality levels exceeding federal ambient air quality standards have been observed for several pollutants. Particulate levels as high as 469 $\mu g/m^3$ for a 24-hr average have been recorded. Nonmethane hydrocarbon levels 10 times as high as the 3-hr standard have been measured, and oxidant levels slightly above the 1-hr average have been recorded.[5]

Several atmospheric dispersion modeling studies have been performed to determine the air quality impact of oil shale development on the region. These studies have been summarized in a report prepared by TRW.[5] The summary shows that:

1.   "Sulfur dioxide levels will meet ambient air quality standards at all sites but will exceed the significant deterioration standard and Colorado's maximum allowable increments at certain sites."
2.   Particulate standards are already exceeded. Incremental increases will exceed the significant deterioration requirements. Many of the modeling analyses did not include fugitive sources, so the particulate levels "are probably underestimates."
3.   Hydrocarbon levels are already quite high, and will get worse due to the additional emissions from oil shale development.

The use of control techniques such as wetting agents and covered conveyors will probably be used to minimize fugitive emissions, but air pollution will still be a major obstacle to oil shale development.

C. Water Quality Impacts

The water quality impacts of oil shale development revolve around two considerations — supply and contamination.

The exact water requirements of an oil shale facility will depend upon many factors, including the process technology and size of the facility, but an approximate estimate is that a 1 million bbl/day oil shale industry will use 200,000 acre-feet of water per year. This amounts to slightly more than 3 bbl of water for every barrel of oil produced. Whether this much water is available in the dry region is currently the subject of lively debate. It is expected that most of the water will come from rivers in the area, although the use of groundwater is also receiving attention. Depletion of water resources in the area will increase the salinity of surface streams, and use of significant amounts of groundwater will lower the water table, drying up water holes and lowering the water flow of creeks and streams. This could have an impact on wildlife and other ecosystems in the area. The construction, mining, and other site activities will also increase the dissolved solids loading in surface streams.

Water is used in the oil shale facility for a variety of tasks, including cooling, moisturizing retorted shale, and gas cleaning (air pollution control), and is subsequently contaminated. Water is also obtained from the oil shale itself. Approximately 2 to 5 gal/ton of shale is obtained, but it is "contaminated with ammonia, chlorine, carbonates, sulfates, mercury, selenium and arsenic and various organics such as phenols and carboxylic acids."[1] All proposed plants will require wastewater treatment facilities to deal with the contaminated water.

A number of other water quality problems exist. Erosion and leaching of spent shale deposits will occur, and it may be necessary to construct retaining dams below the deposit areas to prevent water runoff into the local water shed. Various types of spills could occur when the plant is in operation. Water supply and treatment facilities will be required to support the additional population in the area introduced by the oil shale industry.

In addition to these problems, there are also certain unknowns. For example, the impact of leaching of the *in situ* retorted oil shale on groundwater quality is still to be determined.[2]

D. Solid Waste

The environmental impact which has received the most attention in oil shale development is the solid waste problem.

Spent shale from the retorting process "will vary in consistency — depending on the retorting process — from a lumpy ash-like material resembling dry chunky peanut butter to a fine ash-like substance with a carbon residue that looks like grey talcum powder."[1]

The amounts of spent shale which must be disposed are staggering. A hypothetical example given by Buonicore[6] is illustrative: "Using 20 gallons of oil per ton of oil shale as an average raw material, a 100,000 barrel per day shale oil plant, which would supply considerably less than one percent of the 1972 petroleum demand in the U.S., would have to dispose of over 200,000 tons per day of spent shale. Assuming a packed density of 100 pounds per cubic foot, five weeks of operation would fill a city block to the height of the Empire State Building in New York City (1,472 feet)."

It is currently anticipated that most of the spent shale will be disposed in gullies and canyons. Extensive efforts must be made to control leaching and runoff from rain and snow, including compaction, the use of impervious materials under the piles, and retention devices.

Research is currently being conducted on the ability of the spent shale piles to support vegetation, but the "establishment of vegetation directly on the surface of retorted shale piles is partially limited by inherent properties of retorted shale itself, including the high soluble salt content of the shale, the alkalinity of burned shale, the dark heat absorbing color of carbonaceous retorted shale, and the lack of nutrients needed for plant growth."[5] The uptake of contaminants by the plants, the types of plants likely to grow on the spent shale, and the likely results of removing extensive care and irrigation are all factors which require additional study. Certain small piles have supported vegetation over 10 years, but the long-term success of this type of program is not yet known. Even if the program is ultimately successful, the physical beauty of the scenery in the area is likely to undergo many changes.

Another option for dealing with the spent shale is to return it to the mine. This procedure eliminates a good portion of the visual problems, but it presents the same problem outlined earlier for *in situ* retorting (i.e., the impacts of leaching will be very difficult to control).

In addition to the spent shale, other solid wastes such as spent catalysts from the shale oil upgrading operations and sludges from the wastewater treatment facilities will also require environmentally sound disposal.

E. Other Environmental Impacts

There are a wide range of other environmental parameters which will be impacted by development of an oil shale industry. The development of "boom towns", with their associated health, housing and social problems, is quite probable. Large areas of land will be disrupted for the industry, and wilderness and recreation potential will be affected. The impact of the development of an oil shale industry on national parks in the region has been studied by Schein,[7] who notes: "Certain impacts are common to most of the parks. Increased visitation and the attendant problems which accompany greater use of the park's resources is the most likely and most visible early impact. The guaranteeing of the parks' water supply and its quality will be an on-going concern as an oil shale development program matures." Other impacts will be site specific. For example, "Shadow Mountain National Recreation Area was established to provide recreation on a reservoir whose purpose is to store water for diversion out of the Colorado River Basin across the Continental Divide for use on the dry Eastern Slope of the Rocky Mountains. If downstream depletions become a problem, some of this stored Colorado River water may be allowed to flow downstream to alleviate salinization or appropriation problems. If this occurs, it would certainly restrict recreation on the reservoir."[7]

It is apparent, then, that while the potential energy resources from oil shale are extremely large, environmental impacts present a considerable obstacle to their development.

III. GEOTHERMAL SYSTEMS

Geothermal sources have a reputation for being "clean" reservoirs of energy, and they do have one very important advantage. The environmental impact is localized at the geothermal site. The significant environmental impact of the fuel cycles inherent in other energy generating systems (e.g., the mining and transportation of coal for fossil fueled power plants, and the mining and enrichment of uranium for nuclear power generation) does not occur.

While the geothermal systems are very promising, there are certain environmental impacts which must be considered. These include air, water, and noise pollution, land subsidence, and induced seismic activity. The magnitude of these impacts varies according to the type of geothermal system and the end use of the energy recovered.

The term "geothermal energy" actually covers a wide range of systems. The first to come to mind are usually the hydrothermal systems, causing geysers such as "Old Faithful" in Yellowstone National Park. A large portion of the research, and all of the commercial experience, has been with this type of geothermal system. Hydrothermal systems are usually classified as one of two types: vapor dominated or liquid dominated.

The vapor-dominated systems are more desirable from a commercial viewpoint,[8] but they are not very common. There are only three systems in the U.S. — The Geysers in Sonoma County, Calif., the Mud Volcano System in Yellowstone National Park (including "Old Faithful"); and a "likely, although not yet confirmed, system in Mt. Lassen National Park, California."[9] Pacific Gas and Electric Company is currently

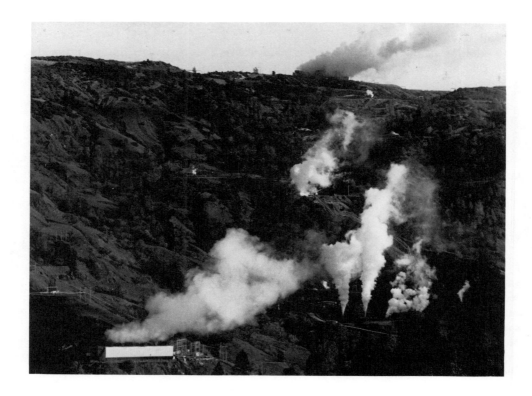

FIGURE 2.   The Geysers. This is part of the geothermal steam field where Pacific Gas and Electric Company generates 502 MW of electricity from underground steam. On top of the hill are Units 7 and 8, which went into operation late in 1972. In the lower left corner of the photo are Units 3 and 4 which became operational in 1967 and 1968, respectively. Units 3 and 4 each generate 27 MW and Units 7 and 8 generate 53 MW apiece. Steam at the right and center comes from active geothermal wells. The steam field is located in Sonoma and Lake Counties, about 90 mi northeast of San Francisco. (From Pacific Gas and Electric Co., San Francisco, Calif.)

generating over 500 MW (electric) at the Geysers site (see Figure 2) and it is one of four commercial operations at vapor-dominated, geothermal sites in the world (there is one site in Italy and two in Japan). Liquid-dominated sites are more common, and there are nine electric generating plants for these types of systems worldwide (most are in New Zealand, Japan, and Mexico).[9] There are no commercial electric operations for liquid-dominated systems in the U.S., but plans are being developed.

Geothermal energy also includes various schemes which do not rely on hydrothermal systems. These use molten rock occurring near the surface (magma), hot dry rock (the solidified margins around the deposits of magma),[9] the normal temperature gradient of the earth's crust, or geopressurized fluids as the ultimate energy source. These systems are just beginning to receive attention, and considerable research will be required before they become commercially feasible.

A list of potential environmental impacts associated with geothermal power production is included in Table 3, and is described in more detail in the following sections. It should be noted, however, that electrical power generation is not the only commercial use of geothermal systems. The steam or hot water can be used for desalting seawater for heating houses, greenhouses, and swimming pools and for providing non-electrical energy for refrigeration and air conditioning.[10] Research is currently being conducted for other nonelectric uses of geothermal energy.

TABLE 3

Potential Environmental Impacts of Geothermal Power Production[9]

Impact	Estimate probability	Technology/resource type	Severity of consequences
Land subsidence	moderate	hot-water	variable — can be high
Induced seismic activity (earthquakes)	low	all	high
Air pollution resulting from discharge of noncondensable gases (e.g., hydrogen sulfide, carbon dioxide)	high	all except hot-water binary/fluid and other "closed-cycle" use of geothermal fluids	variable — depends on emission controls
High noise levels of drilling and plant operation	high	all; worse for vapor-dominated	moderate
Chemical or thermal pollution of surface and groundwaters	moderate	all; greatest probability with hot-water	high
Well blowouts	low	hot-water; vapor-dominated	moderate
Increased erosion and sedimentation resulting from site disturbance	high	all	moderate
Consumption of water for cooling purposes	high	hot-water binary fluid; hot dry rock	high
Consumption of land for wells, power plants, transmission lines	high	all	moderate
Short-term climatic changes resulting from release of heated steam and carbon dioxide	high	hot-water; vapor dominated	low
Disturbance of habitat; alteration of ecosystems	moderate to high	all	moderate to low

TABLE 4

Sources of Steam and Noncondensable Gas Emissions During Geothermal Development[9]

	Relative importance as pollution source
Steam discharge during well drilling and clean-out	Moderate
Production testing of wells	Moderate
Well blow-outs	Low
Venting or "bleeding" of test wells prior to power generation	Low
Steam line vents during power plant operation	Moderate
Accidental steam line breaks	Low
Venting of wells during plant shutdown	Low-Moderate
Power plant operation	High

A. Air Quality

A number of noncondensable gases are released to the atmosphere during the drilling, testing, and operations phase of the geothermal plant development. The nature and quantity of these emissions are site specific, since the chemical composition of the geothermal fluid can vary considerably from site to site. Carbon dioxide is usually the principal component (75 to 95%); ammonia, methane, hydrogen sulfide, and nitrogen are usually present in smaller amounts; and radon, mercury vapor, and argon are typically present in trace amounts.[9,11] Small quantities of particulates are also found in the steam released to the atmosphere. Table 4 lists the various types of operations leading to air pollutant emissions during geothermal development.

Much of the air pollution abatement efforts have gone into control of the hydrogen sulfide emissions. This gas, which is best known for its "rotten egg" odor, is highly toxic and chemically reactive. Its conversion to other compounds of sulfur (SO_2, SO_3, H_2SO_4) leads to an increase of ambient levels of sulfur oxides in the region. Atmospheric dilution is usually sufficient to keep its concentration below critical levels near the plant site, but the concentrations might still create a problem for occupational safety.

B. Water Quality

Water pollution problems are also introduced at various stages in the geothermal development. Construction, site preparation, and related efforts can lead to erosion and increased solids content in surface waters. Blowouts during the drilling operations could also lead to problems, although the air pollution considerations are usually more substantial. The primary water pollution problems occur with actual operation of the plant. Ammonia and boron in the blowdown waste water from the cooling towers caused surface water pollution and harm to aquatic life at The Geysers, and the waste water is now reinjected into the geothermal reservoir. Reinjection appears to be a very promising technique for minimizing waste water impacts. As might be expected, the magnitude of the water pollution problems is considerably larger at liquid-dominated systems. The Wairakei plant in New Zealand (143 MWe) must dispose of 30 million gal of waste water each day.[9]

The nature of the geothermal fluids varies widely from site to site. Many have a high total dissolved solids content and many are saline, but some are pure enough to be used in agriculture and industry. This wide variability has contributed to a broad range of disposal techniques, including direct release to surface waters, evaporation, and reinjection.

The ultimate impact of geothermal development on hydrological resources is not always known. The systems are a depletable resource, and large scale extraction and reinjection of geothermal fluids may significantly alter subsurface hydrology in ways not yet understood.

C. Noise

Noise pollution also occurs at various stages of the geothermal development, including the construction phase and the operation phase. Noise caused by cooling tower fans, steam line vents, and other operating equipment all contribute to substantial ambient noise levels. The greatest noise problem, however, occurs during the drilling phase. The "blowing" of the well after it has been drilled, the testing of the well, and unanticipated well blowouts (rather infrequent) all cause steam at great pressures to escape to the atmosphere, generating high decibel levels. The noise from the air drilling itself, which can continue for relatively long periods of time, is also very high. Extensive work has been done with various types of mufflers to reduce the impact of this type of pollution.

D. Land Subsidence

The withdrawal of large quantities of underground fluids can often lead to both horizontal and vertical ground movement. This has been noted in the petroleum industry where oil extraction has often led to land subsidence. This has been controlled by injecting water around the boundary of the oil field to maintain fluid pressures. A similar phenomenon has been noted at the Wairakei, New Zealand, geothermal plant where vertical movement exceeding 12 ft has occurred since 1956.[11] It should be noted that this plant does not reinject the geothermal water — it is discharged to surface waters. While reinjection can be used to control the land subsidence, it is not without problems of its own (e.g., the plugging of reinjection pipes, high cost, etc.).

E. Seismic Activity

As Bowen notes, "geothermal and seismic phenomena are geographically inseparable."[8] The subsurface conditions which lead to geothermal phenomena also lead to earthquakes and other seismic activity. No data have been presented to date to show that the extraction of geothermal energy has increased the seismicity of an area, but research is focusing on the impacts of reinjection techniques. The use of underground nuclear explosions to fracture the hot dry rock formations discussed earlier is also being considered, but this will require a considerable amount of additional research.

F. Other Impacts

A number of other environmental impacts have been identified. The release of substantial amounts of water vapor has led to instances of local fogging. Waste heat is dissipated to the environment, primarily to the atmosphere through cooling towers, although the use of once-through cooling such as the system used in Wairakei can have a substantial impact on surface waters. The question of land use also arises. As described above, geothermal operations are industrial in nature, but the sites of geothermal resources are often recreational.

Despite the adverse environmental impacts outlined above, a comparison of these with the substantial impacts of other energy generating systems shows that the advantages of geothermal energy may well outweigh the disadvantages. Additional emphasis on nonelectric uses may also minimize the environmental impacts. Barnea also notes that "geothermal energy is perhaps the only natural resource which pollutes the environment if left undeveloped (Yellowstone releases more than 100 tons of arsenic per year)."[10]

IV. SOLAR ENERGY

Solar energy technologies will not have serious environmental implications in the near term because they currently supply only a very small percentage of U.S. power needs. This situation may change significantly by the year 2000, and attention must be given to those environmental problems which may arise from widespread solar energy utilization.

As noted earlier, coal and nuclear fuel systems can have significant environmental impacts in numerous portions of the fuel cycle (e.g., mining, transportation, etc.). Solar energy is quite similar. Since it is a dilute form of power, by its very nature it will require collection devices which must cover a large area and hence require large quantities of material for the construction of these devices. It is the extraction, production, processing, and transportation of these materials which will probably have the greatest environmental impact.

In the following section, three solar energy technologies are discussed: solar photovoltaic energy, solar thermal energy conversion, and solar heating and cooling. First, a description of the technology with some of the associated problems will be reviewed, followed by an environmental assessment of the specific method of solar energy utilization.

Since the potential level of utilization of solar energy is not geographically equal, it might be expected that electricity supplied by a solar station would be cheaper in those areas with greater net radiation. These reduced utility rates might further increase industrial migrations to sunnier regions, in particular the Southwest. This effect, the associated migration of people to these areas, and the resulting environmental impacts are not examined here.

A. Photovoltaic Energy

This technology has been used in cameras, street lamps, and space satellites, but all these previous applications have a trivial impact compared to the impact expected with widespread power generation. The capital cost of solar cells has not previously approached the overriding importance that it will in central electric generating station applications. This fact plus the enormous size of the collectors forces cell efficiency to become an extremely important design if not feasibility parameter.

A photovoltaic central electric generating station will have as its principal components:

1.   The photovoltaic receivers ("panels," "cells")
2.   A storage facility
3.   Power conditioning equipment
4.   Transmission and switching equipment

In contrast to conventional steam electric stations, water requirements are trivial and the absence of reject heat eliminates the need for cooling towers.

1. Photovoltaic Receivers

Photovoltaic solar cells basically are semiconductor devices in which photons are absorbed and charge carriers generated, together with a potential barrier (such as a p-n junction) to separate the charges. These semiconductors must have several very specific properties for photovoltaic application.

Since materials which satisfy the requirements for photocells have generally not been produced in large quantities, little information on pollution control technology, ecological effects, toxicology, and soil chemistry exists. Also, in general, health standards have not been developed for many of the existing and proposed substances to be used for photocells.

Some of the substances being used and others which are under consideration for use are: silicon (Si), cadmium sulfide (CdS), gallium arsenide (GaAs), selenium (Se), and group III phosphides.[12] The materials selected will depend principally on efficiency and cost of production. One process being developed by Tyco Labs and Harvard University, which would significantly reduce costs, is the use of a very thin die which is lowered into molten silicon; silicon is drawn into the die by capillary action. The silicon ribbon is then pulled slowly through the die and holds that shape as it hardens. The ribbons can be cut and fashioned into solar cells without costly grinding and polishing.

2. Photovoltaic Storage Systems

Coal-fired and nuclear steam electric plants can generate electricity upon demand. Since solar generating stations can produce power only in times of adequate insolation the total system requires some amount of storage capacity. These storage facilities would be required unless the solar generating station served only as a peaking station supplying electricity only where peak demand occurred during periods of maximum insolation (e.g., high air conditioning demand). Some storage options are summarized in Table 5.

a. Central Station Photovoltaic Generation on Geosynchronous Satellites

One possibility now being considered as a future source of electricity is to collect sunlight in space and beam it down to earth by means of microwaves.[12] One such conceptual design is presented in Figure 3.

Features of this proposal which are being studied are:

1. The use of large numbers of shuttle launches. One scenario suggests that in 1990-94, 4 stations producing 56×10^3 MWe would require 1444 shuttle flights per year at a cost of $\$68 \times 10^9$ excluding R&D.[16] This may cause serious air pollution as well as other problems.
2. The launching from earth of nuclear cargoes, subsequently used in space propulsion.
3. The use of high intensity microwave beams to transmit energy back to earth. The health hazards of stray microwaves may be significant.

3. Environmental Effects of Photovoltaic Energy Systems

There are a number of direct environmental impacts from photovoltaic energy systems. One of the most obvious effects of large solar energy installations is the land requirement. Table 6 presents expected land requirements for three photovoltaic energy use scenarios.

Space requirements not included in the above calculations are: (1) service roads, (2) transmission lines, (3) power conditioning facilities, (4) power storage facilities, and (5) substation and other related facilities.

TABLE 5

Summary of Candidate Storage Modes[12-14]

Item	Pumped[a] hydro	Compressed[b] air	Batteries[c]	Hydrogen cycle[d]	Flywheels[e]	Magnetic
Minimum economic size, utility application	10⁴ MWh	200 MWh	10 MWh	10 MWh	10 MWh	10⁴ MWh
Estimated costs ($/kW)	200—300	80—700	180	75—350	100—400	500—600
Expected service life (years)	50	20	10—20	30	30	30
Estimated efficiencies (%)	65—70	45 primary 70—75 storage	70—80	50—60	80—95	90—95
Use fossil fuels?	No	Yes	No	No	No	No
Dispersed capability?	No	No	Yes	Yes	Yes	No
Resource limitations	Site limited	Site limited	Unknown	None	None	Yes

a   Conventional pumped hydro storage. This approach is possible only in terrain of substantial relief and ample surface water. About 2500 to 5000 kWh/acre can be stored. There is no prospect of significantly improving efficiency. Besides large land commitment, there are very serious ecological and aesthetic problems associated with draw down.

b   Underground compressed gas experience relates mostly to helium and natural gas. Because auxiliary fossil energy is used, about 4 kWh are recovered for every 3 kWh in, but the real efficiency is 70 to 75% assuming no gas losses through bedding planes and joints. Obviously this can be used only where geological conditions are favorable, or man-made cavities can be exploited.

c   Batteries are becoming attractive at least for utility application. With increased use of the familiar Pb-acid battery, lead may come into short supply. High charging rates cause boiling and H₂ evolution, and high discharge rates cause electrode pitting. However, newer high temperature storage cells using Na, Li, Cl, and S capable of high rate discharge are being developed. The requirement that they be heated makes them unsuitable for residential use, but for utility size load leveling they may become very attractive. R&D needs to be aimed at maximizing reliability at lowest cost, even at reduced charge/discharge rate limits.

d   Hydrogen cycles: water electrolysis, hydrogen storage cryogenically or as hydride, and oxidation in H₂-air or H₂-O₂ fuel cells. These technologies are especially appropriate for photovoltaic application because the dc power can be used directly. Modular factory construction of components allows add-on just as with the panels.

*   Flywheels today are constructed of metal and/or glass fiber and/or organic fibers. Coupled to a photovoltaic generating system, a flywheel would be driven by a variable speed motor-generator receiving its ac supply from the system inverter. One design feature a 100 to 200 ton rotor of 12 to 15 ft diameter rotating at 3500 rpm with a storage capacity of 10^4 to 2×10^4 kWh. It is calculated that a 10^4 kW/hr to 3000 kW unit would cost about $325,000 and have an in-out efficiency of 93 to 95-pc if maintained in H_2 or He. These were 1973 dollars.[15]

/   1970 dollars.

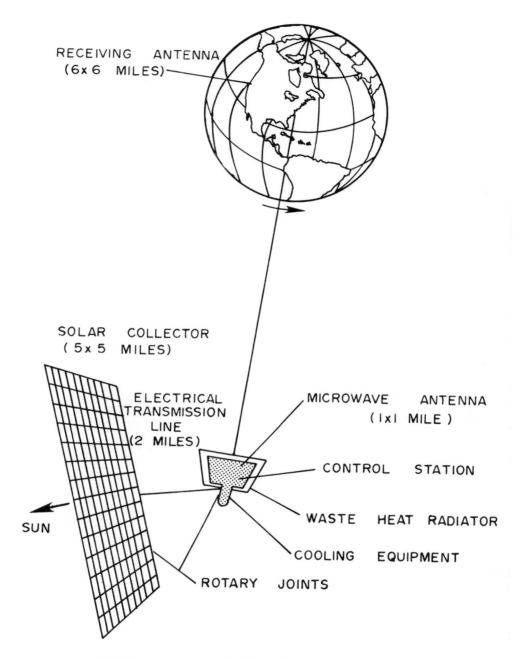

FIGURE 3.   A conceptual 10^4 MW, satellite photovoltaic power station.

Many of the auxiliary facilities will have to be located in the field of solar collectors, and hence, to avoid shadowing the receiving surfaces, much of the equipment such as transmission line might have to be buried or placed in trenches.

There will be a significant visual impact in the area of the solar collector system because of the large tracts of land needed for the facility. But if this is compared to the adverse visual effects caused by coal mining, the solar facility may well come out

TABLE 6

Year 2000 Photovoltaic Power Capacity Projections and Corresponding Land Commitment[12]

Forecast	Total capacity (GW$_e$)	Land area (mi²)	Total contiguous U.S. land area (%)
ERDA-48 scenario III × 40%	20	154	0.005
Project independence business as usual	191	1473	0.05
Project independence accelerated	1100	8492	0.27

ahead. Further, photovoltaic plants will probably have no high structures except possibly departing transmission lines.

Some farmland or grazing land may be taken out of use or production by central-station photovoltaic solar plants or thermal conversion plants, but these plants will most likely be placed in the desert and semidesert southwest. If they become feasible for more choice farm or grazing land, the impacts might be significantly greater.

There are no known direct air pollution effects from solar panels, but possibly from auxiliary energy storage facilities. The type and extent of pollution, if any, will depend upon the method of storage. Photovoltaic receiver systems have basically no water requirements. No thermal pollution occurs because no water is needed. Since no cooling towers are needed, there are no problems with biocides, slimicides, detergents, anticorrosion agents, etc., in blowdown or once-through waters. At least at present, photovoltaic panels are hermetically sealed. This avoids discharge of eroded CdS or other toxic semiconductor materials onto the land and into the surface waters under normal operation.

In addition to the direct environmental impacts outlined above, there will also be a number of indirect impacts. There will be some air pollution as a result of the energy used in conjunction with the production of solar materials and also in the direct production of these materials. Quantities of particulates, SO_x, and NO_x released to the atmosphere will result from the production of the power required and the production of such materials as carbon steel, glass glazing, and aluminizing back panels. (See Reference 12 for pollutant quantity estimates.)

Primary aluminum production will result in emissions of particulates (including particulate fluorides) and gaseous fluorides. Fluorides cause vegetation and livestock injury.

Other air pollutants from cell production include:

Cadmium Sulfide — It is estimated that 10,000 MW equivalent of cadmium sulfide cell production would result in approximately 34 metric tons/year of air emissions from primary cadmium production. All zinc refineries presently emit about 642 metric tons of Cd annually. The OSHA standards for airborne Cd dust are 200 $\mu g/m^3$ (time weighted average) and 600 $\mu g/m^3$ (maximum concentration). Cd inhalation can result in respiratory problems.[17,19] Table 7 presents an estimate of the primary and secondary pollutants generated from the manufacture of cadmium sulfide cells.

Silicon — Silicon cell fabrication can be expected to emit PH_3, $POCl_3$, P_2O_5, BCl_3, and HF to the atmosphere. PH_3 and BCl_3 which are used in the doping process are

TABLE 7

Primary and Secondary Pollutants[a] Generated from the Manufacture of Cadmium Sulfide Cells for 9000 MW/Year (Peak)[b][20]

Pollutants	Front surface cells		Back surface cells	
	kg/yr	%[c]	kg/yr	%[c]
Air				
SO$_2$	6.9×10^6	2.4	7.6×10^6	2.7
Particulates	9.3×10^4	0.4	6.0×10^5	2.5
CO	0.4	Nil	0.5	Nil
Hydrocarbons	0.1	Nil	0.1	Nil
NO$_2$	1.2	Nil	1.5	Nil
Cd	5.2×10^2	120	6.3×10^2	146
Water				
TSS	6.4×10^3	0.1	2.5×10^5	41.1
Oil/Grease	5.6×10^3	1.8	5.0×10^5	164.4
As	5.5×10^1	0.04	6.1	Nil
Cd	1.1×10^2	1.1	1.3×10^2	1.3
Cu	1.4×10^1	3.9	1.5×10^1	4.2
P	2.0×10^2	0.1	1.8×10^4	9.1
Pb	—	—	0.6	Nil
Se	5.2×10^1	0.1	3.1×10^1	0.1
Zn	5.2×10^1	0.1	3.6×10^1	0.1
Solids				
CdO	1.6×10^2		1.9×10^2	
ZnSO$_4$	1.6×10^2		2.0×10^2	

[a]   Excluding emissions from the raw cadmium feedstock (densified, cadmium rich fumes from zinc smelters) and primary emissions from cell surface processing.

[b]   Equivalent to the production of 8820 MT of CdS for front surface cells and 7344 MT of CdS for back surface cells. This represents the demand in the year 2000, from solar photovoltaic power plants producing 1% of the total U.S. demand for electricity (9000 MW).

[c]   Emission as percentage of the corresponding rates emitted from coal-fired steam generators producing 9000 MW/yr of electricity in the year 2000, assuming application of control technology.

particularly toxic. The lowest published lethal concentration (LC1$_o$) for human inhalation of PH$_3$ is 8 ppm.[17,18]

Gallium Arsenide — GaAs is not very toxic in its undissociated state, but arsenic and its compounds are very toxic. Acute airborne exposure to As$_2$O$_3$ has produced skin irritation.[17,18]

Air Pollution Prevented by Not Burning Fuels — If no solar energy electric systems were developed and if it is assumed that fossil-fueling plants would fill the gap, then the "prevented pollutants" can be calculated to be as shown in Table 8.[12]

Water Pollution Impacts — There are three potential areas of significant water pollution caused by the production of solar photovoltaic materials: (1) surface water degradation and groundwater disturbance due to coal, zinc, copper, and bauxite mining; (2) water pollution related to ore roasting, smelting, and refining; and (3) waste water discharges in CdS, Si, and GaAs production and device fabrication.

Cadmium can enter the surface waters in the mining and smelting process. The substance can also leach into ground water from slag heaps, dross disposal, etc.[19] (See Table 7).

TABLE 8

Hypothetical "Pollutants Prevented" by Solar
Electric Substitution for Coal Fired Utility Generation[12]

Pollutant	Emissions prevented (lb/ GWh)	
	No control	Control
Particulates	85,000	8,500
SO$_x$	48,000	4,800
NO$_x$	7,500	7,500

Silicon cell production may have water effluents containing hydrogen fluoride and acetic and nitric acids. The production of gallium arsenide cells will generate considerable quantities of various alumina sludges and waste waters containing the trace metals found in bauxite during the gallium extraction from aluminum ore process.[18]

B. Solar Thermal Energy Conversion

The concept of solar thermal energy conversion is to collect solar radiation over a large area and concentrate it on a small area to produce steam directly or by means of a heat transfer fluid. The heated fluid might supply space or process steam, or be used to store energy. There are generally two types of thermal conversion concentrator systems, the centralized and distributed receivers.

In the central receiver, solar energy is transmitted optically from an array of solar collectors to a centralized receiver located in a tower. In the distributed system the energy is converted into thermal energy by the collectors themselves and is transmitted to the power plant by a heat exchange medium (e.g., air, water, oil, a liquid metal, etc.).

The central receiver system has received the greatest research and development funding. In concept the system has a collecting field of mirrors which focus the radiant energy on the tower which contains a boiler. These mirrors can be either parabolic devices which track the sun separately and focus light on the boiler, or they can be flat mirrors arranged around the tower so that together they act as one large parabolic mirror.

Two major advantages of the central receiver system lie in the efficiency of the energy transfer process and in the resulting high temperatures. Since the energy is transferred as light, the only losses are reflection losses on the receiver. It is anticipated that the central receiver systems being designed will produce supersaturated steam at 900 to 1000°F temperatures, comparable to those in modern coal-fired plants.

In the distributed system the heat exchange takes place at the collector itself. The radiant energy is absorbed on the collecting surfaces and the heat energy is carried to a storage area by means of the heat transfer fluid. The resulting temperatures are lower than those obtained with the centralized collector. They range from 200°F to 500°F and hence are less efficient for power production.

1. Environmental Effects of Solar Thermal Energy Conversion Systems

Many of the environmental effects of these systems are identical or similar to those discussed for photovoltaic systems. Photovoltaic generating stations could be sized almost arbitrarily to meet the specific requirements of particular load centers, the principal restraint being equipment cost. The thermal conversion systems or steam electric generating facilities are not suitable for modular construction. One reason for this is the grid size requirements to achieve adequate temperatures.

The water requirements also limit the placement of these systems. Conventional water cooling towers are being planned which will require large quantities of water.

There are a number of direct environmental impacts of thermal conversion systems. Heat discharges will be similar to conventional fossil fuel plants and hence the same cooling tower problems will arise, such as blowdown and the use of cooling tower chemicals. Some of the problems which will be eliminated in this system versus a conventional coal-fired plant are: no coal pile drainage, fly ash and bottom ash disposal, and scrubber sludge leachate.

The land use effects will be similar to those discussed for photovoltaic systems. Power tower designs will have greater visual impact than flat plate photovoltaic facilities. Towers 200 to 400 m high are under consideration. Mirror glare could be a problem for aircraft. Agricultural impacts will be the same as those for photovoltaic systems. Aside from cooling tower emissions no air pollutant emissions are expected in normal operation. Cooling tower drift may carry some chemicals and could therefore present some problems. As with photovoltaic systems, most of the environmental impacts will come with the production of the required construction materials. At this time, except for cement, concrete, steel, aluminum and glass, many of the other materials which might be used in the production of the thermal systems have not yet been identified.

C. Solar Heating and Cooling

Solar space heating can be categorized as either active or passive. In an active solar house, energy is collected by a system of solar collectors, typically on the roof. The heat energy is carried away by water or air and transferred into some large storage system. From the storage unit, it is then circulated, as required, throughout the house by either a hot water or hot air system of conventional design.

In a passive system there is no circulation to storage. Passive solar houses are most useful in generally sunny regions. They are custom designed and the designs vary considerably.

The active houses are of more commercial interest since the solar heating component is a complete system, often one that can be retrofitted in an existing building. The major components of this system are described below.

Collector — The "flat plate" collector is the most common; a typical size might be a box 1 m by 1 m, 15 to 20 cm thick, covered by a transparent plate of glass or plastic. The back is blackened to absorb solar radiation and the heat that is generated is carried away by water (in pipes or trickling across the surface) or by air. In sophisticated systems the interior is a partial vacuum to reduce energy losses, the windows are double-layered or specially coated to admit incoming radiation but trap outgoing heat radiation. Other special coatings increase the absorptive power of the back plate.

Storage — A second component of a solar heating system is the heat storage unit which is needed to provide for nights and cloudy days. The common storage is water in an insulated tank. When the heating system circulates air, however, crushed rocks or pebbles are often used. Since water has a higher heat capacity than stone, the space required is less for water. The usual rule of thumb for 2 or 3 days of storage is 1.5 gal of water storage per square foot of collector. The rule for rock is 60 lb of rock per square foot of collector.* Other storage materials such as eutectic salts are also under investigation.

Solar Cooling — Evaporative coolers are used in some parts of the country, particu-

* ERDA Factsheet — Solar Heating and Cooling.

TABLE 9

Solar Heating and Cooling Materials Requirements[12]

Material	Cumulative usage, 10^6 tons through year		
	1985	2000	2020
Aluminum	0.07	1.0	5.7
Steel	0.60	9.0	50.0
Copper	0.10	1.5	8.0
Glass	0.40	6.0	32.0

larly the Southwest. Water is evaporated as it runs down over a system of pipes and the water in the pipes, cooled by evaporation, is then circulated through the house.

A more efficient system is based on the "absorption-desorption" principle which is used in refrigerators, air conditioners and heat pumps where energy is obtained from a heat source such as a gas flame or steam (in large units).

1. Environmental Effects of Solar Heating and Cooling

One drawback of using water as a storage and heat transfer fluid is the problem of corrosion. The problem is solvable but, based on current information, the chemical inhibitors which are being used can cause environmental problems. The best solution to the corrosion problem will likely be toxic compounds such as the chromate family of inhibitors. These can get into the groundwater from spillage during installation, maintenance, or corrosion.

Glare from the collectors might well present a problem to people on the ground or in nearby buildings. Since most collector surfaces are made of glass and are elevated, there is also some danger of broken glass falling from buildings.

As discussed previously, the actual materials to be used in large-scale solar collector production is still to be determined. An estimate is presented in Table 9, however. The data are shown as the amount of major materials used for the entire collector system. This includes materials for the plumbing, storage, heat exchangers, and the collector. Many such tabulations appear to have omitted peripheral hardware. Based on these projections, the impact on total U.S. production of these materials will not be significant.

V. HYDROGEN AS AN ALTERNATE FUEL

This section deals mainly with a brief description of the technology associated with hydrogen gas production and the potential environmental impacts related to the production and utilization of hydrogen. The environmental impacts of synthetic fuel production from coal and oil shale are discussed elsewhere in this and other chapters in this book.

Hydrogen may well emerge as a very important fuel toward the end of this century. Since hydrogen is not a basic energy resource (except in the sun), it must be supplied by utilizing some other energy resource to generate hydrogen from water or other hydrogen-containing chemical compounds.

A. Hydrogen Production

The most common method of producing hydrogen in quantities today is by the steam reforming of volatile hydrocarbons. This is not likely to be the method of production in the future because of the increased costs and reduced availability of these feedstocks.

Because water is an abundant resource, it is the favored feedstock. Electrolysis requires a source of electricity, but other energy technologies such as geothermal, solar, nuclear fission reactors, or possibly nuclear fusion can supply this. Obviously, the net efficiency of hydrogen production is dependent on the energy conversion efficiencies of electric generation and electrolysis. Currently available electrolysis units operate at efficiencies of 65%, but research efforts suggest this might rise to 90%.

Research is also underway to develop closed cycle thermochemical processes that could side-step the requirement for electricity and directly use the high temperature heat of a nuclear reactor to produce hydrogen directly. This approach may produce unwanted pollutants because of the highly reactive chemicals expected to be used and the high temperatures.[21]

B. Storage and Distribution

The large quantities of hydrogen requiring storage make gaseous storage improbable. The liquid state, at about 20°K, has been the most likely approach. At the present time liquid hydrogen is routinely shipped by railroad tank car and in tank trucks over the public highways. Cryogenic technology is well developed, and advances relevant to liquid hydrogen containment are being made constantly.

Numerous metal hydrides are presently being researched as possible safe storage media for hydrogen.[21]

Pipelines have been used for many years in Germany for the movement of hydrogen. Some industries in the U.S., such as the chemical and petrochemical industries, have some experience in moving hydrogen by pipeline. It may also be possible to use much of the existing natural gas pipeline network for transporting it.[21]

C. Use of Hydrogen

Hydrogen might be used as an automotive or aircraft fuel. Besides using hydrogen directly as a fuel, one of the most important uses of hydrogen is in fuel cells. A fuel cell combines hydrogen and oxygen to generate electricity with water and heat being the only effluents.

D. Hydrogen Safety

An important aspect of hydrogen use is the question of safety. Hydrogen burns with a faster, hotter flame, and mixtures of hydrogen with air are flammable over wider limits of mixture than natural gas. A special hazard of hydrogen transport and storage is that some metals become brittle immediately upon exposure to a high-purity hydrogen environment. Another potential problem of direct hydrogen use as a fuel is that the hydrogen flame is clear. This problem can be solved by doping the gas with a material to increase flame visibility. Most of the safety problems related to hydrogen use can be handled with little more difficulty than those associated with the use of gasoline and methane.

E. Environmental Impacts of Hydrogen Use

Unlike carbon based fuels, hydrogen used directly as a fuel produces only water at low combustion temperatures. At higher burner temperatures, as in all combustion processes, nitrogen oxides (NO_x) form and must be vented. For small home heating units no vent at all would be required except to perhaps release water vapor, but this water may be a desired side effect to provide humidification.

Hydrogen is also ideal for catalytic combustion at temperatures even as low as 100°C.[22] At this low temperature essentially no NO_x pollutants would be formed.

Large-scale adaptation of hydrogen use technologies may well produce other problems. For example, present water electrolysis cells use an asbestos membrane to separate the hydrogen and oxygen components. Table 10 presents some of the anticipated pollutant releases from a 500 MW electrolysis-fuel cell hydrogen cycle facility.

VI. WIND POWER

Most wind power technologies as presently envisioned would have a benign effect on the environment. The specific effects of windpower systems will depend upon the method of wind energy extraction and the peripheral equipment used for energy conversion, energy storage and ultimate method of use. Figure 4 presents a flow chart of wind machine applications.

In addition to one small or medium sized machine supplying power to one residential or commercial building, the productivity can be increased by grouping machines. Concepts for the placement of large numbers of small to medium size wind generators are (1) structural space array on top of towers, and (2) cable-suspended arrays that would be analogous to hydroelectric dams.

Traditionally, a wind conversion system comprises a support tower, a rotor, a step-up transmission, and an energy converter, such as an electrical generator or a water pump.

Typical overall machine efficiencies generally do not exceed 37%. The theoretical limit for the rotor efficiency is about 59% of the power in the wind stream passing through the area swept out by the rotor blades.

A. Storage of Wind Generated Power

The storage of wind generated power is a requirement similar to that for most solar energy systems — there must be reserve power when the wind is not blowing. Several storage technologies have been used as shown in Figure 4. The most familiar is lead-acid batteries; unfortunately, these can cost as much as the machine itself. Another alternative is to use pumped water or air; that is, either pump water up into a reservoir and let it fall to turn the turbines as needed, or use the wind machine to drive a compressor. The compressed air, which can be stored in tanks or natural caverns, can then be used to drive a turbine. Flywheel storage is also a possibility. Another technique which shows great promise is to use the wind power to electrolyze water and store the hydrogen for use as a fuel, or convert it to electricity in a fuel cell. The environmental impacts of each method of storage will vary considerably.

B. Direct Environmental Effects of Wind Machines

Wind power systems in themselves produce no air or water pollution (unless the storage mechanism would) and little noise except for the very large machines. However, some would regard visual pollution imposed by the wind machines and transmission lines to feed a power network to be the severest wind power system impact. Land use may also be a problem because of the tremendous number of wind plants which would be needed to make a significant contribution to the country's energy needs. Large groups of plants might require considerable land and the clearing of obstructing vegetation. This impact may be insignificant in remote areas where it might be expected that wind machines would be used to meet the power needs of individuals and small communities.

Other potential direct environmental effects include rotor throw, bird collision, and TV interference. There is a possible danger of wind machine rotors being thrown large distances from the wind plant (the machine at Grandpa's Knob threw a blade a distance of 230 m in early 1945). Currently envisioned wind power systems could involve a

TABLE 10

Significant Anticipated Direct Environmental Releases from a 500 MW Electrolysis Fuel Cell Hydrogen Cycle Facility[23]

Component	Atmospheric emissions	Waste water discharges	Solid waste	Accident or malfunction
Process water treatment facility	None	Filter bed backflush (to river) Demineralizer regeneration (to lagoon)	Occasional discard of spoiled resin (to landfill)	Malodorous emissions from anaerobic processes in filter bed
Electrolysis units	Option (a): asbestos Option (b): deteriorated SPE entrained in 65,600 Scfm O_2	Option (a): asbestos in flush (to lagoon) Option (b): deteriorated SPE in flush (to lagoon)	Sludge (Cf. waste water).	Pyrolysis products of SPE
Hydrogen storage	None	None	Discard of spoiled fill (to oxide conversion or recycle facilities)	FeTi and FeTiH$_2$ granular and powdered material (to work place)
Fuel cells	Excess air	Option (a): asbestos in product water and flush Option (b): deteriorated SPE in product water and flush	Sludge (Cf. waste water)	Pyrolysis products of SPE
Cooling towers	Fog and icing, drift (containing treatment chemicals) Heat Noise	Treatment chemicals in blowdown (to lagoon)	Sludge (Cf. waste water)	Wood smoke and pyrolysis products if timber construction used. PVC pyrolysis products
Power handling section	Traces PCBs (SF$_6$) from transformers. Herbicides from rights of way Smoke from slash burning	None	None	PCBs in explosion (SF$_6$)
Sanitary facility	None	Pathogens, BOD, treatment chemicals	Sludge	Raw sewage

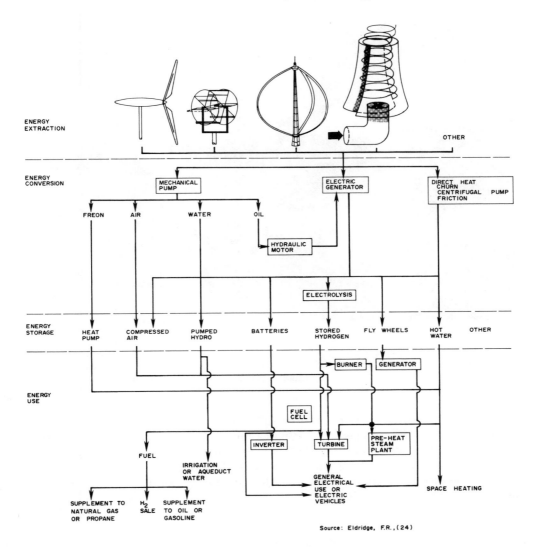

FIGURE 4.   Wind machine applications.

substantially larger hazardous zone area and unless "fail-safe" belt or cable designs to control rotor throw hazards are developed, this might require wind plant development in unpopulated areas.

Studies[17] have shown that there is a significant probability of bird-rotor collisions. Of course, the actual probability depends on the design parameters and the bird density in the area.

Studies performed at the University of Michigan for ERDA indicate that (1) the TV signal reflected by a wind machine increases in proportion to the absolute area of the rotor blades, and (2) reception difficulties might be experienced as far away as 400 m from the machine for higher frequency UHF TV signals. The interference would be seen by the viewer as dark bands traveling across the TV screen.[18]

VII. TAR SANDS

The U.S. has more than 30 billion bbl of oil stored in tar sand deposits throughout

FIGURE 5.   Tar sands excavation. One of three bucketwheel excavators used to strip mine tar sand at the Great Canadian Oil Sands, Ltd. (GCOS) site near Ft. McMurray, Alberta, Canada. Excavators are 210 ft long and 12 stories high. (From Great Canadian Oil Sands, Ltd., a subsidiary of Sun Company, Inc., Radnor, Pa.)

the country, with the major portion (over 90%) in the state of Utah. This amount is dwarfed, however, by the massive Athabasca tar sand deposits in Alberta, Canada (with estimated reserves of 600 billion bbl), where commercial development has already begun. The Great Canadian Oil Sands, Ltd. (GCOS), a subsidiary of the Sun Company Inc., has operated a facility there for over 10 years, and currently produces approximately 50,000 bbl/day of synthetic crude oil.[25]

As in oil shale recovery systems, there are two processes which can be used to obtain oil from the tar sands — surface mining and *in situ* recovery. The environmental impacts of each can be considerably different.

A. Surface Mines

The GCOS facility is a surface mine (see Figure 5), and the environmental impacts are therefore fairly well known. In many respects, surface mining of tar sands is similar to strip mining of coal — the potential for fugitive air emissions from material handling and transfer, problems with increased suspended solids in surface runoff, and the ultimate restoration of the site present similar environmental impacts. There are unique considerations, however. The tar sand deposits in northeastern Alberta are covered by a muskeg swamp (consisting of partially decayed organic material). This must be drained and cleared before mining operations can begin. Tar sands also have the potential for hydrocarbon emissions from volatiles in the bitumen. The magnitude of the hydrocarbon emissions is a function of ambient temperature, elevation, and the nature of the overburden (fractures in the overburden would allow the volatiles to escape over a long period of time).[26] There is also the problem of organic loading of runoff water, which is not usually present with coal mining.

A problem similar to that presented in the oil shale industry is the disposal of spent tar sands after they have been processed through the bitumen extraction plant. The specifics of the operation will often dictate the disposal methodology, but one of two techniques are likely to be used:

1. "Temporary disposal in ponding areas until the sand can be disposed of permanently in mined out areas without interfering with mining operations.
2. Permanent disposal behind dams constructed in valleys near a mine or processing plant."[26]

The potential for unique environmental problems can be found in the experience of a firm preparing to develop a facility in the Athabasca area. The spent sand tailings pond is coated with a thin layer of bitumen, which is toxic to waterfowl. The proposed facility is on a flyway for migratory fowl, and the company is therefore attempting to develop methods to keep the waterfowl away from the tailings ponds.[25]

B. *In Situ* Techniques

When the overburden is too deep, economic considerations discourage surface mining. Research is currently being conducted to determine the feasibility of *in situ* production methods for these areas. Since the methods are so new there are no commercial applications using *in situ* techniques. Little has been reported about the subsequent environmental consequences.

Gases produced in the *in situ* process containing carbon dioxide, carbon monoxide, and methane are expected. The likely quantities of sulfur compound gases (SO_2, H_2S, etc.) are not really known. As with oil shale, the impact of *in situ* recovery processes on subsurface water quality is also an unknown. The *in situ* does offer advantages in that disposal of spent sands is not a problem.

Both surface mining and *in situ* processes are likely to lead to the indirect impacts similar to other extraction systems. This includes the formation of "boom towns" and the loss of land for recreation purposes.

VIII. OCEAN THERMAL ENERGY

The French physicist Jacques d'Arsonval first proposed the concept of generating electricity from ocean thermal gradients in 1881. Technology for the idea has been shown to work, but the economics were simply not competitive. The methodology is receiving attention again, however, as the price of other energy generating techniques increases. Vast amounts of energy are available (i.e., several times the world's present energy consumption) from ocean thermal differences.

There are a number of environmental impacts which must be considered, however. The large-scale mixing of warm and cold water could have impacts on the ocean, biota, and climate. This may not be a negative effect, however. Williams[27] notes that "if nutrient-rich cold water is brought from the ocean depths and released near the surface, this could result in a substantial increase in fish populations, as occurs naturally off the coast of Peru." But the movement of so much water "could create new currents in the vicinity of the unit. Furthermore, the intake may suck in fish and other aquatic organisms."[28]

The large surface areas in the heat exchangers will be continually subjected to the flow of corrosive seawater, and metallic elements will therefore be introduced into the seawater. Loss of the working fluid (typically ammonia) might also be a problem if leaks in the system are significant, or the result of an unexpected spill (e.g., collision with a ship or severe storms).

Other problems include the impacts of techniques used to inhibit biofouling and/or corrosion, the impacts of coastal zone facilities associated with the operations of the offshore plants, and the installation and operation of electrical distribution systems.[29]

IX. OTHER ALTERNATE ENERGY SOURCES

A wide range of alternate energy sources have not been addressed in this chapter, including such sources as tidal power and osmotic pressure systems. Each has environmental advantages and disadvantages which must be addressed. Using the same examples, osmotic pressure systems recover energy where a fresh water river runs into the salt water ocean. The impacts on the estuary could be significant, as the ecosystems there are usually quite fragile.[28] For tidal power sites, the impact on coastal ecosystems must also be determined.

These types of impacts, and the others described in this chapter, can have a significant impact on the ultimate role the various alternate sources will have in the overall energy supply picture. Some of the impacts are substantial, others are unknown. In all cases, however, the shift from "nonconventional" to "conventional" status must be accompanied by attempts to better understand the energy-environmental interactions of the alternate energy systems.

REFERENCES

1. **Anon.**, U.S. Environmental Protection Agency, Oil Shale and the Environment, EPA-600/9-77-033, October, 1977.
2. **Dinneen, G. U. and Cook, G. C.**, Oil shale and the energy crisis, *Technol. Rev.*, 76(No. 3) 26, 1974.
3. Stanford Research Institute, Menlo Park, Calif., Control of Environmental Impacts from Advanced Energy Sources, EPA-60/2-74-002, March, 1974.
4. Tetra Tech, Inc., Arlington, Va., Energy Fact Book — 1976, Office of Naval Research, TT-A-642-76-254, July, 1976.
5. TRW, Inc. and Denver Research Institute, A Preliminary Assessment of the Environmental Impacts from Oil Shale Developments, EPA-600/7-77-069, July, 1977.
6. **Buonicore, A. J.**, Environmental Implications of Energy Use, Proc. 2nd Nat. Conf. on Energy and the Environment, Hueston Woods State Park, Ohio, November 1974.
7. **Schein, D. L.**, Energy or Ecology?: The Impact of Oil Shale Development on the National Parks in the Upper Colorado River Basin, Master's thesis, University of Illinois, Chicago Circle, 1976.
8. **Bowen, R. G.**, Environmental impact of geothermal development, in *Geothermal Energy Resources, Production, Stimulation,* Kruger, P., and Otte, C., Eds., Stanford University Press, Stanford, Calif., 1973.
9. Resource Planning Associates, Inc., Cambridge, Mass., Western Energy Resources and the Environment: Geothermal Energy, EPA-600/9-77-010, May, 1977.
10. **Barnea, J.**, Geothermal power, *Sci. Am.,* 226, 1, 1972.
11. **Axtmann, R. C.**, Environmental impact of a geothermal power plant, *Science,* 187, 4179, 1975.
12. U.S. Environmental Protection Agency, Preliminary Environmental Assessment of Solar Energy Systems, EPA 600/7-77-086, August, 1977.
13. National Science Foundation and Interagency Task Force for Solar Energy, Solar Energy Volume, Project Independence Blueprint Final Task Force Report, Federal Energy Administration, Washington, D.C., November, 1974.
14. Science and Public Policy Program, Energy Alternatives: A Comparative Analysis, University of Oklahoma, Norman, and USGOP, Washington, D.C., May, 1975.
15. **Post, R. F. and Post, S. F.**, Flywheels, *Sci. Am.,* 229, 6, 1973.
16. **Williams, J. R.**, Geosynchronous satellite solar power, *Astronaut. Aeronaut.,* 13, 11, 1975.
17. ERDA, Environmental Impacts of Eight Solar Energy Technologies, ERDA 77-47/1-8, 1977.

18. **Holmes, J. G., Baluss, J. E., Mihlmester, P. E., Miller, S. G., Super, T. L., and Thomian, J. B.,** Energy and Environmental Analysis Inc., Arlington, Va., "Environmental and Safety Implications of Solar Technologies," Proceedings of the 1977 Annual Meeting, Volume 1, The American Section of the International Solar Energy Society.
19. **Fleisscher, M.,** Environmental impact of cadmium: a review by the panel on hazardous trace substances, *Environ. Health Perspect.,* 7, 1974.
20. U.S. Environmental Protection Agency, Assessment of Large-scale Photovoltaic Materials Production, EPA-600/7-77-087, August, 1977.
21. U.S. Environmental Protection Agency, Control of Environmental Impacts from Advanced Energy Sources, NTIS-PB-239450, March, 1974.
22. **Gregory, D. P.,** The hydrogen economy, *Sci. Am.,* 228(No. 1), 13, 1973.
23. **Sears, D. R.,** An Environmental Assessment of a 500 MW Hydrogen Air Fuel Cell Peak Shaving Plant, LMSC-HREC TR D496563, Lockheed Missiles & Space Company, Huntsville, Ala., 1975.
24. **Eldridge, F. R.,** Mitre Corp., McLean, Va., Wind Machines, Prepared for the National Science Foundation, NSF-RA-N-75-051, October, 1975.
25. **Maugh, T. H.,** Tar sands: a new fuels industry takes shape, *Science,* 199, 756, 1978.
26. Battelle Columbus Labs, Columbus, Ohio, Production and Processing of U.S. Tar Sands: An Environmental Assessment, EPA-600/7-76-035, December, 1976.
27. **Williams, J. R.,** Comparative Evaluation of Solar, Fission, Fusion and Fossil Energy Resources. Part I: Solar Energy, N74-18721 (NASA-CR-137242), 1974.
28. **Aulenback, D.B.,** Environmental impact of lesser-known energy sources, *J. Int. Soc. Technol. Assess.,* 2(No. 4), 60, 1976.
29. U.S. Dept of Energy, Washington, D.C., Environmental Development Plan: Ocean Thermal Energy Conversion, DOE/EDP-0006, March, 1978.

Chapter 5

MATERIAL AND ENERGY RESOURCE RECOVERY

J. G. Abert

TABLE OF CONTENTS

I. INTRODUCTION

A. Municipal Solid Waste — Problem or Opportunity?

Unlike air and water pollution, the solid waste problem seems to have a good side — the potential for recovering energy and usable materials. So states a recent article on the subject entitled "Municipal Solid Waste — Problem or Opportunity?."* Dr. Rocco Petrone, President of the National Center for Resource Recovery, summarized solid waste's beneficial aspects when he said, "Resource recovery might be considered an idea whose time has come. It is an appealing concept. It satisfies our awareness of the need for conservation. It goes hand in hand with our desire for environmental improvement. It is a domestic source of supply of ultimately depletable raw materials for industry. For the cities plagued with waste disposal problems, it greatly reduces the volume and weight of the discard that ultimately must be disposed of in some manner." However, communities have been slow to realize the opportunity. In the main, this chapter deals with the technical, economic and institutional realities which inhibit the conversion of problem to opportunity.

There is no question that disposing of solid waste is indeed a problem although the lack of suitable land area to handle the waste by the traditional landfill approach is sometimes overplayed. The difficulty of the political decisions involved in landfill siting is more often the major constraining factor rather than the shear physical non-availability of land. However, there is plenty of waste. U.S. households and commercial sources currently generate over 140 million tons of solid waste annually. This includes household, commercial and institutional waste, but excludes sewage sludge, demolition and construction refuse and industrial wastes. The 140 million tons per year is roughly 3.5 pounds per person per day. The total bill for the collection and disposal of this waste is estimated to be over $7 billion per year and is expected to reach $10 billion by 1980.

There is also no doubt that municipal waste contains some potentially valuable ingredients. Roughly 75% of it is combustible and has value as fuel. On the average, 8% is metal. Approximately 10% is glass. As a fuel, waste's heat energy is about 10 million Btu a ton, somewhat less than half that of a ton of coal. Aluminum recovered to the top re-use specifications will yield between $300 and $400 per ton, steel in excess of $20 per ton and glass $20 or better per ton of cullet recovered. However, the extraction of the metals and glass in marketable form is not inexpensive, nor can waste be used for energy without incurring some fairly high costs, with outlays for both initial capital expenditures and operating expenses. In addition, there is uncertainty as to the technical feasibility of some of the recovery technology. Will it work? Or, even if it does, is there a technologically better approach just over the horizon that may make obsolete an investment made now? Also, the fact that, by their very nature, secondary materials markets are cyclical, works against definitive revenue forecasting, hence against the ability to rationalize with a high degree of certainty public investment decisions to undertake recovery based approaches to solid waste management. Put simply, it is difficult to "sell" the City Council. Today's perspective is then — while the problem of waste is there, for the most part, the opportunity is yet to be realized.

B. Waste Reduction — Reducing the Amount of Waste

Apart from resource recovery, among environmentalists, indeed among ordinary

---

*   Municipal solid waste — problem or opportunity? *EPRI J.,* No. 9, p.6—13, November, 1977. For a good overview of the potential for recycling see chapter 8, Recycling, in *Government and the Nation's Resources,* Report of the National Commission on Supplies and Shortages, December, 1976, p. 155—170.

citizens, there is a general feeling that waste reduction offers a solution to the problem of municipal solid waste. Many give waste reduction a higher priority than resource recovery and often oppose recovery attempts as being a form of "second best" which would not be required if the nation as a whole would pay "proper" attention to waste reduction possibilities. Waste reduction involves waste prevention or diminishing the quantity of waste generated. This is to be accomplished by redesigning products or changing consumption patterns so that reduced amounts of materials are required. More durable and longer-lived products; reusable rather than throw-away or single-use produces and packaging; improvements in materials so that less, particularly the depletable resources, are needed to achieve a desired end purpose; redesigning products and packaging systems to reduce material, and also energy requirements; shifting consumption habits towards a less materials intensive "market basket" of goods and services — all of the above are examples of waste reduction approaches cited by the U.S. Environmental Protection Agency.*

In general, it appears that the ambitions of those who see waste reduction as a panacea for the municipal waste problem far exceed the likely realizations of this approach. The public at large is not as willing as the advocates to reduce consumption. The technical possibilities for better and cheaper — at least not more expensive — products, where better is taken in the context of less material and energy intensive, seem to be not as great as the advocates wish. Finally, the economic, institutional, and behavioral barriers to widespread adoption of "re-use, refill, and make do longer" approaches, seem to be extremely high and in fact may be increasing. The economic system, in terms of product development, distribution, and sale, presumably will continue to respond to the market place wherein consumer preferences for alternative products are displayed. It is unlikely that there will be a dramatic shift in these preferences. Although much has been made of supposed industry restrictions on the number of alternatives available to consumers as a significant barrier to waste reduction, if true, and it may not be, the situation is unlikely to change in any dramatic way so as to allow for a forecast that waste reduction will bring about a significant decrease in the nation's municipal solid waste load.**

C. Source Separation — the Labor Intensive Approach

At present, about 6% of the 140 million annual tons of municipal solid waste is recovered for productive re-use. Virtually all of this is accomplished by source separation which is the segregation of specific waste materials at their point of discard for concentrated collection and reprocessing. While there is some source separation of steel cans and glass bottles, paper and aluminum are the prime materials recycled in

---

* Fourth Report to Congress, Resource Recovery and Waste Reduction, U.S. Environmental Protection Agency, SW-600, p. 1, 1977.

** In fact, with the growing participation of women in the labor force, the use of convenience packaging, which to many is the heart of the solid waste problem, may increase as a larger proportion of householders opt for pre-preparation and other convenience factors which seem to mean "more" packaging. There is fairly extensive literature on waste reduction most of which deals with the issue of whether there should be a deposit on beverage cans and bottles. For example: Bingham, T. H., et al, Energy and Economic Impacts of Mandatory Deposits, Report prepared for the Federal Energy Administration by the Research Triangle Institute, September, 1976; Midwest Research Institute, Resource and Environmental Profile Analysis of Nine Beverage Container Alternatives, Report prepared for the U.S. Environmental Protection Agency, EPA-350-SW-91c, 1974; Ackoff, R. L., et al., A study of the Impacts on the USA of a Ban on One Way Beverage Containers, Report prepared for the U.S. Brewers Association by Busch Center, the Wharton School, University of Pennsylvania, December, 1976; and General Accounting Office, Potential Effects of a National Mandatory Deposit on Beverage Containers, PAS-78-19, December, 1977.

this manner. Programs relying on source separation are dependent on the consumer's motivation to cooperate. This varies from location to location and rises or falls depending on family education, income level, type of housing, frequency of collection, etc. It is markedly increased when there is a financial inducement, either personal or for a worthy group such as the Boy Scouts. Deposits are often mentioned as a means of creating a financial inducement. Containers are brought back to redeem the deposit. Other alternatives are also used. One of the reasons the source separated aluminum recycling program has achieved a level when one in every four aluminum cans sold to the public are returned for recycling is that the redemption centers pay 17 cents/lb. While not the equivalent of receiving a nickle a container, which is the basic tenant of most deposit systems, the 17 cents is not a return to the public of their own money which has been held in escrow, but rather is a payment related to the production price of new aluminum.

Source separation can make a significant contribution in terms of recycling. But, it is not clear to what extent it can contribute to reducing the solid waste load. For example, if all the aluminum were recycled by consumers taking it to a recycling center to realize the offered financial inducement, the solid waste load would be reduced by less than 2% by weight, somewhat more by volume. Collection and disposal costs would hardly be affected since at the margin it is unlikely that there is any cost avoidance associated with a change this small. This is particularly true since equipment is purchased and routes serviced to handle the "high" days and seasons, and for the average collection and disposal day simply would just be somewhat "more" underutilized. Source separation and recycling of glass and steel containers would make a more significant dent in the disposal problem. But, paper recycling is the key to realizing any significant benefit by source separation. Recycling newsprint and other forms of recyclable paper could reduce the waste stream by up to as much as 20% by weight.

For the most part, paper, glass, and steel source separation approaches are based on house-by-house pick up of the preseparated materials. This is generally cost increasing. Without taking into account the revenues generated, the separate collection increases the "burden" of solid waste management. The offsetting feature is, of course, the revenue derived from the sale of the separated products. There is a bit of a Catch -22 here. When the value of the products cycle upwards, householders more and more take steps to realize the potential financial benefits themselves rather than placing the material or materials on the curb for municipal or franchised private hauler pickup. Put simply, the waste is not waste when the householder sees it as having sufficient value to warrant a more purposeful and financially motivated decision to recycle it himself. At an intermediate point to this in the market price cycle is the range when pirating occurs, i.e., when the materials put by the curb do not make it to the designated waste collector, city or private, but are pirated by someone or group of persons whose entrepreneur instincts impose themselves between the householder and the designated collector. When paper prices reached $40 a ton recently, the piracy rate reached about 40% as well and curbside police stake-outs became, somewhat ironically, part of most affected jurisdictions' solid waste management systems. The moral is, you can not make waste waste when it isn't. The Catch-22 is that this is when the economics of substituting recovery for traditional forms of disposal are the best.

To return to the main subject of this subsection, source separation has merit in terms of its contribution to recycling. In some communities, the revenues along with tipping fees avoided many more than offset collection cost increases associated with such programs and in this sense it can also contribute to the solution of the solid waste management problem. More importantly for small communities, labor intensive source separation, even if it is cost increasing, may be the only method of implementing a public decision to participate in the recycling movement.* This is because of the lack of sufficient waste to realize the economies of scale which offset the cost of capital intensive recycling approaches.**

D. Resource Recovery — the Capital Intensive Approach

The approach generally looked at to realize the opportunity of materials and energy conservation with waste as a raw material is capital intensive resource recovery where unsegregated municipal refuse is processed at a central facility using fairly expensive and relatively complex machinery. Taking energy recovery first, there are four major ways to recover energy from the waste: (1) burn the waste in what is called a waterwall incinerator to produce steam, (2) process the waste to remove the bulk of the noncombustible material to produce a fuel known as Refuse Derived Fuel (RDF), (3) use a pyrolysis process to convert the waste to gas, oil, and char as fuel products and (4) extract the methane-rich gas produced by natural decomposition. In addition to conducting this latter process in a capital intensive way at a facility designed for this purpose, the natural production in a landfill can be tapped. In terms of materials recovery, magnetic metals are removed by magnets, aluminum by heavy media or eddy current separators, and glass by froth flotation or optical sorting. There is a great deal of difference in terms of the extent to which development is complete and operational experience obtained among the various approaches proposed for energy and materials recovery. Waterwall incineration and magnetic separation are the most tried, tested, and true. Pyrolysis and optical sorting of glass represent the other end of the risk spectrum.***

E. Outlook for the Future

Conservation through recycling seems to be an inevitability. As land indeed becomes

*   Like other public works decisions, solid waste disposal is a matter of quality of service. How much does a community want to tax itself collectively for those services provided by the public sector and how much of this should go for solid waste?

**   For further reading on source separation see: SCS Engineers, An Analysis of Source Separation Collection of Recyclable Solid Waste, Report prepared for the U.S. Environmental Protection Agency, SW-95; Jackson, D. R., The Other End of the Telescope: A Community Approach to Resource Recovery, *Resources Policy,* Vol. 3 (NO. 3), September, 1977; Bailly, H-C. and Vaccaro, H. S., Source Separation: A Cost Effective Low Technology Resource Recovery Option, *Proc. Am. Soc. of Mechanical Engineers,* Matula, R. A., Ed., Hueston Woods, September 19-24, 1976, p. 218—228; and a series of three articles in the *NCRR Bulletin,* Source Separation of Paper . . . A Growing Practice, Vol. 4 (No. 3), p. 8—12, Summer, 1974, Source Separation . . . A Resource Recovery Option, Vol. 7 (No. 1) p. 3—10, Winter, 1977, and Source Separation . . . the Recycling Center Approach, Vol. 8 (No. 2), p. 31—37, Spring, 1978.

***For state of the art overviews see: Schulz, H., et al., Resource Recovery Technology for Urban Decision Makers, National Science Foundation, Report prepared by the Urban Technology Center, School of Engineering and Applied Science, Columbia University, New York, N.Y. January, 1976; Wilson, M. E., et al, Engineering and Economic Analysis of Waste to Energy Systems, Report prepared by Ralph M. Parsons Co., for the EPA Industrial Environmental Research Laboratory Cincinnati, Ohio, June, 1977; European Waste-to-Energy Systems, An Overview, Report prepared by Resource Planning Associates, Inc., for the Department of Energy, Report CONS-2103-6, June, 1977; Two studies by the National Center for Resource Recovery which deal with Recovery 1 in New New Orleans, (1) Materials Recovery Systems: Engineering Feasibility Study, December, 1972 and (2) New Orleans Resource Recovery Facility: Implementation Study, September, 1977. On Refuse Derived Fuel see in particular Refuse Derived Fuel (RDF) and Densified Refuse Derived Fuel (d-RDF), RM77-2, National Center for Resource Recovery, June, 1978, and Cohan, L. J., et al, Prepared vs. Unprepared Refuse Fired Steam Generators, paper presented at First International Conference on Conversion of Refuse to Energy, Montreaux, Switzerland, November 3—5, 1975.

more scarce and its cost rises, as regulatory actions force improved and higher cost methods of landfilling, as truck fuel costs increase making the trip to distant landfills relatively more expensive, as the fuel value of waste increases because the price of alternative fuels increase and as materials become more scarce because their supply is diminished and as a consequence, their prices rise, more and more communities will add recovery of some sort to their solid waste management system. The remainder of this chapter looks at the recovery decision both from a national and a local perspective.

II. NATIONAL AND LOCAL PERSPECTIVES

A. National Perspective

The conservation potential of recycling is truely impressive. In the Third Report to Congress on Resource Recovery and Waste Reduction, the U.S. Environmental Protection Agency developed figures on the quantity of energy potentially available if the waste of only the more densely populated areas of the country were processed for materials and energy recovery. Based on 1973 data, the aggregate figure was an energy equivalent to 424,000 bbl of oil equivalents per day. Using the 1963 figure, EPA cited some interesting comparisons. The 424,000 bbl/day is equal to 4.6% of the fuel consumed annually by all utilities, or 10% of all the coal consumed annually by utilities, or 28% of all the oil delivered annually through the Alaskan Pipe Line. The savings would have been equal to 1% of all energy consumed in the U.S. for that year. Put differently, it is equivalent to the energy used to light every home and office building in the country and is equal to twice the gasoline savings estimated to be obtained as a result of the 55-miles-per-hour fuel conservation program. These are fairly impressive figures. It is not surprising, therefore, that some attention has been given to the circumstances that surround and the incentives that might bring about a faster adoption of recovery based solid waste management approaches.*

In the Second Report to Congress on Resource Recovery and Waste Reduction, the U.S. Environmental Protection Agency looked at the recycling potential for selective materials is post-consumer municipal waste: iron, aluminum, copper, lead, tin, and paper. Their conclusions were that materials recycling from post-consumer solid waste could provide 7% of the iron, 8% of the aluminum, 19% of the tin, and 15% of the paper consumed annually in the United States.**

These estimates result from recycling 53% of the metals and minerals discarded by consumers and 21% of the paper in the municipal waste stream. According to the Environmental Protection Agency, these so-called *national recovery ratios,* represent practical (maxima) for recycling from a technical standpoint. In deriving them, it was assumed that 95% of the waste generated would be collected, either through mixed waste collection or specialized source separated collection systems; 70% of the collected waste would be processed for recovery; with respect to paper, the assumption was that 40% of the waste which would be collected would be processed for fiber recovery; and with regard to other materials recovery, the efficiency of the processing was assumed to be 80%. These numbers are consistent with the best practice that one would project based on today's experience.

The figures above illustrate that a rather significant proportion of the nation's raw

---

* Third Report to Congress, Resource Recovery and Waste Reduction, U.S. Environmental Protection Agency, SW-161, 33—34, 1975.
** Second Report to "Congress, Resource Recovery and Source Separation, U.S. Environmental Protection Agency, SW-122, p. 14, 1974.

material requirements could, in theory, be met through recycling post-consumer waste. One reason the numbers are not large is that many materials initially go into construction of consumer durables most of which, including automobiles, are not discarded as municipal waste and hence are not in the basic count given here. Nevertheless, the figures are impressive, not only in terms of decreasing the rate of depletion of natural resources, but also in terms of reducing the amount of waste that would need to be diposed of by landfill. Finally, there are significant energy savings associated with the use of recycled materials. For example, to produce a ton of steel from scrap requires only $\frac{1}{3}$ the amount of energy needed to produce it from virgin sources, 1/20 in the case of aluminum and $\frac{1}{3}$ using recycled paper.*

Of course, one should not assume that the amount of materials shown as available for recycling can be automatically consumed by the user industries. A significant expansion in material-user-industry capacity would be needed in most instances. This is because the recycled materials generally require different processing than virgin materials. Offsetting, in a growing economy, the expense of these capital investments are savings in the form of reduced capital equipment and other material input requirements in the mining, ore reduction and benefication, and smelting sections of the virgin mineral industries, as well as similar reductions in tree harvesting, wood preparation wood pulping segments of the pulp and paper industry. In a stagnant economy the offsets are based only on the need to replace worn out plants and equipment.

On a broader plane, the national welfare benefits of these resource savings — both in terms of direct materials savings as a result of recycling and the attendant energy savings — would accrue to future generations in the form of larger resource availability. National policy focuses on these potential savings.

A consideration is the extent to which the energy savings are likely in themselves to provide impetus to bring about substitution between recycled and virgin materials. This mainly is a matter of energy costs. It is easy to overemphasize the possible impact of the recent change in energy prices on the substitution of recycled for virgin raw materials. Standing alone, it is unlikely that the potential for energy savings will bring about a great amount of substitution. This is because energy costs are not a very large fraction of the total cost of virgin material supply. Table 1 gives some data for steel, aluminum, glass containers, and newsprint.

The table highlights the fact that when the recent energy price increase is corrected to take into account that other costs of production have also risen, although not as rapidly, and when the energy cost itself is viewed as a proportion of total production costs, the impact of the energy use differential between virgin and recycled materials loses much of its significance from the perspective of individual producers. As an aggregate viewed from the national perspective, it is still a large figure. Nevertheless, the data in the table show only fairly small cost advantages between secondary and virgin materials except in the case of aluminum. Energy costs and the Bureau of Labor Statistics Wholesale Price Index are given in Table 2. This data is necessary to interpret Table 1. The conclusion that emerges from the tables is that most of the relative cost advantages attributed to changes in energy costs were essentially neutralized by increases in other cost factors and general price inflation. As a result, one can not look to energy use differentials between virgin and raw materials to provide a major stimulation to resource recovery. In a way this is an unfortunate conclusion. One would have preferred a stronger stimulant viewed from the national perspective and consequently, a more rapid implementation of resource recovery. If recovery as a means of

---

* Final Report, Material Needs and the Environment Today and Tomorrow, National Commission on Materials Policy, Table 40.3, p. 4D-8, November, 1973.

TABLE 1

Energy Consumption Differences Among Recycled and Virgin Materials

Products	Energy advantage (million Btu/ton)	Energy cost advantage ($/ton of Product)			Deflated energy cost advantage ($/ton of Product)			Energy cost difference (% of selling price)		
		1967	1974	1976	1967	1974	1976	1967	1974	1967
Carbon steel	7	4.55	10.20	12.06	4.55	6.38	6.59	4—5	4—6	5—6
Aluminum ingot										
Fossil fuel	258	168	375	445	168	235	243	34	55	51
Hydropower	164	107	239	282	107	149	154	21	35	32
Glass containers	2½	1.63	3.65	4.31	1.63	2.28	2.36	1	1.8	NA[a]
Newsprint	9	5.85	13.13	15.51	5.85	8.21	8.48	4.1	7.1	5.3

[a] NA = not available.

Adapted from Smith, F. A., Resource recovery from post-consumer solid wastes, *Proceedings of the Mineral Economics Symposium*, American Institute of Mining, Metallurgical and Petroleum Engineers, Washington, D. C., November 9, 1976, p. 95-109.

TABLE 2

Bureau of Labor Statistics Wholesale Price Index and Energy Cost
Figures

Year	Price index (all commodities) 1967 = 100	Average U.S. manufacturer's unit energy cost ($ per million Btu)
1967	100	.65
1974	160.1	1.46
1976	184.3	1.72

From Smith, F. A., Resource recovery from post-consumer solid
wastes, *Proceedings of the Mineral Economics Symposium,* American Institute of Mining, Metallurgical and Petroleum Engineers,
Washington, D.C., November 9, 1976, p. 95-109.

conservation is going to proceed at a fast pace, other methods of changing relative
prices as they are seen at the local level will be necessary. The local perspective and
how it shapes resource recovery decision-making is discussed at a later point in this
chapter.

The national perspective includes the question of how many plants. If not of particular moment to national policy makers, it is important to those investing in technology
development. How large is the market? For the most part, present day recovery technology seems more amenable to large plants. This is a matter of economies of scale.
For this reason, most studies that have looked at the number of facilities which would
exist if recovery were implemented nationwide, look only at the urban areas. The U.S.
Environmental Protection Agency figures given above on the energy conservation benefits from energy and materials recovery looked at Standard Metropolitan Statistical
Areas (SMSA) which are metropolitan areas in a common labor market whose population exceeds 50,000. Taking the nation as a whole, over 70% of the population reside
in the SMSA's. Narrowing this set to only those SMSA's with 200,000 or more population still leaves the coverage at 65%. The number of SMSA's above 200,000 in population is 150.

Franklin Associates, Ltd., in a recent study looked at the likely number of facilities
(234) and their size which would result from resource recovery being implemented in
these communities. Based on a 1990 projection, this data is summarized by region in
Table 3. For 1990, the percentage of the nation's population covered in these 150 cities
should be higher than 1975's 65% if the current trend showing an increasing proportion of the population moving into SMSAs continues.

The resource recovery projection for 1990 was calculated using a 4.0 lb per person
per day waste generation rate. Processable waste was assumed to be 75% of the waste
generated in each metropolitan area. The basic study gives the number of plants for
each SMSA as well as the regional and national totals shown in Table 3. In determining
how many plants there might be for each area, not all of the waste was necessarily
assumed to go to a single plant. For example, Los Angeles to Long Beach was allocated
two 3,000; three 2,000; three 1,000 and one 500 ton/day facilities.

However, the analysis does not take into account whether this recycling would be
economical when compared to alternative forms of disposal. In many cases, it would
not be, and this is why Federal policy deliberations focus on means to change relative
prices at the local level. The mechanisms that are frequently advocated by those who
feel the implementation of recovery would be in the national interest are described in
a later section of this chapter. They include loan guarantees, and market guarantees

by the U.S. Government, grants, operating subsidiaries, and other types of intervention.

B. Local Perspective

In spite of national concern about saving energy and conserving natural resources through recycling of waste, and the support given by the federal government in terms of technical assistance and limited financial aid, the ultimate responsibility for the yes or no decision rests at the local level. There the decision is made to undertake programs that lead to the construction of resource recovery facilities. Local decisions to expend public funds both for the construction of public works or for services provided to the citizenry are generally made against a criteria of least cost for the type and level of service desired. In most local decisions it is the so-called bottom line that counts. In resource recovery this boils down to "how much per ton for solid waste disposal". Solid waste disposal is a community problem and although resource recovery has all the beneficial national implications discussed earlier, these generally do not carry significant weight at the local level unless the "price is right". Price, in the case of a recovery based disposal option, is the gross disposal cost minus the recovery revenues. The factors which affect the price are highlighted in the next two sections of this chapter, Sections II.C, Key Factors and II.D, Steps to Making a Decision. Since a great many of the factors deal with costs and revenue estimates, Section IV of this chapter, which deals with the economics of resource recovery, is also germane.

A previous section of this chapter gave figures pertaining to solid waste generation estimates and looked at the extent of the resource recovery market. The latter is of interest to those developing technology that they expect to sell into this market. The figures also showed the extent to which resource recovery might aid in abating the nations' use of depletable resources and the extent to which realizing waste's energy potential might contribute to alleviating the energy problem. When these tonnage figures are viewed from the local perspective, it is important to take into account the source of the waste and who has flow control. While, indeed, the per capital waste generated may average 3.3 pounds per person that figure may not be a viable planning factor for determining the feasibility of a proposed recovery facility. An example will illustrate this point.

Franklin Associates found in analyzing waste generation and flow control in a major metropolitan area that while the waste in the area averaged 3.3 lb per person per day, the residential urban solid waste generated averaged only 1.6 lb. per person per day. It is not uncommon to find a proposed recovery plant rationalized on the basis of an areas' equivalent to the 3.3 lb figure used above, but where the community only has access to the 1.6 lb per person per day of residential waste in the urban core, and perhaps it may not even be able to count on all of that.* In the community surveyed, suburban residential waste measured 2.4, unincorporated community waste 1.8 and the urban core residential waste 1.6 lb per person per day. In this community, commercial waste amounted to 1.18 lb per person per day.

C. Key Factors: Pay Less, Pay More, Ownership, and Risk

"Resource Recovery: Is It For Your City?" This is the title of an article that appeared in *Nations' Cities*.** It is the key question. As pointed out above, the principal

---

*   Second Report to Congress Resource Recovery and Source Separation, U.S. Environmental Protection Agency, SW-122, p. 15, 1974.
** Burks, S. and Page, C., Resource recovery: is it for your city? in *Nation's Cities,* 1977, 9.

TABLE 3

Resource Recovery Potential for the 150 Largest U.S. SMSAs, 1990 (Population in Thousands, Waste Generation and Processable Waste in Thousand Tons/Year, and Potential Resource Recovery Plant Sizes in Tons/Day)

Region	Population (000)	Waste generation (000 TPY)	Processable waste (000 TPY)	Potential 50—300	Resource 500	Recovery 1000	Plants 2000	(TPD) 3000
New England	10.804	7,888	5,914	13	7	7	2	1
Middle Atlantic	36,814	26,872	20,155	29	12	14	8	9
South Atlantic	24,786	18,095	13,570	30	13	15	3	4
East South Central	6,391	4,665	3,499	13	7	2	2	—
West South Central	12,341	9,009	6,756	16	10	5	2	2
East North Central	32,277	23,563	17,671	25	19	16	10	3
West North Central	8,822	6,440	4,831	8	7	5	3	—
Mountain	5,924	4,324	3,244	6	5	2	1	1
Pacific	28,228	20,605	15,454	21	16	7	9	5
National Totals	166,387	121,463	91,094	161	96	73	40	25

Notes: Based on a waste generation rate of 4.0 lb per person per day in 1990. SMSA population in 1990 based on Water Resource Council projections. Assumed 75% of waste generated is processable. Assumed resource recovery plants operate 6 days/week, 50 weeks/year.

From Franklin Associates, Ltd., Projections of Regional Resource Recovery in the United States.

factor in answering this question is the bottom line. Is recovery less expensive than alternative methods of solid waste disposal? This presumes of course that a community does not want to pay more for a recovery based disposal option. Surely, a community can make such an affirmative decision since the issue is essentially a political one and the decision can be made through the political process in the same manner that a community collectively decides on other public expenditures — better than *least cost* schools, better police and fire protection, better programs for the elderly, etc. When treated as a quality of service issue, the essential elements of the solid waste management decision are the same as those for the list of public expenditures just given and others like parks and recreation, libraries, and so on. However, by the large, minimum cost for a "satisfactory" disposal solution guides most solid waste mangement decisions. "Satisfactory" may be: push it in the swamp. There do not appear to be any examples of a referendum approach, or anything resembling it, on the specific question of paying more for a recovery based disposal option. For example, recently in a western metropolitan area known for its environmental conscientiousness, a feasibility study found that resource recovery, principally burning waste for energy used in the production of electricity, would be cost increasing over continuing to landfill. The annual increase in cost was a fairly large figure and in the aggregate would run into several millions of dollars. Yet, the population of the metropolitan area is in excess of a million. Per capita, the cost of converting to a recovery based solid waste disposal approach would have been less than $1.50 per capita and less than $5.00 per year for the average family. Many of the citizens were already spending more than this for fuel alone to transport source separated materials, primary paper, to volunteer run collection and redemption centers. For them the central metropolitan approach considered in the feasibility study would have been cost decreasing. For others, a positive decision would have been cost increasing, but had a referendum been held, a cost increasing positive decision by the majority would not have been inconsistent with the general importance given to the environment in the area. The complexity of the decision to spend more is a barrier to substituting recovery for traditional forms of solid waste disposal.

The fear of a "white elephant" is also a barrier to implementing resource recovery. "White elephant" syndromes are a key factor in the consideration of resource recovery potential whether it is a purely private decision or public — made through the executive, legislative, or referendum route. Will the contemplated facility become obsolete during its expected lifetime? Obsolescence can be caused by a number of factors. One is changes in the waste stream. For example, aluminum recovery technology already installed would become obsolete if there was no aluminum to recover. A second is legislation, which may change such that more capital may be needed to control air emissions as an illustration. A third is market prices which may change making an investment *already made* noncost-effective. Finally, the future may bring a better technological solution. The latter may be the more serious factor in the public decision-making arena because of the political overtones. New systems are always being promoted, some of whose benefits are presumably real. More often, the benefits are confined to the imagination of the promoters and a little simple engineering analysis will show that the purported benefits depend on repeal of the second law of thermodynamics or something of the sort. But nevertheless, it is difficult to know which is which and it is easy to make political hay and get media coverage by questioning why the expenditure was made. "Wouldn't it have made sense to have waited?" There is really no way to avoid the possibility of such charges. In a rapid moving technological area such as resource recovery, new and better technical approaches emerge. Indeed, it is hoped that they will. Facing the whims of the market and what are sometimes seen as the whims of governmental regulations are not unusual in business. In fact, they are everyday characteristics of entrepreneurial activity, but they are not as common in government. Many observers would say that activity which exhibits these characteristics should, almost by definition, belong in the private sector rather than the public sector. The other side of this coin is that solid waste management generally is viewed as a public health responsibility and this traditionally has been lodged in the public sector.

Resource recovery, private or public? It is not possible to make a clear cut decision although pressures exerted locally, indeed through national legislation — in the manner in which funds are made available for studies and planning — affect the public vs. private decision. Public money tends to stay in the public sector from an own and operate standpoint. The "who should do it" question and the lack of a clear theoretical basis for a decision on this matter are clear barriers to realizing the potential of waste as a national recyclable resource.

In addition to the above mentioned factor of uncertainty related to the possible obsolescence of an investment once made, there is the basic risk of will the approach adopted work for whatever reason. Of course, this possibility faces every business investment decision. The terminology used in business of upside potential and downside risk is applicable to the resource recovery decision of many communities. However, it is seldom viewed in this perspective. For the most part, communities subscribe to a philosophy of global planning. This equates to bigger is better. Yet, most business strategies would dictate a tactical phase where market penetration is made thorough a test market. To question the total planned approach is almost, as it used to be put, to question the virtues of motherhood. Yet in planning for the possible replacement of traditional disposal by a recovery based approach, total planning generally means "all of the waste to a single centralized facility built now". Seduced by economies of scale might be an appropriate label for this approach. The business tactics referred to above would suggest accepting a higher unit cost but initially going smaller. Upside potential is then the value of successful replication. Downside risk is the cost of failure spread over the entire solid waste stream although only a portion of the stream is involved in the initial trial.

The presumption here is that "success" means a lower solid waste management cost for the initial tonnage and an even greater saving for the replication tonnage. The latter is the amount held out and not put into the initial market trial. This factor, of course, is only germane for the larger metropolitan areas. But these are the ones usually seduced, in a planning sense, by the lower unit cost associated with economies of scale. Suppose total failure occurs, with no salvage value, in a case where one third of an area's waste is committed to the market trial. Suppose further that the cost of this failure is 50 cents/ton/year over a 10 year period spread over the total waste forecast for the metropolitan area. This then is the downside risk. What is the balancing item? Suppose the upside potential, based on the success of the recovery endeavor is a $1.00/ ton saving averaged through replication for 10 years over the total waste of the area. The point here is not one of precise evaluation of probabilities and payoffs but rather to point out that a market penetration, i.e., an investment approach, is an appropriate perspective from which to evaluate resource recovery for the larger metropolitan areas. These, as has been highlighted earlier, are the first areas where recovery will appear to be an economically sound undertaking — if it works. Because of their basic economics, except for special circumstances, smaller metropolitan areas will follow later. Therefore, there is reason to devote more attention in this text to the more likely "early" opportunities and how, in the circumstances that exist in these larger metropolitan areas, the solid waste problem may be converted to the resource recovery opportunity. The barrier here is the presumed need for a total plan which handles all the waste in a single facility, or even if multiple facilities are programmed, the investment is made all at once without the trial — initial and smaller — facility advanced here.

Other advantages accrue to doing it initially on a smaller scale. First, arranging firm markets requires a believable committment to the project on the supply side (generally the public sector). The $100,000,000 and up *grand scheme* generally lacks credibility and is treated so by the potential users of the to-be-recovered materials and the energy product. The smaller project is likely to be believable. Second, the smaller project is less likely to be threatening to existing supply channels. For example, it is less likely to saturate the regional market for secondary ferrous. Hence, there is more likelihood of a buyer executing higher priced letters of intent to purchase than would be the case where he to think his capacity would be saturated. Big enough to be meaningful, but small enough to be cost-beneficial in an investment sense, and less rather than more threatening in terms of existing markets, ought to be the guidelines for any initial recovery project undertaken by the larger metropolitan areas.

Once success is demonstrated by the larger communities the smaller communities will follow. The data given earlier illustrates that the larger communities are the key to significant national coverage. That is, if resource recovery were practiced by the 150 larger SMSAs, 75% of the nation's waste would be processed for recovery purposes. Therefore, to this extent the potential for the nation's waste to be used for the purpose of retarding the depletion of natural resources, including energy, would have been realized. The barrier to the conversion of problem to benefit is total planning. Even in the larger metropolitan areas "small may be beautiful".

D. Steps in Making a Decision

It is possible for a community to do its initial feasibility study almost "on the back of an envelope". Listed below are six steps to making a preliminary determination. To be sure, some outside information is needed such as ascertaining energy prices in the area. However, with this data in hand, the mathematical computations are fairly simple and straightforward. The troublesome part of the feasibility study centers on the fact that there is risk inherent in the venture and as has been pointed out, the risk varies among technologies both from a technical and marketing standpoint. The most difficult part of the feasibility determination concerns the "are you willing to take" questions. The stepwise procedure is as follows:

Are You Ready for Resource Recovery?

1. What are your anticipated solid waste disposal costs by traditional, or present, methods? (Include added transportation costs to distant disposal sites if needed.)
2. Is there a market for steam from burning refuse? If so, what is the reasonable market price to expect for sale of steam, presuming the user will expect some savings over alternative production opportunities?
3. Is there a refuse derived fuel (RDF) or densified RDF market? What is the likely value of the RDF? Are you willing to produce the RDF in a "true market" situation, i.e., without long-term purchase coupled to a price guarantee?
4. Are there markets for recoverable materials — ferrous, aluminum, other nonferrous metals, glass, paper? What are their values? Are you willing to accept the cyclical nature of the market prices for the commodities?
5. Are you willing to float a general obligation bond? If not, are you willing to guarantee community revenues — often in the form of indebtedness?
6. If you convert all of the above into revenue per ton of waste available for disposal and assume either:
    a. Approximately $45 million cost for a steam plant with a life of 20 years, an interest rate of 8% and an operating cost to capital cost ratio of 1:8; or,

b. Approximately $24 million for an RDF/materials recovery facility with a life of 15 years, an interest rate of 8% and an operating cost to capital cost ratio of 1:5, then
You can now compute whether disposal by resource recovery is competitive to the traditional method of disposal (see question 1).*

The six steps above illustrate that the answers to the "are you willing to take risk," and "are you willing to guarantee" questions are key ingredients in selecting a technology and a method of finance. The variability of the prospective markets, in particular, are prime causal factors affecting the recovery decision. And while strong letters of intent to purchase the recovered materials, each with floor prices, can temper the vagaries of the market place, some uncertainty in regard to the potential to realize revenue from the recovered products will always remain. These risks must be faced directly even though market-related risks are not aspects of decision-making in the public sector that local government has in the past knowingly assumed. However, it has happened unknowingly, with the consequence of political embarassment when the forecast of future benefit did not turn out as expected.

III. RESOURCE RECOVERY ECONOMICS

A. Is There Gold in Garbage?

As pointed out in an earlier section of this chapter, there is indeed value in the components of the municipal waste stream. The purpose of this section is to develop an estimate of this value under likely market conditions. Recall, however, that market conditions vary. They move up and down with the business cycle which has an even larger impact on secondary prices than it does on virgin prices. This is because the demand for secondary materials "dries up" first when business conditions begin to slacken. Conversely, secondary markets cycle upwards in greater measure than other business indicators when the economy is prosperous and overall demand is high. Also, recycled materials vary in their market value depending on geographical location; first, in terms of geographically specific markets and second, from location to location depending on the distance to a user facility. An example of the former is the western copper precipitation market for secondary iron. An example of the latter is nearness to one of the three or four newsprint de-inking plants in the country. This section looks at gross revenues, first for materials recovery and then from an energy recovery standpoint. In a later section, the likely overall economies of two types of resource recovery facilities are discussed.

Table 4 presents an estimate for the materials recovery value of one ton of municipal waste. The revenue estimate is $7.40. Note that this figure is derived by multiplying the estimated fraction of the waste for each component assumed to be technologically recoverable times the recovery rate for the technology and an estimated market price. The far right hand column is rounded to the nearest 10 ¢. The proceeds from the recovery of paper fiber are shown for two types of recovery. The first is source sepa-

* The six step "Are You Ready" test was prepared by the National Center for Resource Recovery for *Nation's Cities*, July, p. 14, 1977. The title of the article was Resource Recovery: is it for your city? The dollar figures and operation to capital cost ratios are slightly changed from those that appeared in the article. For other generalized methods of determining initial feasibility of resource recovery see: Abert, J. G., Alter, H., and Bernheisel, J. F., The economics of resource recovery from municipal solid waste, *Science*, 183, 1052, 1974; Mihelich, D. L., Breakeven Economics of Resource Recovery Systems, Proceedings of the Fifth Mineral Waste Utilization Symposium, p. 53—57, April 11—14, 1976. The Proceedings are available from ITT Research Institute, P. O. Box 4963, Chicago, Ill., 60680; Abert, J. G. and Vancil, R. A graphic approach to determine the economics of recovering resources from municipal solid waste *Conservation and Recycling*, Vol. 1, No. 3-4, 299, 1979.

TABLE 4

Materials Recovery Revenues from One Ton of Municipal Waste

Material	Fraction of waste ×	Recovery rate ×	Market price per recovered ton ($) =	Potential revenues per input ton ($)
Newspaper				
Source Separated	.07	.50	30	1.00
Commingled	.07	.20	20	(0.30)
Ferrous	.08	.90	45	3.20
Aluminum	.007	.70	300	1.50
Other Nonferrous	.003	.50	250	0.40
Glass	.10	.65	20	1.30
Total (Assuming source separated news)				$7.40

Based on EPA estimates of waste composition, NCRR estimates of recovery efficiency, and mid-range 1977 prices for recovered materials).

rated paper discussed earler. The second introduces a new term, commingled. This means handpicked from mixed refuse that has been commingled in the traditional packer truck. That is, it is not collected separately. The recovery rate for this approach is low and at present there is a very limited market. It is used here to demonstrate an alternative to source separation which may develop in the future. Also, mechanical methods of separating paper fiber from commingled refuse may also be developed that would make the commingled approach more feasible. Commingled is the least expensive method of collection, hence the interest in methods to recover the paper from the mixed waste.

The table illustrates that the single most valuable materials recovery component of the refuse is ferrous metal which if it is 8% of the waste, with a recovery efficiency of 90% and a price of $45/ton, yields $3.20 per input ton of waste. This is a larger revenue producer than source separated paper, which under the assumptions for composition, efficiency and market price made here yields a revenue of $1.00/ton of household waste discarded. The ferrous revenue is even greater than the two nonferrous fractions taken together — aluminum and other nonferrous such as copper and brass — which total $1.90/ton of waste processed for recovery. At a later point in this chapter further assumptions are made as to market price escalations for the purpose of developing program cost comparisons among the two most likely types of recovery technology. In these projections, under the assumptions made, nonferrous metals (aluminum in particular) become the major revenue producers.

Turning now to energy recovery, the most significant determinant of the value of energy is the alternative fuel that would have been used if refuse were not available. The more expensive the alternative fuel, the higher the value that can be assumed for refuse when it is used as a substitute. Under present prices of conventional fuels, it is better to substitute for oil than for coal. If oil prices continue to escalate and coal does not follow at the same, or roughly the same, rate, then the economics of offering solid waste as an oil substitute will become even more attractive. This will be highlighted later.

The two most likely forms of waste energy are a refuse derived fuel to be burnt with a conventional fuel, most likely coal, as a substitute for part of the normal fuel used, or burnt separately in a 100% waste fired boiler to generate steam. In the former case,

TABLE 5

Potential Energy Revenues

Refuse derived fuel	12 million Btu/ton		
	60 percent of input ton municipal waste		
Market price of competing fuel ($/million Btu)	$ .50	$ 1.00	$ 1.50
Revenue per input ton of municipal waste	$3.60	$ 7.20	$10.80
Steam	By incineration of raw waste		
	(10 million Btu/ton)		
	50% efficiency of incinerator/boiler		
	(5000 lb steam per input ton waste)		
Market price of steam ($/thousand lb)	$1.00	$ 2.00	$ 3.00
Revenue per input ton of municipal waste	$5.00	$10.00	$15.00

the refuse energy is sold as a fuel. In the latter case, steam is the refuse energy product that reaches the market place. Not surprisingly, the market price is higher in the steam case but, as will be pointed out later, the costs of the production of the steam are higher than the cost of the production of the refuse fuel. The significant advantage of steam is in marketing. Since the refuse processor takes the risk of producing the steam, he can generally obtain a firm long-term committment to buy the steam from an appropriate user if located in his area. In the case of refuse fuel production and sale, the risk is mainly one of use and falls on the processor. In the current time frame, because of the lack of operating experience with refuse derived fuel, users are not inclined to sign firm long term contracts to take or pay. Hence, the waste processor faces a risky market situation.

Returning to the economies issue, Table 5 shows ranges of likely revenues for (1) the sale of refuse derived fuel, and (2) the sale of steam. The basis for the estimation is the market price of the competitive fuel. For convenience, no market incentive to enter the "deal" on the part of the consumer is shown. In actual practice, the reader should assume that a refuse energy user will expect some economic advantage from his involvement in the "deal" or else it would be logical for him to stick to his tried, tested, and true fuel or steam source. It is easy enough to adapt the data given in the table to the idea of a discount by simply using the table values for examples where local alternative fuel cost is higher by say 20 to 30%.

The top portion of the table shows a range of refuse energy value from $3.60 to $10.80 per input ton of waste. This corresponds to market prices for competitive fuel of $0.50 to $1.50 per million Btu. Other assumptions made are that the refuse derived fuel contains 12 million Btu per ton as delivered to the user. Also, that 60% of an input ton of waste ends up, after processing, as refuse fuel. The steam alternative is based on an assumed 10 million Btu per ton of waste. This is for the waste in total, including the ferrous and other noncombustibles which by and large are processed out of the fuel fraction in the production of refuse derived fuel. The incinerator efficiency is assumed to be 50%. The result is a range of revenue estimate from $5.00 to $15.00 per input ton of waste corresponding to $1.00 to $3.00 per thousand pounds of steam delivered to a customer in close proximity to the steam generating facility.

Industrial steam produced by burning oil costs, in terms of fuel only, in excess of $2.00 per thousand pounds. A can be used to example, illustrate this. Assume a pre-OPEC price of $9.60/bbl of oil for making the economic comparison. In terms of dollars per million Btu, this is $1.60. At an 80% conversion efficiency, 1000 lb of steam consume $2.00 worth of oil. Now in terms of the substitution of a refuse burning steam generating incinerator, use 50% conversion efficiency such that one ton of waste at 10,000,000 Btu produces 5000 lb of steam. Thus, 1,000 lb of steam are worth $2.00, since this is what it would cost to make them with oil.

Compare this to coal at, say, $0.70 per million Btu after discount. If coal is burnt in a large suspension fired boiler at 80% efficiency, then it costs approximately $0.88 worth of coal to produce 1000 lb of steam. Assuming the alternative steam source is a solid waste burning incinerator operating at 50% efficiency, then again, a ton of waste produces 5000 lb of steam, this time worth $4.40. Exact prices are not important here; the important point is to show the rather extreme differences in the likely energy value of the waste depending on the competitive market. Even before the recent oil price increases, it is seen that the refuse energy was worth roughly twice as much if it were substituted for oil than it was worth if substituted for coal.

What then is the answer to the "is there gold in garbage" question? Fixing the materials recovery revenues at $7.40 as developed in the example and taking a range of from $4.40 to $10.00 for the energy value, one can say that the gold in garbage is on the order of $11.80 to $17.40 per input ton. Energy with ferrous recovery only would produce gross revenues in the range of $7.00 to $13.00/ton of waste processed. The gold in garbage is not large, but when added to the cost avoidance of not having to dispose of the refuse by traditional means, it can be sufficient to offset the processing and residue disposal cost. Two examples using representative values and costs illustrate this in the section that follows.

B. Simplified Recovery Costs and Revenue Comparisons

The purpose of this section is to develop a model for describing the economics of resource recovery for two different technologies: (1) the steam generating mass burning incinerator (Table 6); and (2) an RDF production facility that sells the processed waste to a user who substitutes it for a portion of this normal fuel (Table 7). The figures used are illustrative. They are not meant to pertain to any particular community. What they illustrate is rough overall economics. An important point is that they allow for an examination of at least the first order cost implications of public vs. private ownership of the recovery facility. Controversy over the issue is a significant barrier at the local level to converting the solid waste problem into the resource recovery opportunity.

An initial assumption is that the refuse derived fuel alternative has a useful economic life of 15 years, while the steam generating incinerator has a life of 25 years. The start up date for both alternatives is 1980. The capital cost of the refuse derived fuel option is set at $24 million and the steam generating incinerator at $45 million. Operating to capital cost ratios are used. For the refuse derived fuel plant it is 1/5, for the steam generating incinerator it is 1/8. The effective interest rate is 8%. Municipal bonds or pollution control bonds, both tax free to the investor, should sell at a lower coupon rate — probably under 7%. The higher rate is used here to take into account underwriting and other costs of floating and servicing the bonds. In effect, the 8% figure is the effective rate of interest on the money actually used to construct the facilities. Straight line depreciation is used. Each facility processes 260,000 tons of input waste per year.

Cost avoidance associated with not having to transport to the disposal site and then landfill the refuse that will be recovered under either of the options is assumed to be $10.00/ton in the base year, 1980. A 4% escalation figure is used which brings the average assumed cost avoidance to $14.00/ton for the refuse derived fuel case and $17.00/ton for the steam-generating incinerator. The reason for the difference is the assumed economic lives of the plants. The escalator is applied for only 7½ years for the refuse derived fuel plant, but it is 12½ years for the steam-generating incinerator.

The assumptions made about the energy products are as follows. For the steam produced by the incinerator, oil is assumed to be the competitive fuel. The $9.60/bbl

TABLE 6

Simplified *Pro Forma* **for Steam-Generating Incinerator with Ferrous Recovery**

Revenues
Tipping fee
   ($17.00 per input ton × 260.000 tons/year) $ 4,420,000

Recovery Revenues
Energy
   ($23.30 per input ton × 260,000 tons/year) $ 6,058,000
Ferrous
   ($ 4.90 per input ton × 260,000 tons/year) $ 1,274,000
                                                                     $ 7,335,000
Total Revenues $11,752,000

Costs
Annualized capital costs
   (25 years at 8%) $ 3,600,000
Operating Cost
   (1/8 × $45 million) $ 5,625,000
Total Cost $ 9,255,000

Net Income $ 2,527,000

figure used earlier is escalated at 7% per year. The average price for the 25-year period then becomes approximately $22.50/bbl. Starting with the $2.00/1000 lb of steam figure developed earlier, the escalated value of the refuse as an energy source becomes $4.66/1000 lb of steam 12½ years later and at 10,000,000 Btu per input ton of waste, 50% conversion efficiency, this is $23.30 per input ton of waste. For the refuse derived fuel case, coal is assumed to be the competitive fuel. This is assumed to be $.80 million Btu in 1980. A 4% escalation rate is used. At 4% for 7½ years, the price of coal rises to $1.07 per million Btu. Of the 10,000,000 Btu in an input ton of waste 80% are assumed to be shipped in the refuse derived fuel, the remainder are lost in the processing steps. Therefore, by multiplying 8,000,000 Btu times $1.07 one obtains an estimate of $8.60 for the fuel value of the input waste converted to refuse derived fuel.

The assumptions concerning the recovered materials are as follows.

1. $30.00/ton for mechanically separated commingled paper. The amount recovered is assumed to be 5% of the input waste. This is $1.50 per input ton.
2. $45.00/ton for the recovered glass. The amount recovered is set at 7% of the input waste. This is $2.45 per input ton.
3. $70.00/ton for ferrous metals also at 7% of the input waste. This is $4.90 per input ton of waste.
4. $485.00/ton for nonferrous metals at 1.5% of the input waste. The result is a figure of $7.30 per input ton of waste. This is a 7% escalation on a 1980 estimate of $350/ton.

The ferrous price is assumed to be the same for each type of plant even though the midpoint in the program life is more distant in the case of the steam generating incinerator and hence, if the products were comparable, the escalated value should be higher. The reason for using the same figure is that the products are not the same. The nonincinerated ferrous from the refuse derived fuel plant will undoubtedly bring a higher price. Using the same figure, in effect, produces a discount for the incinerated metal from the ash residue of the steam-generating plant.

TABLE 7

Simplified *Pro Forma* **for Refuse Derived Fuel with Paper, Glass, Ferrous and Nonferrous Metals Recovery**

Revenues	
Tipping fee	
($14.00 per input ton × 260,000 tons/year)	$ 3,640,000
Recovery Revenues	
Energy	
($8.60 per input ton × 260,000 tons/year)	$ 2,236,000
Paper	
($1.50 per input ton × 260,000 tons/year)	$ 390,000
Glass	
($2.45 per input ton × 260,000 tons/year)	$ 637,000
Ferrous	
($4.90 per input ton × 260,000 tons/year)	$ 1,274,000
Nonferrous	
($7.30 per input ton × 260,000 tons/year)	$ 1,898,000
	$ 6,435,000
Total revenues	$10,075,000
Costs	
Annualized capital cost	
(15 years at 8%)	$ 2,560,000
Operating cost	
(1/5 of initial capital cost)	$ 4,800,000
Total Cost	$ 7,360,000
Net Income	$ 2,715,000

Based on the assumptions used in developing these two examples, the net income for the two approaches to recovery turn out be about the same. For the steam generating incinerator the net income figure is $2,527,000 and for the refuse derived fuel option the figure is $2,715,000. However, the rates of return on total investment are considerably different because the steam generating incinerator is twice as expensive. Dividing $2.527 million by $45 million yields 5.6% for the steam-generating incinerator, while dividing $2.715 million by $24 million in the refuse derived fuel case produces a rate of return on total investment of 11.3%. Neither of these returns are such that they are likely to attract investment to the recovery industry. However, because of the market security obtained by selling steam rather than a refuse fuel, it is appropriate to adopt a rate of return on equity approach for evaluating the economics of the steam-generating incinerator. The funds for facilities of this sort can usually be raised on a revenue basis. That is, the owner of the plant pledges only the revenues from the facility to pay off the indebtedness of the project. The owner generally has an equity component of around 20%. Twenty percent of $45 million is $9 million. Using this number as the denominator in the rate of return calculation shows a much brighter picture, i.e., $2.527 million divided by $9 million yields a 29% rate of return on equity. The latter is the amount of invested capital the owner has at risk. If the project fails he stands to lose this $9 million while the investors who brought the bonds, secured only by the expected success of the venture, stand to lose $36 million.

The situation is different for the RDF facility. Because firm markets — take or pay — have not been found for this as yet relatively untested fuel, site owners have had to back bond issues with the credit of the parent corporation. Hence, to continue to use the example developed here, if the project should fail the owner stands to lose the entire $24 million since he must pay off the bond holders. Therefore, the rate of return of equity concept is not appropriate. If the passage of time produces operational data on the continued feasibility of using RDF, the conditions for equity based computations may be satisfied. That is, with bonds sold with only an owner's equity component and the anticipated project revenues backing them. It is clear that in this case the rate of return would rise to rather handsome levels. Alternatively, the tipping fee could be lowered creating disposal savings for communities projected to be in the $14.00 range for alternative means of disposal thus making resource recovery economically viable for cities projected to have lower disposal costs by traditional means. It also should be clear that the uncertainty as to the degree to which the future will allow for equity financing, as that term is used here, with its ramifications on the profitability of the venture, brings on hedging about the future. "Do not move now, but wait." This is one reason communities have not converted as rapidly as many would have wished from traditional means of disposal to resource recovery. This uncertainty is one of the barriers inhibiting the transition from problem to opportunity.*

The examples are also useful to illustrate the economics of private vs. public ownership. If public operation is as efficient as private, and this is of course a debatable issue, then it is appropriate to compare the economics of the two operations by converting the net income figures given in the tables to tipping fee reductions.** The direct implication is that if there is no need to reward entrepreneurial risk, because that risk is taken by the tax paying public at large, resource recovery becomes cheaper. Therefore, being cheaper it can create a dividend for those communities with relatively expensive traditional forms of disposal and can make recovery economically feasible for communities with relatively inexpensive landfill. In the steam-generating incinerator case, net income divided by the 260,000 tons/year of waste burnt produces a figure of $9.72 per input ton. The corresponding figure for the refuse derived fuel plant is $10.44. Applying this to the tipping fee considerably reduces the amount of revenue that must be generated from this source of income. In the steam generating incinerator case the tipping fee could be reduced to $7.28 per input ton and for the RDF example, the resultant figure is $3.56 per input ton, making the latter system, under the assumptions made here, competitive in almost every environment where 1000 tons/day of waste is available for processing and even leaving a fair amount of latitude for diseconomies of scale and perhaps still offering a competitive means of disposal for smaller communities.

This section has used a very basic economic model applied to the steam generating incinerator and the refuse derived fuel cases in order to illustrate how the economics of resource recovery might work out for a particular community. The reader should not look to these examples for precise cost and revenue forecasts. In fact, the oil price used is obviously already out-of-date. Otherwise, the figures used are illustrative of the general magnitude but, for any particular community the estimates given here could be sufficiently off the mark to considerably affect the outcome. However, as a framework to aid in thinking about economic aspects and the complexities of market risk, rates of return and types of ownership, the model and the two examples serve a useful purpose.

---

* The question is often raised as to whether it is better to burn paper as part of the mixed waste or attempt its recovery for the reuse of the fiber it contains. Paper runs about 16 million Btu/ton. Note then that $30/ton as recovered fiber is equivalent to $1.87 per million Btu; $20 a ton as fiber is $1.25 per million Btu and $10/ton is $.62 per million Btu. Fiber recovery is the most attractive when secondary paper is over approximately $20/ton if coal is the alternative fuel. Against oil the case of using paper for energy is quite attractive

** See Savas, E. S., Policy Analysis for local government: public vs. private collection, *Policy Analysis*, 3(No. 1), 1977.

IV. GOVERNMENTAL ACTIONS SUGGESTED TO CHANGE
RELATIVE PRICES

A. Incentives, Disincentives, and Regulatory or Mandated Approaches

It has been the main thesis of this chapter that resource recovery will only take place when it makes economic sense at the local level. While sometimes it makes political sense to spend more to accomplish environmental goals, risk taking is not politically wise and much that is involved in an affirmative resource recovery decision requires risk taking. Until more of the risk is out of the decision, unless there is a externally provided financial cushion to protect the local decision maker or unless an affirmative recovery decision is mandated by higher authority, one will not see a rapid shift from solid waste problem to resource recovery opportunity. In one way or the other, these *unlesses* and *untils* have been considered at the federal level for it is here that the risk of RDT&E can be spread over the tax base rather than falling on an individual community. It is also at the federal level where the relative cost and prices faced by local decision makers can be changed. Finally, the federal policymaker can mandate, through regulatory controls, certain actions at the local level that would accelerate the use of recovery based disposal alternatives. In the sections that follow, possible federal actions are discussed under the headings: Technology Incentives, Capital and Operating Assistance, Market Measures, and Regulatory Actions.

B. Technology Incentives

When it is in the national interest to encourage a faster rate of development of new technologies which promise to accomplish a national goal, the federal government has offered financial assistance to the developers. The defense and space programs are the principal examples, although there are occasions where fairly significant amounts of federally raised public monies have been spent in the health and education areas as well. Often, the federal assistance is direct in the form of research or demonstration grants or contracts. Sometimes it is indirect by providing protection from competition in order that the organization that invests in the development of a new approach can enjoy a market advantage when the development reaches the commercial level.

The research and demonstration grant is the principal method used by the federal government to stimulate technology. The rationale is that improved unit processes and systems will come about if the national government assumes part of the risk. This is generally risk in implementation which occurs after the hardware has been developed or partially developed. There are fewer examples of major governmental support early on in the developmental process. By participating at the implementation stage, the national government gains the opportunity to compare and evaluate the various systems it is supporting as to their costs and feasibility and then can disseminate this information to others at the local level to aid them in their resource recovery decision making.

C. Capital and Operating Assistance

There is a wide spectrum of capital assistance alternatives ranging from direct grants for planning, plant design, building construction, and equipment purchase, to indirect measures that lower what would otherwise be the cost of the plant through loan guarantees and rapid tax write-offs. The federal government's principal cost lowering contribution to the implementation of recovery facilities has been its willingness to underwrite the planning steps and to provide technical assistance. In the latter case, and sometimes in the former as well, the federal dollars are given to states who use them to pay state personnel to provide the technical assistance or for pass through planning grants.

There have been no federal construction grants exclusively for resource recovery facilities other than those facilities which come under the heading of research and demonstration. Undoubtedly, some revenue sharing money has been used locally for resource recovery, but recycling has not been a major beneficiary of this program. The main advantage of construction grants is that they help overcome initial investment cost barriers. In theory, the fact that the plant is less expensive could allow the communities with relatively high disposal costs to market their recovered materials and energy at lower prices. Alternatively, the grant "cheapened" plant would find application in lower cost disposal areas. There are disadvantages to construction grants that have been emphasized by the opponents of such an approach. Many people feel that the solid waste disposal issue is a local and not a national concern and that it is wrong to redistribute funds collected through the national tax system to subsidize local plant construction. Even if there were no redistribution involved, i.e., if exactly as much as were collected from each locality by the federal tax mechanisms were returned to the same locality, the objection would be "let the decision be made locally and let the local tax mechanism, and tax structure, raise the funds for the project".

A study by Resource Planning Associates listed the pros and cons of a construction grant program viewed from the federal perspective. This list illustrates the complexity of federal policy actions as viewed locally where implementation decisions are actually made, particularly when these policy actions involve an attempt to effect national considerations and policy decisions by changing prices.*

Advantages of Construction Grants

• The measure would provide capital assistance to cites for financing solid waste management.
• A construction grant provides for a high degree of control over the allocation and expenditure of Federal funds.
• The measure avoids the windfall that recyclers already in operation would receive under a user tax credit or subsidy.
• The recovery plant would produce a steady reliable supply of secondary material. Whether these materials would be sold is another question.

Disadvantages of Construction Grants

• Due to the uncertainty of the markets for recovery plant outputs, it is questionable as to whether construction grants would result in increased recycling. Plants could be built whose outputs would not be saleable and would require disposal.
• The measure would force acquisition of secondary materials by processing rather than by skimming; skimming provides greater solid waste management savings than processing.
• The grant would stimulate capital intensive, technological approaches to resource recovery. Such approaches may not be required or desirable.
• The measure is not flexible in that it would lock in approaches from the onset. Once a plant has been built, it would not be abandoned even if costs were high and efficiency was low.
• The measure is high risk in that the cost of construction and equipment would be borne by the federal government whether or not the outputs of the plant were recycled.

---

* Resource Planning Associates, Legislative Issue Paper #2, Resource Recovery Incentives, p. 22, August 15, 1972.

• A construction grant program would be very difficult to administer. Both construction costs and secondary material prices vary across the nation. Therefore, a fixed percentage grant would not be applicable, and the federal contribution would have to be variable.

• There are numerous uncertainties in determining how much subsidy is required to achieve a desired level of recycling (e.g., the efficiency of processes and operation costs are not well known); hence, the impact of the program would be highly unpredictable.

• Since the measure only subsidizes recovery by processing, it would only have an effect in areas with sufficient tonnage to justify large scale plants. There are a limited number of such places and recovery in most of the nation would be unaffected.

• A grant program is very vulnerable to political influence in the selection of guarantees.

• The measure would only be available to public waste management organizations, whereas half of the solid waste in the nation is handled by private organizations.

• In public hands, resource recovery plant operation would be handled by a sector least qualified to operate a commercial marketing-oriented enterprise.

The list above illustrates that policy actions are interrelated in terms of accomplishing the main objective, here stimulating the construction of recovery facilities. Their secondary effects are often different. In addition to affecting the cost of recovery at the local level by reducing the capital outlay necessary by giving the local government a federal grant, capital costs would be cheapened through a federal loan subsidy. In this case, the federal government could pay a portion of the interest charge. Loan guarantees, another form of lowering the cost would have two effects. First, the necessary financing could be obtained cheaper, i.e., at a lower rate of interest because of the guarantee. However, this is not a substantial effect. More important is the "bail out" if the project fails. The pay back of the investors would be done by the federal government. Another method of changing local costs would be to operate on the market side by enhancing, with a federal payment, the revenue stream generated by the recovered products sold in the market place. Interest rate subsidiaries and cash payments based on the sale of products affect the cost and revenue streams over the lifetime of the project. The construction grant is upfront.

Parallel methods of affecting the annual cost of a facility that is privately owned are investment tax credits or rapid write-offs. Under the investment tax credit, all or a percentage of the initial cost of a recycling plant and its equipment could be charged against net taxable income in the year of purchase, thus reducing the effective capital requirements for the initial year. Rapid depreciation which is presently permitted for various types of pollution control equipment allows depreciation to be taken in advance of the expected life of the equipment. For example, a magnet with a useful life project to be 15 years could be written off in 5 years. In each case, the successful facility becomes profitable sooner and plants that may otherwise be only marginal investment opportunities have their profit potential enhanced.

The Environmental Protection Agency has conducted a comparative analysis of three alternative programs to "cheapen" the local cost of embarking on a resource recovery effort. The accuracy of their figures is not important here. However, the analysis is a useful illustration of the factors that are important in policy determination. The three incentive program considered were (1) a 75% construction grant, (2) a 75% loan interest subsidy, and (3) a 30% cash subsidy. The analysis appeared in the Second Report to Congress on Resource Recovery and Source Reduction.* The first

* Second Report to Congress, Resource Recovery and Source Reduction, U.S. Environmental Protection Agency, SW-122, p. 44—46, 1974.

two alternatives are self explanatory. The third alternative needs some additional explanation. It is a cash payment to the owner or operator of a recovery facility equal to a percent of the sale price of the plant's products. The impact of the three incentive programs on the net costs of operating six types of resource recovery facilities are shown in Table 8. The interest subsidy has the federal government paying all but 1.25% of a 5% rate. Note the difference in the operating costs among incentive programs and among different types of plants. In part this is due to the difference in the amount of capital required to build the plants and in the difference is the market value of the products.

Table 9 also taken from the Second Report to Congress shows various measures of the effectiveness of the three incentive programs analyzed. Note that the preference for any individual approach depends on the target. If the absolute number of plants is the objective, then this is accomplished best with the construction grant program. If minimizing the so-called "windfall" is important, which is the financial gain made by those jurisdictions and private owners who would have gone into resource recovery in the absence of the incentive program, then construction grants again are preferred. However, the construction grant program is the most expensive. As one would expect, the preferred policy issue is complex which is one reason there has been much debate and little action in terms of a major federal thrust in this area.

This is in contrast to federal involvement in publicly-owned sewage treatment plants. There is a political consensus that sewage treatment is a federal responsibility. The "water shed" and "air shed" analogies apply. As mentioned earlier, no such consensus has formed behind the "waste shed" argument. This is, that the responsibility for better waste disposal and greater implementation of resource recovery should be laid at the feet of the federal decision-maker and paid for out of federal tax receipts. Nevertheless, it should be pointed out that if only 10% of the nations' $25 billion, 5-year federal program for sewage treatment plants were diverted to financing resource recovery facilities there would be sufficient funds to build the capacity to process 75% of the nation's refuse for recovery purposes.

D. Market Measures

In a sense the cash subsidy mentioned above was a market measure, although the payment would be made to the plant operator. However, the principal measure advanced for increasing the demand for recovered materials has been a tax credit to users of secondary materials, and to those who use waste-based energy such as RDF or steam from a waste burning steam generating incinerator. The users of materials and energy recovered from waste would receive a tax credit equivalent to a percentage of the cost of purchasing the recycled materials and energy. Also mentioned as a possible market incentive are investment tax credits and rapid write-offs for plant and equipment to use recycled materials. This is in contrast to the use of such incentives to encourage putting in place plant and equipment to initially extract the materials from the waste stream or to make a RDF, including waste-based gas or oil. There would be an overlap in terms of straight burning of waste where the initial process is also the final step in recycling.

According to the Resource Planning Associates study cited earlier, it has been estimated that a tax credit rate of 15% would overcome significant secondary materials economic disadvantages. The results of a 1972 analysis show that a tax credit of 15% available to post-consumer wastes, should result in new recycling of 11.2 million tons by 1980. The cost of the program in 1980 would be $50.2 million in tax revenues foregone. Of this total, $9.5 would be compensated for by revenue losses (depletion allowances, etc.) avoided, for a net cost of the program in that year of $40.7 million.

TABLE 8

Impact of Selected Incentives on the Economics of Municipally Owned Resource Recovery Plants

Net Plant Cost (dollars/ton)

Type of incentive	Fuel recovery	Materials recovery	Pyrolysis	Incineration with residue recovery	Incineration with steam recovery	Incineration with electricity recovery
None	2.70	4.77	5.42	7.18	7.05	8.97
75% Construction grant	1.46	2.86	3.40	5.33	5.15	5.95
75% Loan interest subsidy	2.09	3.86	4.42	6.33	6.12	7.75
30% Cash subsidy	1.78	3.45	3.76	6.64	6.05	6.99

From Second Report to Congress, Resource Recovery and Source Reduction, U.S. Environmental Protection Agency, SW-122, p. 45, 1974. The calculations appearing in the table are based on data from Midwest Research Institute, Resource Recovery; the State of Technology. Washington, D.C., U.S. Government Printing Office, February, 1973.

TABLE 9

Recycling Impact of Selected Incentives to Municipalities for Development and Operation of Resource Recovery Plants[a]

Type of incentive	Approximate number of plants constructed, 1976—85	Total recovery from constructed plants,[a] (1976—85)					Total recovery over the lifetime of the plants[b]		Total cost to the Federal Government (millions of dollars)	Windfall[c] (percent)	Federal cost of additional recycling[d] (dollars/ton)
		Heat content (10^{12} Btu's)	Materials (10^6 tons)				Heat content (10^{12} Btu's)	Materials (10^6 tons)			
			Ferrous metals	Glass	Paper	Aluminum					
75% construction grant	80	592	6.4	4.4	3.9	0.31	1,813	46.1	600	44	2.20
75% loan interest subsidy	55	410	4.4	3.0	2.8	.22	1,247	31.7	320	64	2.60
30% cash subsidy	65	485	5.3	3.6	3.2	.26	1,453	37.4	440	54	2.40

[a] It is assumed that there is a mix of the following six plant types: shredded refuse as a fuel, pyrolysis to produce oil, incineration with steam recovery, incineration with electricity generation, incineration with residue recovery, and wet pulping for materials recovery. As presently envisioned, four of these plants recover energy, four recover ferrous metals, three recover glass, three recover aluminum, and one recovers paper. It is assumed that plant construction proceeds at a constant annual rate throughout the period.

[b] The plants are assumed to have a 20-year life.

[c] This example is based on the assumption that 35 plants would be constructed with or without the subsidies.

[d] This is the total cost to the Federal Government divided by the waste processed at all plants except the 35 that would have been constructed without incentives.

From: Second Report to Congress, Resource Recovery and Source Reduction, U.S. Environmental Protection Agency (SW-122), 1974, 46.

Conversely, this expenditure would result in solid waste disposal savings of $77.4 million in 1980.

Advantages and disadvantages of the tax credit are listed below:

Advantages of Tax Credit

• The tax credit provides an incentive for using additional secondary materials since the financial reward increases as more secondary materials are used. This should result in substitution of secondary materials for virgin materials to maximize the benefit.

• The tax credit stimulates the most efficient means of acquiring waste materials whether it be through skimming or through processing mixed wastes. Skimming would effect savings of both collection and disposal costs.

• The tax credit is flexible in that it subsidizes a percentage of waste materials purchase costs. As secondary material prices drop, the dollar incentive drops, and as prices rise, a larger dollar incentive is provided. In a similar manner, the tax credit adjusts for differences in materials prices across the nation.

• The measure would provide payments to the recycling industry, segments of which are marginally profitable and threatened with financial disaster due to increasing pollution abatement costs.

• The measure would provide an incentive to the private sector to increase its resource recovery activity, and the private sector is best qualified to implement recovery, which is a market-oriented activity.

Disadvantages of Tax Credit

• The measure employs the tax mechanism to disburse funds. This is politically unattractive at a time when major tax reform measures are contemplated.

• The measure results in a large windfall payment to present users of secondary materials, and to those who would use such materials in the absence of a tax credit.

• The measure would result in a loss of revenues to the Federal Government — but these would be partially offset by depletion allowances not taken on the virgin materials displaced by wastes.

• The full value of the credit would not be available to industries which are not making a profit or are making a very small profit (unless it is carried backward or forward to tax returns for other years).

• This measure requires enforcement and administration by the Internal Revenue Service.*

There has been no action on tax credits of the sort described above although there has been considerable discussion. For reasons already mentioned, the federal government has been reluctant to effect policy actions which would change relative prices in regard to resource recovery. This pertains to affecting the demand side as well as the supply side.

E. Regulatory Actions

As the reader might suspect, the federal government has been active in the regulatory

---

* Resource Planning Associates, Legislative Issue Paper #2, p. 18—19. The sources given by Resource Planning Associates for the data on the tax credit magnitude and impact are: A Recycling Tax Credit, a draft memorandum submitted to the Treasury Dept. by the Council of Economic Advisors, the Council on Environmental Quality and the Environmental Protection Agency, June 2, 1972, and Federal Encouragement for Recycling, a memo submitted to the Council on Enviornmental Quality and the Council of Economic Advisors by the Environmental Protection Agency, August 3, 1972.

front. The principal actions here have stemmed from the federal government's responsibility for public health, not through a desire to conserve materials or develop a relatively untapped energy source. Of course, tighter waste disposal regulations promulgated to protect public health have an effect on disposal prices as seen at the local level. There is an expectation among many that the increased cost of landfill which follows from higher standards and the increased enforcement activity will be the prime factors that bring about the adoption of recovery-based disposal methods and this may, in fact, be true.

An early regulatory action that benefited resource recovery by making financing cheaper was the 1975 decision by the Internal Revenue Service to allow the use of tax-free bonds, called Pollution Control Revenue Bonds, to finance both materials and energy recovery. The 1975 rule interpretation allows tax-exempt status for all types of equipment at the recovery plant necessary to beneficiate the recovered products to make them more commercially acceptable or to increase their market value. The rules specifically exclude beneficiation facilities and equipment for further processing at the commercial user's plant.

With respect to energy recovery, the rules allow tax-exempt status for all assets to convert the waste into usable energy, including extra equipment that may be necessary to upgrade the product to meet the specifications of its particular market. The rules exclude equipment for transporting the product after processing "into the form in which it is sold" (e.g., via steam pipes or trucks). The rules also exclude electricity-generating equipment from tax-exempt financing, "since the equipment transforms the commercially salable steam into another form of energy".

Also among federal regulatory actions are rules governing federal procurement in terms of federal purchases of products with increased percentages of recycled materials. There have been some specifications issued, particularly for paper and paper packaging which call for a higher proportion of secondary fibers, but even if all federal purchases were of recycled goods this would be less than 2% of the market, on average. There is potential here, particularly if the change in federal specifications causes other levels of government to change and perhaps federal contractors as well. It should be noted that the federal government is not willing to pay more for a comparable product made from secondary materials. It prefers the secondary product if it is equal in cost, or costs less, than that made from virgin sources.

Other regulatory measures that have been discussed, in some cases very heatedly, are the removal of tax substitutes to virgin materials and a readjustment of freight rates between primary and secondary goods. Producers of virgin materials and fuels benefit from tax-saving depletion allowances, accelerated tax write-offs of exploration costs and advantageous capital gains treatments. Secondary material processors are treated differently and the proposals in one way or the other seek to even up the tax treatment among the two industrial sectors. Some proponents of the increased use of recycled materials would see the pendulum swing over such that the rules work in favor of the secondary producers. The pros and cons of these proposals are a subject in their own right and beyond the scope of this chapter. It is sufficient to note that changing the rules would certainly affect the price of virgin materials. Also, new cost relationships would be set up on the secondary materials side through the interaction of demand and supply. Finally, these costs, like those associated with the differences in the cost of transporting virgin and secondary materials are only a segment of the overall production decision which determines the location of plants, methods of production and the type and mix of input materials. Significant changes in the demand for secondary materials will take time.

In concluding this section, it is important to point out that the casual observer of the regulatory debates should not be mislead by the frequent use of the term "discrimination". What is "discrimination" to one side of the argument may be "fair" to the other side. The prices that are charged for goods and services seldom relate accurately to the costs of production. They are hopefully market determined and hence there should be a tendency for goods and services which essentially are substitutes to bring the same price. However, past policy decisions concerning national objectives and goals have perturbated many price relationships. What is "fair", viewed in the broader political sense, is what is. It becomes discriminatory if national goals shift.

V. SUMMARY

A. Problem or Opportunity?

There is clearly a prospect that the solid waste problem can be transformed into the resource recovery opportunity. However, progress has been slow. Only a very small percentage of the nation's waste is presently being recycled and as far as materials recycling is concerned, most of this is through consumer programs, mainly newspapers. On the energy side, there are a few mass burning steam-generating incinerators and an increasing number of RDF projects. However, the surface is barely scratched and it is not clear that the rate of implementation is accelerating in any large measure. The main reasons for this are uncertain technology and questionable economics, partially because of the technology and partially because of the natural variability in the markets for the recovery products.

B. Technology and Economics

There is still a good deal of uncertainty associated with most resource recovery technology. The principal exceptions are the mass burning steam-generating incinerator and the magnetic separation of ferrous metals. The RDF concept is just beginning to generate operating data but even this is biased by the fact the projects are still mostly in the shakedown stage. As the economics portion of this chapter showed, the refuse derived fuel option exhibits, at least on paper, better systems economics than the steam-generating incinerator. However, this advantage is not gained without significant disadvantages. Lack of operating data means that the fuel market is soft in terms of a long term certainty that the customer will indeed take the fuels thus enabling the community to completely amortize off its investment. Until this issue is resolved, there is not likely to be a great rush to implement RDF systems. Likewise, until this uncertainty is resolved, many communities will be hesitant to invest in the more capital intensive steam-generating incinerator because of the potential that a better system may come along and make the incinerator obsolete before the end of its useful life. Notwithstanding the RDF option, other new approaches appear with great frequency. There is much room for innovation, particularly for small-scale systems. Today's more developed technologies are not adaptable, in an economic sense, to the smaller communities. Therefore, for these communities resource recovery, apart from consumer programs, awaits a technological breakthrough or some policy action that would make the prices they face, when considering a move to resource recovery, favorable in comparison to continuing to rely on landfill.

C. Governmental Actions

There is hardly a tactic of government that has not been considered as a means of encouraging the adoption of recovery-based solid waste disposal systems. These include everything from mandated regional solid waste planning; government provided technical assistance; construction subsidies in the form of grants; various operating subsidies, mandated federal procurement of recovered materials, etc. Only a few of these have been adopted. This is mainly because there is no consensus as to the extent that the federal government should be involved in the resouce recovery issue. There probably is no clear cut "rule of government" that would allow for a consensus to form. If the federal government should become more active than it has so far, it probably will be motivated by a concern for saving depletable resources, the energy question and a desire to spawn more conservation mindedness on the part of the public rather than by some philosophical federal interest determination that moves resource recovery higher up on the priority list. It is fairly clear that recovery will happen over time. The uncertain question is to what extent government actions will be taken to speed up converting the waste problem to conservation opportunity.

Chapter 6

CONVERSION OF WASTE ORGANIC MATTER TO ENERGY

E. P. Lynch

TABLE OF CONTENTS

I. INTRODUCTION

The term waste organic matter covers a wide field of material. It includes: urban waste (garbage); some industrial wastes such as those from the plastics industry and from timber processing plants; residues of grain crops such as corn stover, wheat straw, rice straw, etc; sewage sludge; animal manure; water hyacinths used for metal scavenging in tertiary waste water treatment; forest residues; and many other materials. Any waste organic material which will burn, pyrolyze, or undergo biological degradation is a candidate for producing energy. Many methods have been devised and/or proposed for obtaining energy from these materials either in the form of direct heat, combustible gases, or combustible liquids. All of these methods fall into one of two categories — biological and thermal.

II. BIOLOGICAL PROCESSES

A. Anaerobic Digestion

This is more properly referred to as fermentation, after Pasteur, who defined fermentation as "Life without air". However, digestion is the term in common usage and most people associate the term "fermentation" with aerobic processes.

Anaerobic digestion can occur only with materials such as cellulose or starch which can be biologically degraded to simple sugars. Cellulose is a polymer of glucose with linkage occurring in the beta position at the 1-4 glycosidic bonds. Starch contains amylose and amylopectin both of which consist of polymers of glucose linked in the alpha position at the 1-4 glycosidic bonds. The α 1-4 bond can be broken (hydrolyzed) by enzymes secreted by many microorganisms, plants, and animals. Very few enzymes can hydrolyze cellulose. Also, cellulose usually contains both crystalline and amorphous regions of which the amorphous hydrolyzes more readily. For an in-depth treatment of this subject refer to Gascoigne.[1]

The overall digestion process occurs in three steps. They are:

1. Hydrolysis of the substrate to glucose
2. Formation of organic acids from glucose
3. Conversion of the organic acids to methane and carbon dioxide

The first step we have discussed. The second step is also an enzymatic process. It generally proceeds via the Embden-Meyerhof pathway and then from pyruvic acid (or pyruvate) to acetic acid and some propionic acid. This is much too involved for discussion here. For proper treatment of this subject refer to any modern text on microbiology.

It should be noted that the first two steps listed above are common to both anaerobic and aerobic processes, at least as far as the production of pyruvate.

The third step requires the presence of methanogenic bacteria. A number of these exist and are generally found as a mixed population in sewage sludge, which is used to seed the digester. These bacteria reduce the volatile acids to methane and carbon dioxide, usually in equimolar quantities. The gas leaving the digester has a heating value of approximately 500 Btu/Scf (water-free basis). If the gas is dehydrated and the carbon dioxide removed, the heating value is 1000 Btu/Scf methane. The quantity of gas which will be produced per pound of substrate fed will vary widely with the composition of the substrate.

One of the more widely used applications for anaerobic digestion is in the treatment of sewage sludge. The gas from such a unit is usually burned to provide process heat in the sewage treatment plant. The residue from the digesters, when filtered and dried, makes an excellent fertilizer. The digesters used for sewage sludge are usually large diameter, agitated concrete tanks. All three of the process steps occur in one vessel. The first two steps in the process function best at a pH of 4.0 to 6.5. Production of methane, however, is optimum at a pH of 7.0 to 7.8. The digesters are operated at a compromise pH of 7.0. If the digester "sours", i.e., the pH drops too low, production of methane will cease. Also, certain materials are toxic to the methanogenic bacteria and will cause a decrease in methane production or a cessation of production if the entire population is toxified. A study of the toxic effects of various substances is presently underway at Drexel University.[2] The digesters may also be operated in the mesophilic range (30 to 45°C) or the thermophilic range (55 to 75°C). The former gives a higher yield of methane and does not usually require an external source of heat but requires a retention time of approximately 20 days in the digester. The latter gives a somewhat lower yield of methane and requires an external source of heat but requires only one half the retention time. An excellent analysis of anaerobic digestion has been given by Bailey and Ollis.[3]

The decomposition of urban waste by anaerobic digestion is under active investigation. The heterogenous nature of urban waste makes it much more difficult to handle than sewage sludge. To process urban waste the metals and glass present must be removed and the waste shredded and air classified. The plastic material in the waste is particularly troublesome because it is not biodegradable under anaerobic conditions and there is evidence that it collects in a scum layer at the liquid level in the digester. The cellulosic portion of the waste is also very difficult to slurry. The state of the feed material and the degree and type of agitation within the digester are important. In general, the more finely divided the feed is the easier it is to keep in suspension and the more readily it will react. Stringy, fibrous material will accumulate in the scum layer and cause heavy, tough, rope-like tendrils to form on the agitator shaft. Very little information is available on the percentage of solids which can be successfully handled in a conventional (stirred tank) digester. Studies made by Systems Technology Corp.[4] using both mechanical and gas agitation indicate that this quantity is low, possibly as low as 4% (vol.). These tests were made at their Franklin, Ohio plant using urban waste which had been processed in a Black-Clawson hydrapulper. A 50 to 100 ton/day proof-of-concept-plant is being operated by Waste Management, Inc.[5] This plant is designed for 12 to 15% (vol) solids in the digesters which are also of the conventional stirred tank design. To date, information is not available on the results of this operation. The residue or sludge from a digester operating on urban waste is not suitable as a fertilizer. It must be dewatered and landfilled. Digesters other than the conventional stirred tank type have been used or proposed. Horizontal, plug flow types with minimal agitation have been used successfully on animal manure. These work best when no bedding straw is mixed with the manure. Vertical plug flow and vertical fixed bed digesters have been proposed. To date these have been tested only on a laboratory scale. Many investigators have also proposed using multistage, both two-stage and three-stage, conventional digesters with the different steps of the process occurring in different stages. It is known that the generation of methane and carbon dioxide is the rate-limiting step of the process. There is some evidence that multistaging will permit greater flexibility and throughput.

B. Aerobic Fermentation

1. General Considerations

The use of aerobic fermentation is widespread in the production of pharmaceuticals, sugars, yeasts, and alcohols. Enzymatic hydrolysis is involved in most, if not all, of these processes. The sugars produced are sometimes the product but may be intermediates for the final product. The processes which convert the sugars to ethanol are the ones of most interest to us.

Most of the ethanol produced by fermentation and subsequent distillation is beverage grade at 95% concentration and is used for blending with whiskeys or as a base for vodka and gin. This alcohol is designated as "grain neutral spirits" in blended whiskey. Small amounts of fusel oil are also made in the process and must be removed. Some industrial grade alcohol is also produced for use as a chemical intermediate. The greatest interest in ethanol as a fuel is in the production of anhydrous ethanol for blending with gasoline to produce "gasahol". For this purpose fusel oil may be left in the product.

There are many materials which may be fermented to make ethanol. Among these are all of the cereal grains (corn, wheat, barley, rice, oats, rye, etc.), potatoes, corn stover, barley straw, rice straw, sorghum straw, wheat straw, molasses, and newsprint and other cellulosic products. Of these, only corn stover, the straws, and newsprint could be considered as waste products. Logistics would favor the use of newsprint as a raw material.

2. Ethanol From Cellulose (Newsprint)

An excellent study of the conversion of newsprint to ethanol has been made at the Lawrence-Berkeley Laboratory, University of California, by C. R. Wilke.[6] This study well illustrates the concepts of enzymatic hydrolysis of cellulose to glucose and the fermentation of glucose to ethanol. Preliminary cost data are also presented. Excerpts from Wilke's report are presented in this section to illustrate these concepts, which are common for most fermentable feed stocks.

Cellulose may be hydrolyzed by acids as well as by enzymes. In the presence of dilute acid cellulose is hydrolyzed to glucose according to the reaction:

$$(C_6H_{10}O_5)_n + H_2O \xrightarrow{\quad [H^+] \quad} n\,C_6H_{12}O_6 \qquad (1)$$

Unfortunately with respect to obtaining a maximum yield of sugars, acid also catalyzes the decomposition of glucose to 5-hydroxymethy 2-furaldehyde (HMF) and thence to levulinic plus formic acids.

$$C_6H_{12}O_6 \xrightarrow{\quad [H^+] \quad} HO-CH_2-C \overset{\overset{\displaystyle CH}{\|}}{\underset{\displaystyle O}{\diagdown}} \overset{\overset{\displaystyle CH}{\|}}{\diagup} C-C \overset{\displaystyle O}{\underset{H}{/\!/}} + 3H_2O$$

glucose (hexose)   5-hydroxymethyl 2-furaldehyde   (2)

$$C_6H_6O_3 + 2H_2O \rightarrow CH_3-\overset{\overset{\displaystyle O}{\|}}{C}-CH_2-CH_2-\overset{\overset{\displaystyle O}{\|}}{C}-OH + HCOOH$$

(HMF)   levulinic acid   formic acid

$$(3)$$

Sugars produced by acid hydrolysis are generally fermentable, although the rates

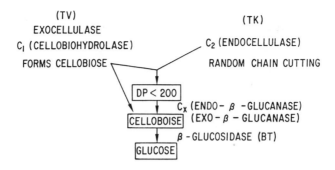

FIGURE 1.   A tentative scheme for enzymatic hydrolysis of cellulose.

may be slow due to inhibitory effects of various substances in the hydrolyzates. Hexoses may be fermented to ethanol in satisfactory yield by *Saccharomyces sp.* Pentose may be fermented to butanol and acetone by *O. butylicum* or to 3,2 butylene glycol by *Aerobacter aerogenes.* Various pretreatments of sugar solutions have been employed to reduce inhibitory effects including addition of sodium sulfite, heat treatment, use of large quantities of inoculum, removal of lignin and furfural, and clarification with activated carbon.

The use of enzymatic hydrolysis is more common than use of acid hydrolysis. Many microorganisms, including particularly species of fungi, produce enzyme systems or "cellulases" which depolymerize and hydrolyze cellulose to lower oligosaccharides and ultimately to glucose. One of the most powerful cellulase producers is the fungus *Trichoderma viride* in the form of the mutant QM9414 developed at the U.S. Army Natick Laboratories.

Enzymatic hydrolysis involves at least five separate types of enzyme activities as illustrated in Figure 1. An endocellulase (C_2) cuts long cellulose fibers into short lengths and along with cellobiohydrolase (C_1) breaks down the highly polymerized crystalline parts of the cellulose to a degree of polymerization in the range of 200 or less. Two *Beta*-glucanase components (C_x) carry the degradation to cellobiose followed by action of *beta*-glucosidase, or cellobiase, to form glucose.

An enzymatically formed hydrolyzate will typically contain glucose plus some higher oliogosaccharides, primarily cellobiose with the relative amounts of each depending upon the relative strength of the various enzyme components, the degree of crystallinity of the cellulose and the hydrolysis time.

It has become customary to characterize the activity of cellulase in terms of C_1 activity (action against cotton, a crystalline cellulose) and C_x activity (action against carboxy methyl cellulose) and on overall activity (action against Whatman filter paper) or filter paper activity (FPA) according to Mandels and Weber.[7]

Hydrolysis of cellulosic materials results upon immersion of the substrate into the enzyme solution. The rate and extent of hydrolysis will depend upon the particular substrate and upon the type of pretreatment employed. Chemical pretreatments must be carefully evaluated for the substrate involved since the cost of chemicals may be prohibitive. A dilute acid pretreatment may be economical for substrates having a high hemicellulose (polymerized pentose) content.

For substrates such as newsprint containing appreciable quantities of crystalline cellulose, a mechanical pretreatment such as ball milling, which reduces the crystallinity, improves the hydrolysis.

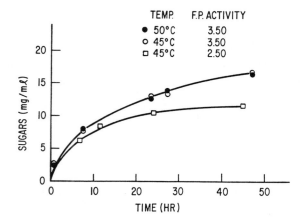

FIGURE 2.   Hydrolysis of 5% suspension of −20 mesh newsprint.

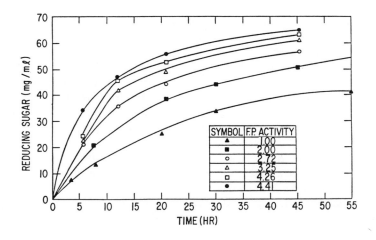

FIGURE 3.   Hydrolysis of 10% ball milled −200 mesh newsprint.

Figure 2 shows typical hydrolysis curves for 20 mesh Wiley milled (shredded) newsprint in 5% suspension, containing 61% *alpha*-cellulose, 16% hemicellulose and 21% lignin. Approximately 50% conversion of the cellulose to sugars occurs in 40 hr producing 15 lb of sugars (as glucose) per lb of enzyme protein at an activity of 3.5 FPA. A representative composition of the hydrolyzate sugars is 72% glucose, 22% cellobiose, 4.4% xylose and 1.5% mannose.

Figure 3 shows data for hydrolysis of 10% suspensions of −200 mesh ball milled newsprint at 50%C. At 3.5 FPA the hydrolysis is approximately 85% complete producing 54 lb of sugars per lb of enzyme protein.

During hydrolysis the enzyme components are strongly adsorbed on the cellulosic substrate. In the case of newsprint hydrolysis, after about 50% conversion approximately one third of the original enzyme activity remains in the liquid phase from which it can be recovered by adsorption on fresh solid entering the process.

The enzyme protein remaining on the residual solids is not readily removed and must

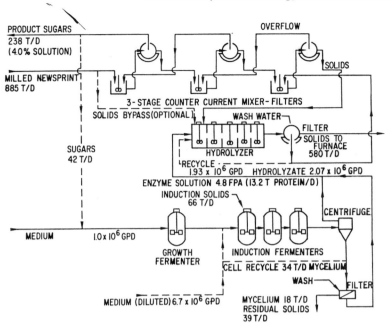

FIGURE 4.   Flow diagram of the base case process.

be considered as lost in the present technology. However, it would be very important economically if a low cost desorbing agent could be found.

Wilke, Yang, and von Stockar[8] have developed a preliminary process design and cost analysis for enzymatic hydrolysis of 885 tons/day of newsprint. While confirmation of the process assumptions by pilot plant studies are needed, the analysis provides a rough economic perspective of the relative importance of various processing operations. Detailed equipment specification and justification of the process assumptions are available in the original report.

Figure 4 is a schematic flow diagram of the hydrolysis process. Flow quantities correspond to the base case process specifications given in Table 1. For simplicity the facilities for milling, heat exchange, induction solids sterilization, and residual solids combustion have been omitted in the flow diagram, although they were designed and are included in the processing cost analyses.

The primary plant feed consists of 885 tons/day of newsprint containing 6% moisture. By means of moderate shredding and hammer-milling the feed is reduced to approximately −20 mesh. The size reduction is not critical so long as the material will form aqueous suspensions which can be pumped, agitated, and filtered. An additional 66 tons/day of feed material is diverted to the first enzyme induction fermentor after sterilization with steam. The product sugar stream from the hydrolyzer is contacted counter-currently in three mixer-filter stages with feed solids for enzyme recovery. Each mixer filter stage consists of a mixing tank to provide 30 min contact time and a horizontal belt vacuum filter to separate the solids from the liquid. A total enzyme recovery of 95% is predicted by theory.

Hydrolysis is conducted over 40 hr at 45°C at a solid/liquid ratio of 1/20 w/w based on inputs to the hydrolyzer. The latter consists of five agitated cylindrical concrete digestors of the type used for solid waste treatment in sanitary engineering. Cellulose conversion of 50% is assumed, at an overall enzyme strength equivalent to 3.5 FPA

TABLE 1

Base Design Case Specification

Feed (−20 mesh newsprint)	885 ton/day
Cellulose content[a]	61% (dry)
Enzyme activity	3.5 FPA
Cellulose hydrolysis	50%, 40 hr., 45°C
Enzyme recovery	34%
Product (as glucose)[b]	238 ton/day
Product concentration	4%
Cell recycle fraction	0.65

[a]   Assumed newsprint composition: 61% a cellulose, 21% lignin, and 16% hemicellulose

[b]   Representative sugar composition: 72% glucose, 22% cellobiose, 4.4% xylose, and 1.5% mannose.

TABLE 2

Medium Raw Materials — Base Case

Component[a]	GM/LIT	$/ton	tons/day
$(NH_4)_2SO_4$	1.4	90	9.3
KH_2PO_4	2.0	120	13.2
$CaCl_2 \cdot 2H_2O$	0.3	33	2.0
$MgSO_4 \cdot 7H_2O$	0.3	110	2.0
$(NH_2)_2CO$	0.3	160	2.0
Protein Nutrient[b]	0.5	300	3.3

[a]   Trace elements are assumed supplied by the process water.

[b]   Pharmamedia, Traders Protein Corp., Ft. Worth, Tex.

in the hydrolyzer. Provision is made for the recycle of a portion of the product solution (plus enzyme) back to the hydrolysis vessel. A sugar concentration of 4.0% is obtained for the case shown. A range of sugar levels is possible depending on the mode of operation and amount of sugar recycle employed.

Make-up enzyme is produced in a two-stage fermentation system, employing the fungus *Trichoderma viride* QM9414 obtained from the U.S. Army Natick Laboratories. Cell growth is obtained in the first stage at a dilution rate of 0.2 hr⁻¹ employing a medium containing 1% product sugars plus minerals and protein nutrient given in Table 2. The induction system is operated at an overall dilution rate of 0.017 hr⁻¹ excluding the cell recycle stream. Both stages employ agitated stainless steel vessels operated at 30°C with aeration rates of 0.15 and 0.015 vvm in the growth and induction stages, respectively. The growth stage feed is sterilized in a heat exchange system (not shown). The induction section effluent is passed through a centrifuge from which a portion of the underflow is fed back to the first induction stage. Ten induction stages in series are employed. The flow quantities in Figure 4 correspond to a cell recycle fraction of 0.65. Recycle fraction is the fraction of cells leaving the last induction stage which is returned to the first stage. For the case shown the use of recycle will maintain the cell density in the induction system at 7 g/ℓ, assuming negligible growth in the induction system when newsprint is employed. The resultant enzyme production is sufficient to provide an enzyme concentration of 3.5 FPA in the hydrolyzer. A portion of the centrifuge underflow is filtered and the cells are discarded to maintain adequate

TABLE 3

Process Cost Analysis — Base Case. Raw Material (Newsprint) Cost Excluded.

	Hydrolysis	Pretreatment	Enzyme recovery	Enzyme make-up	Total
Fixed capital cost ($)	6,200,960	2,816,130	2,060,410	12,309,260	23,386,760
Annual investment related costs ($)	1,482,030	673,060	492,440	2,941,910	5,589,440
Annual labor related costs ($)	122,990	61,500	122,990	122,990	430,470
Annual utilities costs ($)	239,415	132,290	26,650	446,850	845,115
Annual raw materials costs ($)	—	—	—	1,312,190	1,312,190
Annual manufacturing costs ($)	1,844,435	866,850	641,990	4,823,940	8,176,140
Daily manufacturing costs ($)	5,589	2,626	1,945	14,618	24,778
Sugars cost (c/lb)	1.17	0.55	0.41	3.07	5.2

cell viability. The centrifuge overflow will contain a small concentration of cells. Removal of these cells prior to hydrolysis is assumed unnecessary because *T. viride* will not grow at the hydrolysis temperature. However, further study of other possible problems of microbial contamination in the hydrolysis system is needed.

Spent solids from the hydrolyzer following filtration are fed to a furnace and steam-power plant to provide process steam and electricity for the process. A substantial excess of energy is available in the spent solids, sufficient to operate an alcohol fermentation plant, for example, and to produce some additional by-product power. No credit is assumed for this excess energy in the processing cost analysis described below. For the process described above, a preliminary cost estimate was made for the required capital investment and cost per pound of sugars produced in aqueous solution.

The fixed capital cost is estimated as a multiple of purchased cost of the principal items of equipment. In the present case a multiplier of 3.1 was used, except in the case of the concrete digesters for which the multiple was reduced to 1.68 because the unit cost already included engineering construction and contractor's fees. The total manufacturing cost is broken down into investment related costs, labor related costs, utilities costs, and raw material costs. Taxes are omitted on the assumption that the installation would be part of a municipal waste processing complex. No charge or credit has been assigned to the newsprint. Costs of process steam and power were estimated assuming that they could be generated on the plant site using spent solids as fuel. Capital costs for steam power facilities are not included in the fixed capital costs on the assumption that the specified unit costs for steam and electricity include both investment and labor charges. An on-stream efficiency of 90% is assumed, corresponding to 330 days operation per calendar year.

The resulting fixed capital cost, total manufacturing costs and costs per unit of product are listed in Table 3 for each of the major processing sections: (1) hydrolysis, (2) pretreatment, (3) enzyme recovery, and (4) enzyme make-up.

For the base case a fixed capital cost of $23,390,000 and a sugar cost of 5.2 cents/ lb is obtained. Enzyme make-up is the major cost factor, comprising nearly 60% of the total. Cysewski and Wilke studied the continuous fermentation of glucose with *Saccharomyces cerevisiae* and have made a preliminary process design and cost estimate for the production of ethanol and torula yeast from the enzymatic hydrolyzate

TABLE 4

Ethanol Fermentation Design Basis

Sugar concentration	14.3%, 70% Fermentable
Dilution rate	0.17
Temperature	35°C
Cell yield factor, Y(X/S)	0.1
Ethanol yield factor, Y(P/S)	0.465

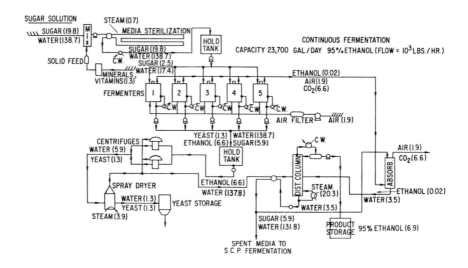

FIGURE 5.   Flow diagram for ethanol product.

of newsprint. Some results of their study will be reviewed briefly. More detailed information is available in the original report.[10]

The fermentation process was designed to produce 24,000 gal of 95% ethanol per day from the sugars produced from newsprint hydrolysis (Figure 4).

The design basis is shown in Table 4. The hydrolysis product was found to be 70% fermentable by *Saccharomyces*, thus requiring a 14.3% solution of hydrolyzate sugars to obtain the optimum feed of 10% fermentable sugars. Preliminary cost analysis showed it economically favorable to concentrate the sugar to 14.3%. The concentration costs of 2.7 cents/gal of ethanol produced (see below) is more than offset by the savings in fermentation and distillation costs. A computer process model was used to design and optimize the ethanol fermentation plant and a single cell protein process which consumes the residual sugars left after the alcohol fermentation.

Figure 5 shows a schematic flow diagram of the ethanol fermentation process. The evaporator which concentrates the hydrolyzate sugar solution is not shown, although it has been included in the process analysis.

After the hydrolyzate sugars have been evaporatively concentrated from 4.0% to 14.3% solution, protein and mineral supplements are mixed with the sugars. Sterilized by steam injection, the fermentation broth is distributed to five continuous fermenters, each operating at a dilution rate of 0.17 hr^{-1}. A low flow of air (8.0 × 10^4 vvm) is sparged through the fermenters to maintain the oxygen tension at the optimum level of 0.07 mmHg. The fermented beer then passes to two continuous centrifuges and the yeast is removed. The yeast is subsequently dried and stored for sale as a protein feed

TABLE 5

Capital Investment Summary

	10^6	% of total
Sugar concentration	0.58	10.8
Alcohol fermentation	2.36	43.9
Distillation	0.39	7.3
SCP fermentation	2.04	3.80
Total	5.37	100.00

supplement. The clarified beer from the centrifuges is next distilled to concentrate the ethanol to 95wt%. An absorber using the distillate bottoms as the absorbing liquid is employed to recover ethanol lost in the exit gases (air and CO_2) from the fermenters. The ethanol rich stream from the absorber is also fed to the main distillation unit for final ethanol recovery.

Saccharomyces cerevisiae used in the ethanol fermentation will ferment only 70% of the reducing sugars in the hydrolyzate. The remaining 30% of the sugars (xylose and cellobiose) are fed to an aerobic fermentation process to produce single cell protein from a torula yeast. Although torula yeasts will ferment the remaining sugars, it is a facultative aerobe and does not produce ethanol.

The single cell protein fermentation, although not shown, resembles the alcohol fermentation process excluding the distillation and absorption columns. Of course the aeration and agitation rates are much higher for the production of cell mass. Also the fermenters were operated at a total pressure of 2.6 at to enhance the oxygen transfer.* After the yeast has been removed from the broth by centrifugation, the yeast stream is spray dried and packaged for sale.

A preliminary cost estimate was made for the above mentioned ethanol and SCP fermentation processes to determine the required capital investment and cost per gallon of 95% ethanol.

The sugar cost was taken at a base cost of 5.2 cents/lb as presented above. The steam and power costs were estimated assuming that they would be generated using spent solids from the hydrolysis process as fuel.

The fixed capital costs for the overall process are shown in Table 5. A total fixed capital of 5.37×10^6 is required to produce 24,000 gal/day of 95% ethanol from the hydrolyzate sugars. A breakdown of ethanol production costs is shown in Table 6. Of the $1.05/gal production cost, 68.6% is related to the sugar cost of 5.2 cents/lb.

The importance of sugar cost in the SCP fermentation is shown in Table 6. The sugar cost amounts to 39% of the yeast production cost of 30.0 cents/lb. A somewhat heavy charge is made for nutrient supplements in the SCP process. The nutrient requirement was based on the yeast cell mass composition assuming no vitamin or protein components are in the hydrolyzate sugars. These media supplement costs would be reduced if agricultural or municipal wastes, which contain many vitamins and minerals, were hydrolyzed instead of the newsprint used in the base design case.

The above costs for ethanol and SCP should be considered within the context of the particular cellulose processing scheme, of which they would be a part. Such an analysis is presented elsewhere,[10] in which alcohol is taken as the primary product resulting from enzymatic hydrolysis of newsprint, and cost credits are estimated for by-product yeast and electrical power.

---

* These conditions were found to be optimal for the SCP fermentation from a computer model of the fermentation process.

TABLE 6

Processing Cost Distribution — Ethanol Production

	c/gal 95% ETOH	Percent of total
Sugar concentration	2.7	2.6
Fermentation	5.4	5.1
Distillation	2.5	2.4
Yeast recovery	1.0	1.0
Raw materials	21.4	18.3
Sugar	72.2	68.6
Total	105.2	100

3. Other Fermentable Wastes

Much work has been done on the biological conversion of forest residues, wood chips, bark, sawdust, etc. using both aerobic and anaerobic systems. The intractability of lignin in such systems has proved to be a stumbling block. Research is underway at several universities to develop biological systems to which lignin will be susceptible.

III. THERMAL PROCESSES

A. General Considerations

There are several ways in which thermal energy or combustible fuels may be obtained from waste materials. Among these are:

1. Direct combustion (incineration) of combustible waste or the combustible portion of waste with heat recovery, usually as process steam
2. Cofiring of refuse derived fuel (RDF) with other fuels in central power stations
3. Partial oxidation of waste to produce combustible gases and liquids
4. Flash pyrolysis of waste to produce combustible gases and liquids
5. Thermal cracking of molten thermoplastics to produce combustible gases and liquids

All of these systems have been successfully operated, some on a commercial scale, others on a pilot plant scale.

B. Direct Combustion

Several incinerator type units have been installed in the U.S. Many of these are used only to dispose of trash. The trend now, however, is to recover heat from these units in the form of process steam. Large installations generally use waterwall incinerators and generate steam at 150 to 175 psig. One of the more sophisticated units of this type in the Northwest Incinerator Plant of the City of Chicago. This plant processes 1000 tons/day of municipal refuse and generates 150 psig steam. The economic viability of such a unit depends upon the ability to sell the steam. However, the main purpose of such plants is to dispose of municipal refuse and the overall economics is of secondary importance. These plants must be equipped with electrostatic precipitators and scrubbers to remove particulates, and sulfur and nitrogen oxides. The incoming refuse receives absolute minimal screening. Noncombustibles discharged from the incinerator grate pass through a magnetic separator to remove ferrous metals which are sold. The remaining noncombustibles are trucked to a landfill.

There are many types of direct combustion units which are equipped with waste heat

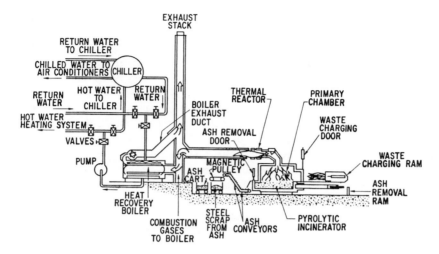

FIGURE 6.   Kelley pyrolytic incinerator.

boilers. One of these is made by the Kelley Co. of Milwaukee, Wis. This system is unusual in that it incorporates two-stage combustion, which they refer to as pyrolytic incineration, and provides both hot water and chilled water. A flow diagram for this unit is shown in Figure 6. Solid waste is pushed into the pyrolytic incinerator at the far right when the waste-charging door to the primary chamber rises. Burned under low oxygen conditions, the waste generates a gas that rises with the smoke into the thermal reactor (right center). There both gas and smoke are burned, thus preventing air pollution. The hot air that remains is drawn through the heat recovery boiler (bottom left), and returns to the exhaust stack. Water heated in the boiler is fed either to the heating system in cold weather or to the absorption chiller (upper left) for air conditioning in warm weather.

C. Cofiring of RDF

Refuse derived fuel is essentially the cellulosic portion of urban waste and is shredded to a maximum size of about 1 in. This material may be cofired with other fuels in boilers if the necessary adaptations are made to the boilers. The RDF is pneumatically transported and injected into the firebox. If the point of cofiring is close to the source of RDF, no further treatment is required. Several manufacturers make forms of RDF which can be stored and shipped. Among these firms are Combustion Equipment Associates, National Center for Resource Recovery, and Occidental Research Corp. The Browning-Ferris Co., Houston, Tex., has made tests of cofiring RDF in cement kilns.

D. Partial Oxidation

1. Types of Reactors

Partial oxidation is usually, and erroneously, referred to as pyrolysis. In true pyrolysis no combustion of the material takes place. All heat for the process is supplied from external sources and no products of combustion are mixed with the process off-gas. In partial oxidation processes a portion of the feed material is burned and the hot gases heat the balance of the feed to a temperature where thermal decomposition (pyrolysis) occurs. The pyrolysis gases are mixed with the combustion gases.

Pyrolysis is a complex process of simultaneous and consecutive chemical reactions. While a complete description of the specific reaction types occurring has not been determined, it is generally believed that reactions such as crosslinking, isomerization, deoxygenation, denitrogenation, etc., do occur. The reactive portion of the solid waste is composed primarily of cellulosic material. Decomposition starts to occur at about 360°F (182°C), producing a mixture of solids, liquid, and gas, the proportions and composition depending on reactor conditions and environment.

Pyrolysis reactors have been designed to handle a variety of refuse feedstock conditions and therefore may be adapted to agricultural biomass. Conceptually, a system may be designed to handle either a raw feed or a preprocessed feed. The preprocessing decisions are dictated by characteristics of the feedstock, but will also have a direct effect on required reactor equipment such as feed and discharge devices, etc. In general, a dried, finely shredded feedstock is most desirable from a reaction viewpoint.

Several basic reactor types have been used for pyrolysis reactions. The most common can be classified as follows: (1) shaft, (2) rotary kiln, and (3) fluidized bed.

Shaft reactors (horizontal and vertical) are conceptually the simplest and lowest in capital cost. In the vertical type, the feed material is fed into the top of the reactor and settles into the reactor under its own weight. Generated pyrolysis gases pass upward through the shaft and are removed from the top. Typical feed mechanisms include screw conveyors, rotary devices, and rams.

The horizontal shaft type incorporates a feed conveyor system through the reactor housing. Feedstock is thus continuously pyrolyzed from the conveyor system. Feed and discharge problems are minimized but reliability of conveyors at elevated temperatures can be a problem. Both types of vessels are constructed of metal capable of withstanding high temperatures or are lined with a refractory material.

The rotary kiln is a rotating cylinder usually slightly inclined to the horizontal. Feed material is charged into one end of the kiln and progresses through the kiln by means of rotation and slope of the cylinder to the opposite end where it is discharged. The metal cylinder is normally lined with a refractory brick. The rotary kiln has mixing advantages over the shaft type reactor, but the sealing of the rotating cylinder from the stationary feed and discharge ports can be a problem.

The fluidized bed reactor consists of a bed of solid particles (e.g., sand) suspended by an upward flowing gas stream. For pyrolysis applications, the solid particles are heated and serve as the heat source for the pyrolysis reactions. A chemical reaction involving the solid particles may occur. The major advantage over other reactor types is improved heat transfer and temperature control. The primary drawbacks include erosion and carry-over problems associated with the solid particles, gas velocity control, and solids transfer and separation problems.

Table 7 lists 24 pyrolysis projects in progress or completed (1974). The status of each project is indicated.

2. Union Carbide Purox Process

The Union Carbide Purox process is one of partial oxidation where combustion is supported by 95% pure oxygen. This is high temperature process which gives a medium Btu gas (approximately 300 Btu/Scf) and a slagging ash. Aside from the advantages of a medium Btu gas, the process results in a minimum formation of nitrogen oxides. These can be formed only from nitrogenous material present in the solids feed. The reactor is the vertical downflow type with a lock mechanism for feed. Another advantage of this system is that raw urban waste with minimum preparation (such as removing old refrigerators, hot water tanks, and other ferrous metal) can be fed to the reactor. The disadvantage of the system is, of course, the cost of providing pure oxygen.

Figure 7 is a flow diagram for this process with a material balance shown for one standard module (350 tons/day).

As illustrated in Figure 7, municipal refuse is charged at the top of a shaft furnace

TABLE 7

Pyrolysis Reactor Classifications

	Heating Method		Product distribution				Feed conditions		Reactor temperature °C	Status		
	Direct	Indirect	Solid (Btu/lb)	Liquid (Btu/lb)	Gas (Btu/Ft³)	Raw	Size reduction	Separation		Research	Pilot plant (TPD)	Commercial (TPD)
Vertical shaft												
Garrett		X	9,700	10,500	550		X	X	900		4	200
Batelle		X			170		X		1800		2	
Ga. Tech.	X		10,000	13,000	200		X		750		25	
URDC	X				150	X			2600		120	
Torrax	X				150	X			3000		75	
Union Carbide	X				300	X			3000		5	200
Horizontal shaft												
Kemp		X	X	X	X		X		1100		5	
Barber-Colman		X			500		X	X	1200		1	
Rotary kiln												
Monsanto	X		2,500		130		X		1800		35	1,000
Devco	X		X		X		X	X	1000		120	1,500
Rust Eng.		X			450				1250			260
Pan Am Res.		X					X		200	X		
Fluid bed												
W. Virginia		X			450		X	X	1400	X		
A. D. Little		X			X		X	X	1400	X		
Coors	X				150		X	X	1400		1	
Other												
Battelle		X							1800	X		
Hercules			X							X		
Bur. Mines	X				500		X	X	1800	X		
NYU	X								1700	X		
USC	X									X		
Anti Poll. Syst.		X								X		
Univ. Calif.		X					X			X		
Wallace-Atkins		X	3,000	16,000	500		X		1600	X		
Res. Sci.		X					X		1800		2	

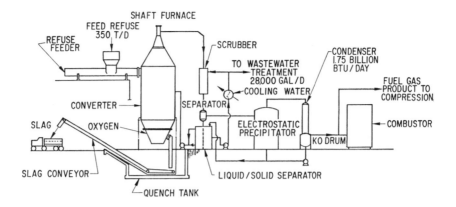

FIGURE 7.   Purox module flow diagram.

and is pyrolyzed as it passes downward through the furnace. Oxygen enters the furnace through tuyeres near the furnace bottom and passes upward through a 1425 to 1650°C (2600 to 3000°F) combustion zone. The products of combustion then pass through a pyrolysis zone and exit at about 93°C (200°F). The off-gas then passes through an electrostatic precipitator to remove the fly ash and oil formed during pyrolysis, both of which are recycled to the furnace combustion zone. The gas then passes through an acid absorber and a condenser. The clean fuel gas has a heating value of about 2.7 cal/cm³ (300 Btu/ft³) and a flame temperature equivalent to that of natural gas. As the solid waste passes downward through the furnace, it contacts the exiting pyrolysis products and traps a portion of the oil and fly ash while itself losing moisture. After passing through the pyrolysis and combustion zones, the remaining solid waste is removed as a slag from the furnace bottom.

The Purox system has a net thermal efficiency of about 65% in converting solid waste to fuel gas. Process losses include energy losses in the conversion process and energy required for the operation of the onsite cryogenic gas separation unit which produces 95% pure oxygen for use in the system.

Table 8 describes the composition of the clean fuel gas. This gas is low in sulfur (about 15 ppm) and essentially free of nitrogen oxides. It can be burned in existing utility plants or by other large fuel consumers as an auxiliary fuel without contributing to corrosion of the boiler or undesirable stack emissions.

Process residues from a 350 ton/day system include granulated metal and glass from the quench tank and about 28,000 gal/day of condensed water containing organics that must be treated or discharged to a sanitary sewer.

Most other vertical shaft reactors are similar to the Union Carbide unit except that they use air for combustion. This causes more formation of nitrogen oxides which must be removed from the gases produced.

3. Multiple Hearth Reactors

An example of this type of unit, which is based on the well-known Nichols-Hereschoff furnace, is one developed by Garrett Research Corp.

This type of equipment has been successfully employed for continuous high temperature processing in the chemical and metallurgical industries for over 100 years. It consists of several vertically stacked compartments with a common central shaft. Rabble teeth are mounted on arms attached to a central shaft, whose slow rotation imparts a positive mechanical motion to the solid material on each hearth. The downcomers

TABLE 8

Purox System Fuel Gas Composition

Component	Vol %
CO	50
H_2	30
CO_2	15
CH_4	3
C_2H_x	1
N_2	1
	100

through which the solid drops onto the hearth below are located alternately near the inner and outer periphery. They may have star valves for good sealing. The hearths are sufficiently isolated to enable the conditions at each hearth to be optimized for its particular function. Since the solid is spread in a thin layer with some constant raking and tumbling action, the residence time is adjustable, and efficient solid-gas heat- and mass-transfer are achieved. For these reasons the multiple-hearth furnace is well suited for thermally processing biomass materials that are usually moist, fibrous, sticky, and susceptible to ash fusion at high temperature.

In the Garrett process high thermal efficiency is obtained by:

1. Double-effect drying, in which most of the latent heat of evaporation of the moisture content of the raw material is usefully recovered in a second, vacuum drying stage.
2. Multi-stage processing with the heat for pyrolysis being supplied by the combustion of char in a separate ompartment — thus, the gaseous products of pyrolysis are not diluted by combustion flue gas (unlike many partial oxidation systems), and the Btu content is considerably higher.
3. Heat exchange is obtained among the appropriate streams, e.g., the combustion air is preheated by hot ash and flue gas.

A simplified flow diagram of the process is given in Figure 8. The raw material may be first chopped and mechanically dewatered if necessary. It is then loaded into a hopper and conveyed to the top of the multiple-hearth converter by means of a jacketed screw conveyor. The material is partially dried under a modest vacuum by moist flue gas flowing countercurrently through the conveyor jacket and screw, and condensing inside it. The conveyor has star valves at each end to maintain a good seal and may have a hollow screw to provide a larger surface area for heat transfer.

One or more of the uppermost hearths are devoted to direct-contact drying by hot flue gas from the combustion zone. The material, with a moisture content of about 5%, falls to the pyrolysis hearth. Here it gets heated mainly by hot char from the combustion zone, and also by the hot gases accompanying the char. The char is introduced through an external steam lift in which some synthesis gas and the gaseous products of pyrolysis are cooled and condensed. The tar (water-insoluble portion of the condensate) may be recycled to the pyrolysis zone.

Char from the pyrolysis zone drops onto the combustion hearth where it is burned to generate steam. The hot flue gas preheats the incoming air in an external heat exchanger, then goes to the drying section at the top. Most of the hot char is directed back to the pyrolysis zone, while the rest drops to the clean-up burner where it is

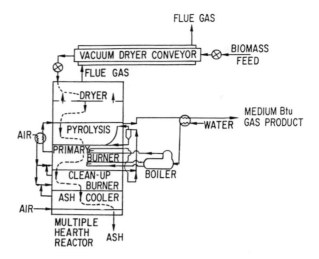

FIGURE 8.   Gas production by the Garrett Energy Research and Engineering Company multiple hearth pyrolysis process.

completely burned. The ash drops to the lowest hearth where it is cooled by incoming air which is preheated. The ash is then discharged from the reactor for disposal.

The gas leaving the condensate collector may either be utilized directly or sent to a scrubber in which H_2S, CO_2, and moisture are removed. This product gas may be piped for use at a nearby industrial plant, or blended into a natural gas pipeline. The only by-product is ash which could have application as a fertilizer or source of chemicals.

E. Rotary Kiln Reactors

The best known of these is the Landgard process developed by Monsanto Chemical Company. This system consists of a receiving and shredding process followed by storage of the shredded material in an Atlas style silo. The shredded refuse is then conveyed at a constant rate to the pyrolysis reactor. The decomposition of the organic matter is controlled at 1200°F gas and 2000°F residue temperatures. Produced gases move countercurrent to the burning waste stream and exit the reactor at the feed end.

In this process the reactor residue is water quenched and then flotation separated into carbon char, ferrous metal, and glass aggregate products. The only commercial operation of this type was installed by the city of Baltimore. Major problems were encountered in the operation of this unit. These problems have not yet been completely resolved.

F. Pyrolysis
1. General Considerations

Many continuous pyrolysis units have been proposed which rely upon heat transfer through metal walls. These may be considered to be "sustained" or "slow" pyrolysis units as distinguished from "flash" pyrolysis. The difference between the two types is the residence time of the solids in the pyrolysis zone. One of the few sustained pyrolysis units which is offered commercially is produced by the Enterprise Company.

2. The Enterprise Pyrolysis System

The Enterprise process is unique in that the pyrolytic reactors are designed for opti-

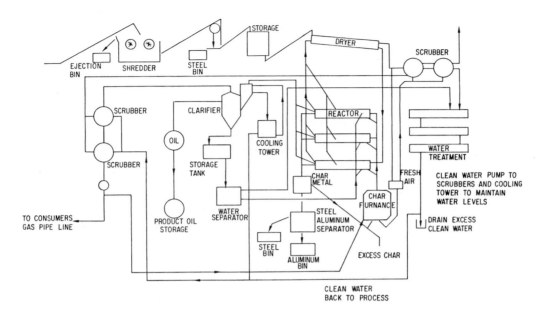

FIGURE 9.   Flow diagram.

mum temperature control so that the yield is in the form of three marketable by-products, pipeline quality gas (approximately 1000 Btu/cf), medium weight industrial fuel oil, and a high Btu char. The reactor's capability, coupled with a "front-end" subsystem for resource recovery, make the total system a profitable operation. The oil yield averages 1.25 bbl/ton of refuse and has a Btu value between 15,000 and 17,000 per pound. The gas averages 5000 Scf/ton of refuse and has a Btu range of 900 to 1100 per Scf. The char by-product averages about 400 lb/ton and has about 8000 Btu/lb.

Figure 9 is a flow diagram for the system. Refuse collection vehicles dump their loads on a level concrete dumping floor where a "front-end" loader pushes the waste into a pit that is approximately 4 ft deep and 6 ft wide. A conveyer transports the waste material to the top of the shredder.

A platform is provided on each side of the conveyer. Workers stand on each platform to ensure that engine blocks, steel cable, pieces of industrial steel, etc. do not proceed into the shredder. Winch devices are provided to assist in lifting out heavy items. The conveyer may be manually controlled by these men.

Prior to entering the feed chute into the shredder the waste material passes under a unit called a floating feeder. This unit resembles a large steel paddle wheel that is the same width as the conveyer belt. It is spring mounted and free to raise or lower. It is separately powered and equipped with sensors for automatic control of conveyer operation. Its primary function is to provide an even flow of waste material into the shredder.

The shredder reduces incoming solid waste to a −4 in. particle size, including washers, dryers, and refrigerators. Because of its dual rotor design, there is no need for a secondary shredding system. One rotor has 32 hard-faced free swinging hammers and the other has 28. The hammers are arranged on each rotor in a spiral pattern so that only two hammers are at the point of impact with the waste material at any one time. Operations of this shredder is smoother and requires less hammer maintenance than is experienced on conventional shredders. These shredders are powered with four motors that are started with a sequential start control system. A spring loaded tramp material reject chute is incorporated in each shredder. If a sorter should miss a motor block, it would kick out through the reject chute and prevent damage to the dual rotor hammers.

From the dual rotor shredder, the processed material is gravity fed into a shredder discharge conveyor, which transports it to a magnetic separator chute and housing assembly. At this point approximately 90% of ferrous metals are extracted and diverted to containers for storage until delivery to a scrap metal processor. A drum type magnetic separator is used along with a blower in the separation process.

After leaving the ferrous metal separation point, the remaining waste stream fraction is transported on a steel belted, elevating conveyor to a drag type distribution conveyor. Both of these conveyors have the same width as the conveyors described. Each conveyor has its own motor and drive system controlled automatically through the central control panel. The purpose of the drag type distribution conveyor is to distribute the waste evenly into several storage modules. This conveyor is equipped with sensors and a control so that a preselected level of refuse is always maintained in each storage module.

Each storage and feed module consists of three rectangular shaped bins measuring 8 ft × 8 ft × 100 ft long. These bins are stacked on top of each other and each bin is equipped with a bottom that is a steel belted conveyor powered with an individual motor. In operation, the top bin feeds to the middle bin which in turn feeds down to the first or bottom bin. The bottom bin feeds into a transfer conveyor that is in a pit under all of the storage and feed modules. Each bin in the module has the capacity for storing 50 tons of refuse and since each has a conveyor bottom, the constant movement eliminates any bridging or packing.

The primary purpose of the storage module is to store and feed shredded waste to the continuously operating pyrolysis section of the plant. The grinding or "front-end" part of the plant is in operation only 8 hr a day for 6 days a week whereas the "back-end" is designed to operate 7 days a week on a 24-hr basis. The number of storage modules needed is regulated by the capacity of the plant. Generally, storage capacity is based on 1 days' in-feed requirements to the reactors.

A transfer conveyor receives the shredded waste from the bottom of the storage and feed modules and conveys it to a distribution conveyor for feeding into the cylindrical rotary dryers. The transfer and distribution conveyors are less wide than the pit and feed conveyors (approximately 48 in. wide). They are steel belted and are individually powered and equipped with automatic controls through the central control panel. The drag type distribution conveyor is designed to maintain an even flow of shredded waste into each dryer.

The cylindrical rotating dryers function to reduce the solid waste moisture content to approximately 7%. Movement through the dryers is by gravity. Hydraulic ram lifts at one end of the dryer automatically adjusts the tilt of the rotating drum, thus controlling the feed of the shredded refuse into each reactor's infeed conveyor. Excess heat taken from the reactor is used for operation of the dryers. Moisture-saturated air is vented from the rotating dryers to flue gas scrubbers, where the moisture is removed and the clean air exhausted to the atmosphere.

Enclosed steel belted conveyors take the dried waste from the dryers and feed it into the inlet ends of the pyrolytic reactors. Each of these conveyors is equipped with a hydraulically operated ram to ensure even feeding into the reactor.

The pyrolysis reactor is manufactured in two sizes. For plants up to 400 tpd capacity, 50 tpd reactors are used. Larger plants, 600 tpd and up to the largest 1800 tpd size, use the 200 tpd reactors. Each reactor consists of two coaxial cylindrical chambers with a screw type conveyor to transport the shredded waste material through the inner cylinder where it is subjected to controlled temperatures in an oxygen-free environment. This action converts the reactive portion of the waste to a gaseous state; the remaining material is reduced to a char. Each reactor is designed to operate independently of the others in the event one or more have to be shut down for maintenance.

To maintain adequate temperatures in the reactor (normal range is 1000 to 1400°F) a char furnace is provided. The furnace provides heat for the reactors and the rotary tumble dryers. Flue gas scrubbers are provided to control air pollution. Char from the reactor is passed over a secondary magnet to remove residual ferrous metal. The char and heat process system for each reactor consists of:

1.   A char and metal separator consisting of a steel shaker conveyor. Following this unit in the stream is an air classifier to separate char from glass, sand and other heavier materials.
2.   The separated metals pass over a secondary drum type magnetic separator to remove any ferrous metals that were missed during the primary ferrous metal separation function. The remaining metals will consist of the nonferrous category.
3.   A screw type auger conveyor, completely enclosed, transports the char to the kiln where it is used as the energy source to maintain the reactor's operating temperatures.
4.   The char kilns are designed to fire primarily with char. However, provisions have been incorporated so that either the process gas or commercial natural gas can be burned. Under normal conditions, the process is started with natural gas and when operating temperatures have been reached, char is introduced and takes over as the prime energy source.
5.   Insulated ducting is provided to furnish heat to the reactor's screw conveyor shaft and to the reactor's outer heat area. The heat exhausting from the reactor is ducted to the inlet of the rotary dryer.
6.   Flue gas wet scrubbers receive all excess hot air for cleanup prior to venting to the atmosphere.

The plant includes a gas processor that is sized to correspond with the total rated capacity of the plant. The gas processor system consists of:

1.   Heat exchangers to separate the hydrocarbon fluids from the pyrolytic gases.
2.   Clarifier tanks to separate the oil from water and to pull off any sludges. The water is routed to a treatment process unit while the sludges are returned to the input end of the pyrolytic reactor.
3.   Wet gas scrubbers to clean the pyrolytic gas and to furnish a source of vacuum for the process. Each scrubber is equipped with Venturi nozzles for this purpose.
4.   Vapor eliminators to remove moisture from the gases.
5.   Dry filter units to further clean and dewater the gases to make it suitable for industrial use.
6.   Cooling towers to supply water for the system's heat exchangers.
7.   An oil storage tank sized to store oil produced during four days of operations.
8.   A water treatment facility that will physically and chemically process all contaminated water generated by the system to make it suitable for reuse or disposal. After treatment, most of the water is recycled back for reuse in the gas processor, flue gas scrubbers, and the cooling tower. Any remaining "cleaned" water is piped to a drain or it may be used for plant property cleaning or irrigation.

3. Occidental Flash Pyrolysis System
This is a complicated system that is very similar in appearance to an oil refinery.

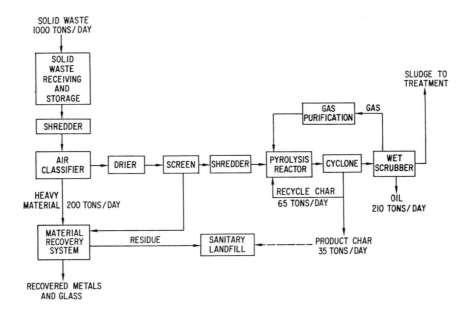

FIGURE 10.   Occidental flash pyrolysis system.

The received refuse is first coarsely shredded and the ferrous metals removed with magnets. From here the refuse is air classified to remove the light fraction, consisting of organic materials. The organic fraction is then dried and receives secondary shredding to produce a finer feed before introduction into the flash pyrolysis reactor. The air classified heavy fraction, comprised primarily of inorganic materials, is then processed to recover glass and nonferrous metals. The unrecovered solids, about 8% by weight, are then collected for landfill.

The light organic fraction when leaving the second set of shredders resembles vacuum cleaner bag fluff. After the moisture content has been reduced, it is carried into the flash pyrolysis reactor by recycled product gas. The pyrolysis takes place at about 950°F. Upon leaving the reactor the solid residue (char) is separated from the product vapors by cyclone separators. The char is then combusted with air and the resulting hot ash is recycled to supply the heat in the reactor.

Following separation of the solids, the pyrolytic product vapors are quenched rapidly for separation into pyrolytic oil, gas, and water. The water is then routed through a cleaning unit to make it suitable for sewage disposal. The gas is recycled to the reactor leaving the oil as the only saleable product.

The oil yield, about 1 bbl/ton of refuse, is similar in consistency to roofing tar and has to be heated to 160°F for pipeline transport. The Btu value for this oil is about 10,600 per pound. Current plans are to use this oil as a supplemental fuel with No. 6 industrial fuel oil. A flow diagram for this system is shown in Figure 10.

The properties of the pyrolytic oil are shown in Table 9. The effect of 0.3% chlorine, ash, and the organic acids present in the oil on corrosion have not been determined.

Residues from 1000 ton/day plant include any unrecycled solid waste inerts, 68 tons of solid residue in slurry form from the scrubber, and about 27,000 gal of process water high in biological oxygen demand (BOD) and methyl chloride that must be treated.

TABLE 9

Typical Properties of Garrett Pyrolytic Oil

Carbon (wt %)	57.5
Oxygen (wt %)	33.4
Hydrogen (wt %)	7.6
Nitrogen (wt %)	0.9
Chlorine (wt %)	0.3
Sulfur (wt %)	0.1—0.3
Ash (wt %)	0.2—0.4
Cal/gram	5,830
Btu/pound	10,500
Sp. gr.	1.30
Pour point, °C (°F)	32 (90)
Flash point, °C (°F)	56 (133)
Viscosity SSU @ 88°C (180°F)	3,150
Pumping temperature, °C (°F)	71 (160)
Atomizing temperature, °C (°F)	116 (240)

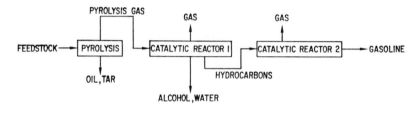

FIGURE 11.   Basic chemical conversion scheme.

4. Arizona State University Flash Pyrolysis System

This system, which is now at the pilot plant stage, is probably the most sophisticated of the flash pyrolysis units.[11] It is designed to convert cellulosic waste material and polymeric waste material to gasoline. This is an advanced concept, third generation pilot plant. Second generation processes are just now reaching the demonstration scale phase, e.g., Occidental Research Corp. at El Cajon, Calif., with EPA funding (thermal approach) and Waste Management, Inc., at Pompano Beach, Fla., with DOE funding (biological approach).

The research in progress at Arizona State University falls into a third generation category. Here, gas from a thermal conversion step is converted into materials with higher value and enhanced market flexibility. The desired products are equivalents of current commercial liquid fuel products, i.e., *not* a fuel alternative such as alcohol blends ("Gasohol"), etc. The analogy to a petroleum refinery is apparent. Projects in the third generation category are all in the research and development stage at the present time.

The conversion system consists of thermal gasification (pyrolysis) and liquid fuels synthesis steps (Figure 11). All units are operated continuously. System capacity is about 25 lb/hr of solids feedstock. Products yields of 20 to 100 gal liquid fuel per ton feedstock are to be expected, depending on type of feedstock and operating conditions.

The pyrolysis system consists of a dual fluidized bed arrangement (pyrolyzer, combustor) where one bed is operated as a gasifier and the other as a heat source for a solids medium continuously transferred between the two beds. Both inert and catalytic solids media are under investigation. The primary advantages of the fluidized bed in

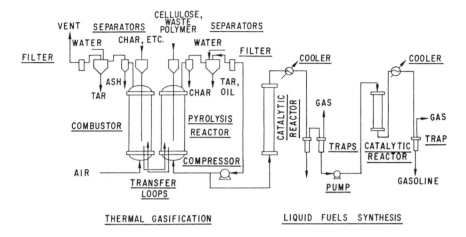

FIGURE 12.   Conversion system schematic.

this application are efficient heat transfer and continuous catalyst regeneration. The dual system minimizes the possibility of contamination of the pyrolysis gas with combustion products. Several solids feeder configurations are used (dependent on feedstock). The control element in each case is either a rotary valve or screw. The overhead system on both the pyrolyzer and combustor consists of a cyclone separator (particle remover), cyclone scrubber (cooler and tar removal) and filter (solid fines removal). Some pyrolysis gas is recirculated to the pyrolyzer via a compressor while the balance is fed to the liquid fuels system. Combustor gas is vented.

The liquid fuels system consists of a fluidized bed catalytic reactor (CATALYTIC REACTOR 1) and a fixed bed catalytic reactor (CATALYTIC REACTOR 2). The fluidized bed utilitizes a Fischer-Tropsch type catalyst. The fluidized bed is used in this application to achieve good temperature control (exothermic reaction). A two-phase liquid product is obtained: (1) water-alcohol, and (2) paraffinic hydrocarbon. The hydrocarbon phase is a candidate for a paraffinic fuel such as kerosene but lacks the structural complexity for a high octane rating. If a high octane gasoline is desired, the paraffinic hydrocarbon phase is processed in the fixed bed reactor where the desired reforming reactions are introduced. Auxiliary equipment for the liquid fuels reactors includes condensers, traps and a liquid feed pump (for the reforming step). A flow diagram of the process is depicted in Figure 12.

Feedstocks under investigation include the organic fraction of municipal refuse, kelp residue, synthetic polymers and agricultural biomass sources. A typical pyrolysis gas composition (cellulose source) is as follows:

C_2H_4	5—15 mol %
CO	35—45
H_2	10—20
CH_4	10—15
C_2H_6	1—5
CO_2	15—30

Typical gas phase yields are 75 to 85% (feedstock to gas). Reactor temperatures in the 500 to 1000°C range have been explored with pressure at 0 to 5 psig. The particular composition (and gas phase yields) will vary with feedstock type and operating conditions such as reactor temperature, solids feedrate, etc. Studies in progress include an assessment of the effect of catalysts on pyrolysis gas composition and yields.

TABLE 10

Liquid Hydrocarbons Analysis — Liquid Fuels System

Grouped composition analysis (wt %)

Sample	Straight chain		Unsaturated straight chain		Branched chain		Cyclo-paraffins	Aromatics	Unknowns	Specific gravity	ASTM 10% (°F)	ASTM 90% (°F)	Octane number
	C_3–C_7	C_7+	C_3–C_7	C_7+	C_3–C_7	C_7+							
CAT. RX1 product	15.0	34.4	2.0	5.6	5.1	16.8	0.9	6.3	13.9	0.753	138	494	52
CAT. RX2 Product (CAT. A)	27.8	19.9	0.0	0.0	11.2	8.4	0.6	22.1	10.0	0.744	52	428	82
CAT. RX2 Product (CAT. B)	11.2	13.7	0.0	0.0	14.4	8.4	0.4	46.1	5.8	0.792	106	349	115
Chevron unleaded	14.1	6.3	0.0	0.0	23.3	19.9	1.5	29.9	5.0	0.745	88	340	85
JP-4 jet fuel	10.1	23.8	0.0	0.0	10.1	16.5	2.2	19.8	17.5	0.765	160	448	65

The pyrolysis gas is passed to the liquid fuels synthesis reactors with minimum treatment (solid fines, liquids, and tar removal). The product composition from the fluidized bed catalytic reactor (CATALYTIC REACTOR 1) is insensitive to changes in operating conditions (temperature, pressure, catalyst loading, feed composition) for a fixed catalyst type. However, liquid hydrocarbon yields are directly affected. Reactor temperatures up to 300°C have been explored with pressure limited to a maximum of 125 psig. The hydrocarbon/water phase product ratio is about 10/1 on a volumetric basis. The water phase contains about 15% (wt.) low molecular weight alcohols. The hydrocarbon phase contains about 45 to 55% (wt.) saturated straight chain hydrocarbons, 5 to 10% unsaturated straight chain hydrocarbons, 20 to 25% branched straight chain hydrocarbons, and 5 to 10% cycloparaffins and aromatics. Liquid product yields are in the 20 to 100 gal/ton pyrolysis feedstock range (depending on pyrolysis gas composition). This material probably could be tailored to match paraffinic fuels such as kerosene and diesel. It is unsuitable, however, as an internal combustion engine fuel due to low octane rating (roughly 50). The required structural complexity (and thus high octane) is achieved in the fixed bed catalytic reactor (CATALYTIC REACTOR 2). Here, heat effects are fairly mild allowing for the use of the relatively simple fixed bed. Hydrocracking and aromatics production dominate with aromatic compositions of up to 50% wt observed in the product (corresponding to an octane rating of about 115). In general, octane rating increases for increased reactor temperatures, pressures, are 300 to 500°C with pressures in the 400 to 600 psig range. Product yields (volume product per volume liquid feed) are in the 50 to 70% range for an acceptable octane rating (80 to 100).

Example liquid hydrocarbon analyses for the liquid fuels synthesis reactors are shown in Table 10. Two listings are shown for the reforming step, corresponding to alternate catalysts. Some commercial samples (Chevron unleaded, JP-4 jet fuel) are listed for comparison. Studies in progress in the liquid fuels system include the use of a hydrogenation catalyst (to eliminate unsaturation after the first reactor), and the use of an isomerization catalyst (to isomerize low molecular paraffins from the first reactor). Also an assessment of recycling off gases from the downstream reactors to the gasification system is in progress (to increase overall product yields). Considerable flexibility exists although the need for sequential steps seems apparent.

G. Thermal Cracking

Any thermoplastic can be melted and thermally cracked by pumping it through a heating coil. The products will be gases, a light oil, and a heavy oil. The composition of the products will depend upon the temperature of the coil and the residence time in the coil. An interesting application of this is found in a pilot plant for cracking atactic polypropylene. This unit was designed and built by the Procedyne Corp. of New Brunswick, N.J. Although the work was done under a DOE contract, the design is proprietary to Procedyne.

One advantage of a unit of this type is that there are no particulate emissions. The major portion of the vent gases should be combustible and may be disposed of in an afterburner.

REFERENCES

1. Gascoigne, J. A. and Gascoigne, M. M., *Biological Degradation of Cellulose*, Butterworths, London, 1960.

2. Recovery of Anaerobic Digestion After Exposure to Intoxicants, Drexel University, Philadelphia, Pa; Principal Investigator, Dr. R. E. Speece, DOE Contract EC-77-S-02-4391.

3. **Bailey, J. E. and Ollis, D. F.**, *Biochemical Engineering Fundamentals,* McGraw-Hill, New York, 1977.

4. Best Mixing Concepts for Refuse/Sludge for ERDA's Biogasification Project, Systems Technology Corp., Xenia, Ohio, Principal Investigator; Dr. J. T. Swartzbaugh, ERDA Contract E(40-1)-5175.

5. A.S.E.F. Solid Waste to Methane Gas, Pompano Beach Fl, Prime Contractor; Waste Management Inc., Oak Brook, Illinois, DOE Contract EY-76-C-02-2770.

6. **Wilke, C. R.**, Production of sugars and ethanol based on the enzymatic hydrolysis of cellulose, in Proc. of the Fuels from Biomass Symp., U.S. Department of Energy, C00/4255-1, University of Illinois, Urbana, April 18-19, 1977.

7. **Mandels, M. and Weber, J.**, *Adv. Chem. Ser.,* 95, 391, 1969.

8. **Wilke, C. R., Yang, R. D., and Stockar, U. V.**, Preliminary cost analyses for enzymatic hydrolysis of newsprint, *Biotechnol. Bioeng., Symp.,* 6, 155, 1976.

9. **Cysenski, G. R. and Wilke, C. R.**, Utilization of cellulosic materials through enzymatic hydrolysis. I. Fermentation of hydrolyzate to ethanol and single cell protein, *Biotechnol. Bioeng.,* 18, 1297, 1976.

10. **Cysenski, G. R. and Wilke, C. R.**, Utilization of cellulosic materials through enzymatic hydrolysis. II. Preliminary assessment of an integrated processing scheme, *Biotechnol. Bioeng.,* 18, 1315, 1976.

11. Conversion of Cellulosic and Waste Polymer Materials to Gasoline, Arizona State University, Tempe, Arizona, Principal Investigator, Dr. J. L. Kuester, DOE Contract EY-76-S-02-2982.*000.

Chapter 7

WASTE-TO-ENERGY SYSTEMS: THEIR NATURE AND ENVIRONMENTAL IMPACT

L. J. Shannon and K. P. Ananth

TABLE OF CONTENTS

I. INTRODUCTION

Energy recovery from materials contained in urban, industrial, agricultural, and forestry waste streams has been of increasing interest in recent years. Urban and industrial wastes encompass the already well-defined solid waste burdens of municipalities and industry, the sludge produced in waste treatment systems, and such wastes as oils, greases, and solvents. Agricultural wastes include crop residues which normally would be returned to the land as well as the residues generated by the crop/food processing industry. Forestry wastes include the debris of logging and sawmill operations and forest management practices such as thinning, disease control, and fire control.

Variations in compositions inherent in the above waste streams have led to the development of several concepts for energy recovery. Systems proposed include various mechanical separation systems, cocombustion with fossil fuels, several versions of pyrolysis, chemically oriented processes involving hydrolysis or solvent/extraction-liquefaction, and biochemically based processes — fermentation, digestion — to convert wastes to specific substances such as ethanol and metahne plus edible single-cell protein. Energy products recovered from the waste streams may be in the form of solids, liquids, or gases — or energy may be recovered more directly as hot water or steam. Some systems recover combinations of these several types of energy. The form, or forms, of energy and other products recovered depend on the type of process, its operating conditions and economic factors. Recent concerns with fossil fuel reserves and maldistributions of available supplies have focused increasing attention on the utilization of wastes as a supplementary or substitute fuel for use in heat-recovery incinerators and industrial or utility boilers.

Table 1 presents a summary of representative unit processes or operations which do or could comprise steps in an energy recovery system. Table 1 emphasizes the energy recovery mode and includes only the initial steps in a materials recovery system (i.e., size reduction and segregation).

Various combinations of the unit processes listed in Table 1 have been proposed to convert the energy contained in waste materials into steam, oil, gas, and electricity. The major waste-to-energy systems, on a generic basis, are:

1. Waterwall incinerators
2. Hog fuel boilers
3. Combined firing systems
4. Thermochemical processes (pyrolysis)
5. Advanced combustion systems (CPU-400)
6. Biochemical systems

The systems are listed in a rough order of their degree of commercial availability. With the exception of biochemical systems, all of the above systems involve thermal processing of the waste materials. Preprocessing of the waste material (i.e., shredding, air classification, screening, etc.) is required in many of the systems prior to the energy conversion step.

The simplest form of energy recovery is the use of a waste heat boiler with a conventional refractory incinerator, that is, extracting heat from the flue gases usually to make low pressure steam. A more effective type of heat recovery unit utilizes furnace walls made of closely-spaced steel tubes welded together, with water or steam circulated through the tubes to extract heat generated during combustion. This procedure not only leads to heat recovery, but allows a major reduction in air requirements.

The performance of waterwall incinerators which generate steam has been fully

TABLE1

Summary of Representative Unit Processes or Operations in an Energy Recovery System

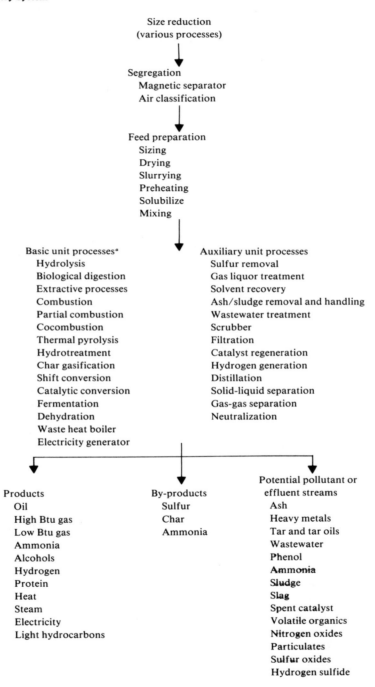

Size reduction
(various processes)

Segregation
   Magnetic separator
   Air classification

Feed preparation
   Sizing
   Drying
   Slurrying
   Preheating
   Solubilize
   Mixing

Basic unit processes[a]	Auxiliary unit processes
Hydrolysis	Sulfur removal
Biological digestion	Gas liquor treatment
Extractive processes	Solvent recovery
Combustion	Ash/sludge removal and handling
Partial combustion	Wastewater treatment
Cocombustion	Scrubber
Thermal pyrolysis	Filtration
Hydrotreatment	Catalyst regeneration
Char gasification	Hydrogen generation
Shift conversion	Distillation
Catalytic conversion	Solid-liquid separation
Fermentation	Gas-gas separation
Dehydration	Neutralization
Waste heat boiler	
Electricity generator	

Products	By-products	Potential pollutant or effluent streams
Oil	Sulfur	Ash
High Btu gas	Char	Heavy metals
Low Btu gas	Ammonia	Tar and tar oils
Ammonia		Wastewater
Alcohols		Phenol
Hydrogen		Ammonia
Protein		Sludge
Heat		Slag
Steam		Spent catalyst
Electricity		Volatile organics
Light hydrocarbons		Nitrogen oxides
		Particulates
		Sulfur oxides
		Hydrogen sulfide

[a]   Some unit operations, notably sulfur removal, are a combination of more than one unit operation.

proved both in Europe and North America. However, no waterwall incinerator projects in the U.S. are yet on sound footing with regard to external steam sales. Waste is not normally processed before firing except to remove large items and the lack of need for preprocessing of the waste is an advantage of the waterwall incinerator. Disadvantages include difficulty in maintaining uniform steam production because of uneven burning rates, corrosion on boiler tubes and grates, and high capital and maintenance costs.

Burning wood under a boiler is not a new concept. There were 230 boilers with capability to burn wood, either as the primary fuel or as an alternate fuel, sold in this country between 1965 and March 1975. The technology is available and vendors are able to supply equipment designed to burn wood.

Hog fuel boilers are an established technology in the pulp and paper industry. The waste from sawmills and other forest products industries could be used to supplement other sources of wood as fuel for a power plant. The practice would benefit those industries by providing an outlet for otherwise waste material. The major uncertainties in the concept lie in the logistics and the economics of the procurement of wood chips for fuel.

Combined firing systems produce steam and/or electricity through the combustion of processed solid waste and a fossil fuel, such as coal or oil, in a fossil fuel-fired boiler. Combined firing systems using refuse and coal have been demonstrated and tested at St. Louis, Mo.; Ames, Iowa; and Columbus, Ohio. The Ames, Iowa, facility has been operational for over a year.

In the pyrolytic process, organic materials are heated in an oxygen-deficient atmosphere to produce a gaseous and/or liquid product, char, and slag. The nature of these products depends primarily on the composition of the waste, pyrolysis temperature, pressure, and residence time. Unlike incineration which is highly exothermic, the addition of heat to the pyrolysis chamber is usually necessary. The method of heat introduction is a major distinguishing factor between various pyrolysis processes. For example, auxiliary fuel combustion, preheated air, circulating heated solids, and limited oxygen introduction to produce heat by oxidizing part of the carbon present in the waste have all been used. Pyrolysis systems have been tested at the pilot scale, but problems have been encountered in the full-scale systems at Baltimore and San Diego.

The coupling of a fluid bed combustor and a gas turbine-generator to produce electrical power forms the basis of an advanced combustion system to recover energy from waste material. The system developed in Menlo Park, Calif. consists of two modules, one for solid waste processing and the other a power module. Development of this system has progressed to a pilot-scale facility.

An alternate way of recovering energy from wastes is to allow anaerobic organisms to digest them and release methane gas. Experimental studies have indicated the capability of these organisms to degrade complex municipal paper waste and garbage. A facility to demonstrate, on a commercial scale, the feasibility of the anaerobic digestion process is nearing the operational stage in Pompano Beach, Fla.

The recovery of energy from wastes is desirable provided that the recovery processes do not cause significant insults to the environment. Because of relative infancy of U.S. waste-to-energy technology, operating experience is not extensive and the environmental impacts of many of the energy recovery systems are ill defined at this time.

Potential pollutants or effluent streams are shown in Table 1 in order to indicate the scope of the potential environmental impacts on air, water, and land which may result. Several types of pollutants such as particulates, heavy metals, POMs, chlorides, NO_x, SO_x, etc., have been identified in air emission streams exiting energy recovery operations. Wastewater effluents from energy recovery plants can be in the form of ash quench water, sluice water from ash rejection, discharge of intermediate process liquids, and scrubber waters from particulate removal of flue gas desulfurization processes. Wastewater effluents from pyrolysis processes may contain concentrated amounts of soluble organic and inorganic compounds. In addition, trace elements contained in waste may be entrained in liquid discharges in higher concentrations than in the waste material itself. Solid waste from energy recovery systems presents primary disposal problems. Furthermore, the ashes, sludges, and residual materials may cause a secondary impact, e.g., water contamination resulting from leaching of materials disposed of on land.

Requirements for pollution control technology to minimize environmental impacts of waste-to-energy processes are quite diverse because of the wide range of potential impacts. Both add-on control devices and process modifications may be viable approaches. Pollution control equipment in use at existing plants varies in effectiveness. Several types of air pollution control devices have been employed on waste combustion, cofiring, and pyrolysis processes. There is very little operational experience relating to wastewater and residue pollution control. Air pollution control has, to this point, received the most attention at waste-to-fuel plants, and particulate control has been the subject of most interest.

A more extensive discussion of the nature of waste-to-energy systems and their associated environmental impacts is presented in the remainder of this chapter.

II. SPECIFIC WASTE-TO-ENERGY SYSTEMS

A brief description of each generic system, a discussion of the nature of emissions, and control technology for these emissions are presented in the following sections.

A. Waterwall Incinerators

1. System Description

Originally incinerators were designed to dispose of refuse and other unwanted combustibles by thermal decomposition. Increasing emphasis on energy conservation had led to incorporation of heat recovery systems in the most modern incinerators.

The use of raw refuse as a fuel for steam production in waterwall incinerators began in Europe and has now been technologically developed to a fine degree. The European design has generally served as the basis for a few recent U.S. installations, listed in Table 2.

Refuse is normally burned "as received" in a waterwall incinerator, with size reduction equipment only for oversize or bulky refuse. Firing is usually accomplished by using traveling grates. Combustion gases exchange heat in the boiler section, superheater, and economizer, thereby reducing the flue gas to an exit temperature of approximately 93 to 232°C. Flue gas exit temperatures and excess air levels are generally much higher than for suspension firing, and boiler efficiencies are proportionately lower than those found in electric utility boilers. Auxiliary fuels such as oil or coal are usually provided for supplementary steam generation.

2. Emissions From Waterwall Incinerators

Emissions from waterwall incinerators include particulates, gases, wastewater from ash sluicing, bottom ash, and captured fly ash. Recent tests[1] on the Nashville incinerator showed average inlet grain loadings of 2746 mg/nm³ and an average outlet loading of 55 mg/nm³ after the electrostatic precipitator (ESP). Similar tests performed at other U.S. and foreign waterwall incinerators indicate that fly ash emissions range from approximately 0.06 to 0.65 g/10⁶ J of heat input, with the lower values (0.06 to 0.13 g/10⁶ J) representative of U.S. installations.[2]

TABLE 2

Waterwall Incinerators in the U.S.

Location	Start up date	Capacity (Mg/day)	Processing steps[a]	Products
Akron, Ohio	1979	907	SH, AC, MS	Steam, ferrous
Braintree, Mass.	6/77	217	None	Steam
Chicago, Ill. (Northwest)	7/71	1451	None	Steam
Dade County, Fla.	1/79	2721	WP, MS, OS	Steam, glass, ferrous, aluminum
Detroit, Mich.	UN	2721	UN	Steam
Harrisburg, Pa.	10/72	653	MS	Steam, ferrous
Lexington-Fayette Urban County Gov., Ky.	[b]	952	SH, MS	Steam, ferrous
Minneapolis-St. Paul, Minn.	1980	1089	UN	Steam
Nashville, Tenn.	7/74	653	None	Steam
Norfolk, Va.	1967	327	None	Steam
Saugus, Mass.	4/76	1089	SC, MS	Steam, ferrous
Haverhill, Mass.	UN	2721	UN	Steam, ferrous
Memphis, Tenn.	UN	1814	UN	Steam
New Haven, Conn.	UN	1633	UN	Steam
Onondaga County, N.Y.	UN	907	UN	Steam, ferrous
Beverly, Salem, Lynn, Mass.	1980	454	UN	Steam

[a] SH, shredding; AC, air classification; MS, magnetic separation; SC, screening; OS, other mechanical separation; UN, unknown; WP, wet pulping.

[b] Construction of facility deferred until market conditions for recovered materials improve.

TABLE 3

Analysis of Flue Gas from Nashville Incinerator[4]

Test number and date

Gas	1 2-21-75	2 2-21-75	3 2-23-75	4 2-26-75	5 2-26-75	6 2-27-75	Average
CO_2 (%)	10.0	9.8	11.4	10.8	10.3	10.3	10.4
O_2 (%)	10.5	10.3	8.5	9.0	9.3	9.6	9.5
Excess air (%)	102	100	69	73	79	83	84
NO_x ($\mu l/\ell$)	107	120	177	150	165	154	146
SO_2 ($\mu l/\ell$)	46	51	39	30	22	38	38
CO ($\mu l/\ell$)	158	179	100	—	—	—	153
Chloride ($\mu l/\ell$)	63	—	177	120	78	—	110

Particle size data for fly ash particulates from municipal incinerators indicate that 30 to 45% by weight are less than 10 μm, 23 to 40% are less than 5 μm, and 13 to 30% are less than 1 μm.[2]

A more important environmental consequence of fly ash particulates from waste incineration is the enrichment or preferential concentration of several trace elements in the smaller-sized particulates. Gordon et al.[3] report enrichment factors from municipal incinerators of 1000, 270, 18, and 10 for cadmium, lead, copper, and zinc, respectively. The same phenomenon is likely to occur in waterwall incinerators.

Gaseous emissions consist of SO_2, NO_x, chlorides, and CO in addition to CO_2, oxygen, and hydrocarbons. Table 3 summarizes the concentrations of these gases observed in tests conducted at Nashville.[4] Similar tests conducted at the municipal incinerator in Babylon, N.Y. showed NO_x concentrations ranging from 53 to 115 $\mu l/\ell$.[5] The SO_2 and chloride concentrations at the same facility were observed to be 56 to 195 $\mu l/\ell$ and 214 to 1,250 $\mu l/\ell$, respectively.[5] The differences in the gas concentrations could be a result of using different sampling and analysis methods and/or different incinerator operating characteristics.

In general, SO_2 emissions from incinerators will be lower than those observed from coal-fired power plants since refuse has a lower sulfur level. Chloride emissions can be high, since refuse can contain significant quantities of plastics. Chloride emissions can create a significant problem; even though they can be easily scrubbed from the gas stream, their subsequent removal from the scrubbing water can result in water pollution.

Hydrocarbon emissions from municipal incinerators are reported to be in the range of 0.4 to 42.5 $\mu l/\ell$.[5,6] Methane and ethylene appear to be the predominant species. C_1 through C_5 hydrocarbons are minor constituents of incinerator emission when combustion conditions are good.[5]

Meager information is available on water pollutants from waterwall incinerators. The only significant water usage, other than for steam generation, occurs in ash sluicing. Water quenching of ash from the boiler is usually necessary to break up clinkers and to quench burning materials. Thus, water pollution problems occur and create the need for treatment facilities to be constructed as part of the incinerator plant. Other wastewater sources include the sanitary system's boiler blowdown, demineralizer backwash, and quench channel overflow. At Saugus, the average wastewater discharge is estimated to be approximately 0.006 m^3/sec.[7] No information is available describing wastewater quality from the various waterwall incinerator plants.

Solid waste emissions from waterwall incinerators consist of bottom ash and captured fly ash. These wastes can be disposed of in landfills.

Midwest Research Institute (MRI) has conducted a comprehensive multimedia environmental assessment of the Braintree waterwall incinerator in January 1978. At the time this chapter was prepared, the results of the test program were not available. The test report is scheduled for publication at a later date.

3. Control Technology for Waterwall Incinerators

Information presented here is based primarily on the Nashville and the Saugus systems. Data on other locations are not available. However, since the two systems discussed here are among the most recent facilities, the discussion is representative of current control technology.

a. Nashville

Air emissions from the Nashville incinerator have been controlled at various times using different types of wet scrubbers. The system now has an electrostatic precipitator that meets the local regulation, and a second electrostatic precipitator is in the process of being installed.

Recent test data on the American Air Filter ESP unit operating at Nashville showed the following inlet/outlet particulate loadings when corrected to 12% CO_2:[1]

	Inlet (mg/nm³)		Outlet (mg/nm³)
	2153		64
	2220		41
	3838		62
Average	2737	Average	56

The tests were conducted using U.S. Environmental Protection Agency (EPA) methods, and were done only to determine particulate loadings at full load. No particle sizing or gas composition measurements were made.

Experience with wet scrubbers at Nashville was reported to be both frustrating and expensive.[8] The original low-energy scrubbers were ineffective in collecting fine particulate. Stack sampling indicated that 90% of the particulate escaping the scrubber had an average diameter of less than 6 μm. Modifications to the original scrubbers increased the pressure drop and the collection efficiency, but not sufficiently to bring the units into compliance.[8]

Pilot tests of two other wet collection devices (high pressure spray scrubber and high temperature water flashing nozzle) indicated possible compliance. However, excessive steam usage and stringent recycle water cleanup requirements were factors that caused their rejection in favor of electrostatic precipitators.[8]

A pilot baghouse program was also conducted at Nashville. In the initial baghouse program, five fabrics of glass, stainless steel, and synthetic fibers were utilized in two baghouses, a pulse type and a backflow type. Meaningful stack sampling was not conducted, although visible emissions appeared to be well controlled. The five fabrics held up for the test period of approximately 3 months. Burst tests and other analyses of one of the fabrics (an aramid felt) indicated a projected total life expectancy of only 5 to 6 months. This result is not surprising because the fiber is not acid resistant.

A second-phase EPA-sponsored program on fabric filters was scheduled for summer 1977 at Nashville. An 85 m³/min slip stream from the heat recovery incinerator was to be used as the gas source. Objectives of the testing program were:[8] (1) screen three types of high-temperature, acid-resistant filter media; (2) determine efficiency and optimum air-to-cloth ratios for the various filter media; (3) make technical economic comparisons of a baghouse using these media versus other particulate control methods such as ESPs and wet scrubbers; and (4) recommend a prime filter media candidate for follow-up life expectancy programs. Unfortunately, due to a change in management at Nashville Thermal Transfer, this program came to an abrupt halt sometime in September of 1977.

Solid waste at the Nashville facility primarily consists of captured fly ash and bottom ash. These materials could be disposed of in landfills. No information is apparently available on any wastewater treatment facility at Nashville. However, treatment of wastewater from this facility should not pose any control problems.

b. Saugus

The Saugus system has two Wheelabrator-Lurgi electrostatic precipitators capable of handling 6800 m^3/min each at 220°C. They are designed to control particulates to 57 mg/nm^3, corrected to 12% CO_2, and they are apparently operating satisfactorily under the Metropolitan Boston Air Pollution Control District requirement of 114 mg/ nm^3 at 12% CO_2. No test data are available.

Wastewater sources are the sanitary system, boiler blowdown, demineralizer backwash, and quench channel overflow. All blowdown and backwash are neutralized as required, and pumped to a holding tank that feeds the ash quench conveyor channels. No ash quench water is recirculated since it is progressively removed in the wet ash with overflow to the sewer. Under operating conditions, total flow to the sewer is expected to consist primarily of the sanitary system discharge.[7]

The front ash discharge from the furnace and the mechanically conveyed ash from the boiler and precipitator hoppers are mechanically conveyed from a quench tank to a classifying house. In the house, the drag conveyor drops the ash into a trommel screen where it is classified into three fractions. Pieces larger than about 8 cm drop into a truck, and the ash that drops through the screen is further classified into magnetic and nonmagnetic fractions, each of which goes to a separate truck for sale to a steel plant and disposal, respectively.

B. Hog Fuel Boilers
1. System Description

In the manufacture of lumber, about 50% of the material from the log is removed to produce sound lumber.[9] Though the total waste usually averages approximately 50%, distribution of the different types of waste such as slabs, edging, trimming, bark, sawdust, and shavings may vary depending on mill conditions and product desired. The mills frequently use sawdust or sawdust and shaving mixtures for steam production because they can be burned without further processing. The remainder of the waste products requires further size reduction in a "hog" to facilitate storage, feeding, combustion, etc. These newly sized products together with varying percentages of sawdust and shavings present constitute "hog fuel".[9]

The most prevalent size for wood-fired boilers is reported to be in the range of 114 to 1140 kg steam per minute. The most common firing method for wood-fired boilers in all size ranges is the spreader stoker, with overfeed stokers also being common in sizes less than 1900 kg steam per minute.[10]

There are several important considerations in burning wood. These relate to the fouling potential of wood as a result of its ash composition. Wood ash is high in CaO (50 to 60%), and high in Na_2O and K_2O (4 to 7%). Generally speaking, substituting wood for residual fuel oil will increase problems with fouled heat-receiving surfaces. Burning wood in boiler furnaces designed for pulverized coal will not be likely to pose fouling problems worse than with coal alone, except that alkalies may tend to accumulate more rapidly in the cooler parts of the boiler, such as the superheater.[10]

The substitution of wood firing in existing coal-fired stoker boilers presents the fewest problems. In most cases, only minor modifications to the boiler are necessary, such as addition of a wood-feeding system or firing ports. Hogged fuel of less than about 5 cm in size, with a minimum of slack (less than 0.6 cm) should be acceptable to most spreader and overfeed-type stokers.[10]

Wood can also be fired in suspension in boilers designed for pulverized coal or heavy oil. The wood should be reduced in size to less than 0.60 cm and dried as much as possible to insure rapid combustion. Most suspension wood-fired boilers have a small grate at the base of the unit to insure complete burnout of any wood chips that do not burn in suspension. Firing wood in boilers designed for natural gas or light fuel oil would represent a difficult problem since extensive boiler modifications will have to be undertaken to provide ash handling capabilities.

2. Emissions From Hog Fuel Boilers

The combustion of wood will result in particulate pollutant emissions and ash in the form of captured fly ash and bottom ash. Wood, unlike coal or oil, has a negligible sulfur content and should therefore create no SO_2 problems. Nitrogen oxide emissions should also be lower than that observed during coal combustion because of the low nitrogen content of wood (see Table 4).

Typical emission factors for wood and bark combustion, as reported in the literature, are presented in Table 5. Values presented in Table 5 are uncontrolled emissions.[10] Based on these values, it appears that control of criteria pollutants from wood or bark combustion should pose no serious problems.

Particulate emissions from wood-fired boilers can vary, depending on the extent of char reinjection, boiler type, excess air used, wood waste type (e.g., logs, sawdust, chips), and wood moisture content. Hall et al. report that the single most significant factor is probably the extent of char reinjection utilized.[10]

Char reinjection systems, which return collected particles to the combustion zone to achieve more complete combustion of the carbon, represent a compromise between two conflicting objectives. While reinjection increases boiler efficiency and minimizes the emission of uncombusted carbon, it also increases boiler maintenance requirements, decreases the average fly-ash particle size, increases the dust load to the collector, and makes collection more difficult.[10] Properly designed reinjection systems should separate the sand and the char from the exhaust gases, reinject the larger carbon fraction to the boiler, and reinject the fine sand particles to the ash disposal system.

3. Control Technology for Hog Fuel Boilers

Emissions from hog fuel boilers primarily consist of particulates. The other environmental aspect is the generation of captured fly ash and bottom ash, which can be disposed of in landfills.

Fly ash particulates from hog fuel boilers are light in density and larger in size than fly ash from coal-fired boilers.[10] Also, particulate emissions from wood-fired systems can vary depending on the extent of char reinjection, boiler type, excess air, wood waste type, moisture content, etc. Because of these variations, a specific dust loading cannot be established. It is reported that dust loadings range from 1,144 to 11,441 mg/nm^3 and that multicyclones are the sole source of particulate removal for most hog fuel boilers.[10] Wet scrubbers with moderate pressure drops can also be used effectively on this source, since particle size is considered to be large. However, this may result in secondary wastewater pollution. High temperature fabric filtration systems may also be another alternative control system. The use of ESPs, however, will depend on particle resistivity, which for this source might be in the lower range.

TABLE 4

Comparative Chemical Analysis of Wood and Bark, Coal, and Oil[a]

| | Wood and bark | | | | | | Coal | | | Residual fuel oil — range of No. 6 oil |
Item	Pine bark	Oak bark	Spruce bark	Redwood bark	Redwood	Pine	Washed Pennsylvania coal	Western coal	Pennsylvania coal	
Proximate										
Volatile matter	72.9	76.0	69.6	72.6	82.5	79.4	35.8	43.4	37.6	—
Fixed carbon	24.2	18.7	26.6	27.0	17.3	20.1	57.3	51.7	52.2	—
Ash	2.9	5.3	3.8	0.4	0.2	0.5	6.9	4.9	10.1	—
Ultimate										
Hydrogen	5.6	5.4	5.7	5.1	5.9	6.3	5.1	6.4	5.0	9.5—12.0
Carbon	53.4	49.7	51.8	51.9	53.5	51.8	78.1	54.6	74.2	86.5—90.2
Sulfur	0.1	0.1	0.1	0.1	0	0	1.2	0.4	2.1	0.7—3.5
Nitrogen	0.1	0.2	0.2	0.1	0.1	0.1	1.6	1.0	1.5	—
Oxygen	37.9	39.3	38.4	42.4	40.3	41.3	7.1	33.8	7.1	0.01—0.5
Ash	2.9	5.3	3.8	0.4	0.2	0.5	6.9	3.3	10.1	—
Heating value, J/kg	21×10^6	19.47×10^6	20.33×10^6	19.42×10^6	21.44×10^6	21.24×10^6	32.49×10^6	21.91×10^6	30.96×10^6	40.5×10^6—44.17×10^6
Ash analyses										
SiO_2	39.0	11.1	32.0	14.3	—	—	—	30.7	49.7	—
Fe_2O_3	3.0	3.3	6.4	3.5	—	—	—	18.9	11.4	—
TiO_2	0.2	0.1	0.8	0.3	—	—	—	1.1	1.2	—
Al_2O_3	14.0	0.1	11.0	4.0	—	—	—	19.6	26.8	—
Mn_3O_4	Trace	Trace	1.5	0.1	—	—	—	—	—	—
GaO	25.5	64.5	25.3	6.0	—	—	—	11.3	4.2	—
MgO	6.5	1.2	4.1	6.6	—	—	—	3.7	0.8	—
Na_2O	1.3	8.9	8.0	18.0	—	—	—	2.4	2.9	—
K_2O	6.0	0.2	2.4	10.6	—	—	—	—	—	—
SO_3	0.3	2.0	2.1	7.4	—	—	—	12.2	2.5	—
Cl	Trace	Trace	Trace	18.4	—	—	—	—	—	—

Note: Dry basis, % by weight, except as noted.

TABLE 5

Emission Factors for Wood and Bark[a] Combustion in Boilers with No Reinjection[10]

Pollutant	Emission (g/kg)
Particulate[b]	12.5—15
Sulfur oxides (SO₂)[c]	0—1.5
Carbon monoxide	1.0
Hydrocarbons[d]	1.0
Nitrogen oxides (NO₂)	5

[a]   Moisture content assumed to be 50% in wood and bark.
[b]   This number is the atmospheric emission factor without fly ash reinjection. For boilers with reinjection, the particulate loadings reaching the control equipment are 15 to 17.5 g/kg fuel with 100% reinjection.
[c]   Use 0 for most wood, and higher values for bark.
[d]   Expressed as methane.

C. Combined Firing Systems

1. System Description

Combined firing systems use refuse-derived fuel (RDF) or wood with coal or oil for production of electric power or steam in boilers. Combined firing systems being planned for the U.S. generally utilize both materials and energy recovery. Figure 1 presents a simplified schematic for this type of system when municipal waste is the source material. As shown in the figure, preconversion processing of the waste is required for enrichment of the waste to RDF. The preconversion processing also facilitates the recovery of ferrous and nonferrous metal and glass from the waste. RDF and a fossil fuel (coal or oil) can then be readily combusted to generate steam or electricity. A representative list of combined firing systems is given in Table 6.

On a smaller scale, particularly in industrial boilers, wood waste (wood chips) is commonly used with coal. In this case, there is usually no need for processing the waste. However, in systems where bark is used with coal, the bark must be shredded. Combined firing systems utilizing wood and coal are generally located in areas where there is an adequate supply of wood waste, and they are generally operated on a smaller scale than systems using RDF and coal or oil.

2. Emissions From Combined Firing Systems

Combined firing systems can consist of coal and RDF, oil and RDF, coal and wood waste, and oil and wood waste. Where RDF is used, processing of municipal solid waste (MSW) is required. Depending on the type of wood waste (wood chips or bark), processing may become necessary. If processing of MSW or bark is undertaken, then the processing plant becomes the first emission source in the waste-to-energy conversion chain. MSW processing usually involves shredding, air classification, and removal of ferrous and sometimes aluminum metal. Emissions from such a facility can include solid residue from processing and particulate pollutants from the air classifier system. If washdown operations are involved, this will result in wastewater discharge. Bark processing will usually involve only particulate discharge.

Only coal + RDF systems have been studied to any extent. Information on emissions from various types of combined firing systems is discussed next.

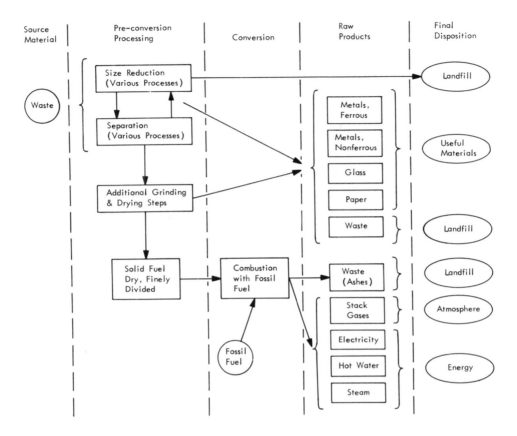

FIGURE 1.   Schematic of combined firing system.

a. Coal + RDF Systems

The facilities in St. Louis, Mo., and Ames, Iowa, have been used to conduct tests to determine the environmental consequences of combined firing systems. Highlights of the results of the test programs follow.

1) St. Louis-Union Electric System

The St. Louis-Union Electric System was the first demonstration plant in the U.S. to process municipal waste for use as a supplementary fuel in a utility boiler. Two separate facilities comprised the system — a processing plant operated by the City of St. Louis and receiving and firing operations at the Union Electric Company's Mera-mec Plant near St. Louis. At the 272 ton/day capacity processing plant, raw solid waste was milled to a nominal 3.8 cm particle size and air-classified into light and heavy fractions. The light or RDF fraction, approximately 80% of the received solid waste, was temporarily stored and then hauled 29 km by transport truck to the Union Electric Company Meramec power plant.

2) Processing Plant

A detailed characterization of emissions from the MSW processing facility at St. Louis has been reported by Fiscus et al.[11,12]

Studies conducted at the processing plant were directed to quantifying emissions and evaluating other environmental aspects of the facility and its operations. Specific tests were conducted to:

1. Determine mass emission rates and particle size for particulate matter discharged from the Air Density Separator (ADS) and from the hammermill (HM) cyclone for both regular* and fine grind** refuse
2. Quantify water effluents and pollutant levels therein
3. Evaluate the leachability of all solid waste effluents that do or can occur from this facility
4. Carry out a noise survey in and around the processing plant

Mass emissions from the ADS cyclone for the regular grind tests ranged from 9.0 to 34 kg/hr (20 to 80 lb/hr) with an average of 27 kg/hr (60 lb/hr) with corresponding emission rates from 0.3 to 2.0 kg/mg (0.6 to 4.0 lb/ton) with an average of 0.95 kg/mg (1.9 lb/ton). This emission rate indicates the need for controlling or reducing the emissions in future plants of this type.[11]

Particle size tests on the ADS cyclone discharge during regular grind operations showed that at least 80% of the particulate emissions were larger than 10 μm. Based on visual observations, it was suspected that a considerable number of the emissions were probably much larger than 10 μm.[11]

A second series of mass emission (and particle size) tests was conducted on the ADS system when fine-grind RDF was being produced. Data from these tests showed that emissions averaged 57 kg/hr (126 lb/hr), which is about twice as high as the average for the regular grind tests. Perhaps more importantly, the average emission rate was 2.7 kg/mg (5.5 lb/ton), about three times higher than that for regular grind refuse. The reduced processing rate for fine grind necessitated reduced air flow in the ADS system, which may have impaired removal efficiency in the ADS cyclone. The particle size distribution of the ADS emissions during the fine-grind tests was similar to the regular grind tests, indicating no significant increase in the percent of particles smaller than 10 μm.[11]

The emissions from the HM are less than from the ADS system, but the data for regular grind RDF cover a wide range of 0.008 to 3.9 kg/hr (0.02 to 8.6 lb/hr). Particle size distribution tests were also conducted on the emissions from the HM cyclone. As was the case from the ADS cyclone emissions, the tests showed that most of the particulate matter (>80%) was greater than 10 μm in size.[11]

The only liquid effluent from the processing plant in St. Louis occurred from periodic washdown of the asphalted processing area of the plant (not including the floor of the raw refuse receiving building). This cleanup effort removed dust and settled particles, much of which resulted from blowoff from conveyor belts and ADS cyclone emissions. Sampling and analysis of the runoff were conducted. Comparison of analysis data for the raw water and the runoff indicates a large increase in total suspended solids (TSS) as expected. There was also a significant increase in biochemical oxygen demand (BOD) and chemical oxygen demand (COD).[11]

The processing-plant residue includes all material not converted to RDF or recovered as ferrous metal. Plant residue which is landfilled averages approximately 15% by weight of the incoming material. Another 5% by weight of ferrous materials are recovered. The residue contains about 5% of the energy content of the incoming waste. It is composed primarily of glass, wood, metals, paper, plastic, rock, and dirt. A limited series of tests to evaluate the leachate which may result from landfilling of this waste, indicated that drinking water standards were exceeded in the laboratory-pro-

---

*   Regular grind refuse refers to refuse obtained when grates with 76 mm square openings were used in the hammermill.

**   Fine grind refers to refuse obtained when grates with 32 mm diameter openings were used in the hammermill.

TABLE 6

Combined Firing Systems

Location	10⁶ lb/hr Steam production design capacity	Processing steps[a] of refuse	Products[b]
Ames, Iowa	0.36	SH, MS, AC, SC, OS	RDF, ferrous, aluminum
Akron, Ohio	UN	SH, MS, AC	RDF, ferrous, nonferrous
Bridgeport, Conn.	UN	SH, AC, MS, FF	RDF (Eco-Fuel II), ferrous, glass, nonferrous
Brockton, Mass.	UN	SH, AC, MS, OS	RDF (Eco-Fuel II), ferrous
Capital District, N.Y.	UN	SH, AC, MS	RDF, ferrous
Columbus, Ohio	0.15	SH, AC, MS	RDF, ferrous
Chicago, Ill.	1.5	SH, AC, MS	RDF, ferrous
Ft. Wayne, Ind.	UN	UN	UN
Milwaukee, Wis.	2.0	SH, AC, MS, SC	RDF, ferrous, glass, aluminum, paper
Monroe County, N.Y.	UN	SH, AC, MS, FF, OS	RDF, ferrous, nonferrous, glass
New York, N.Y.	UN	SH, AC, MS	RDF, ferrous
St. Louis, Mo.	UN	SH, MS, AC, OS	RDF, ferrous, nonferrous, glass residue
Houston, Tex.	UN	SH, MS, AC	RDF, ferrous
Hagerstown, Md.	60	SH, AC, SC	d-RDF[c]

[a] Processing steps at RDF production facility: SH, shredding; AC, air classification; MS, magnetic separation; SC, screening; OS, other mechanical separation; FF, froth flotation; and UN, unknown.

[b] Principal product of cofired systems is electric power. RDF can be a product only if all of the RDF generated in the processing plant is not used as a supplementary fuel in the cofired system.

[c] Densified RDF.

duced leachate solutions for many elements.[11] Since the leachate produced for the tests reported in Reference 11 was the result of only a single set of laboratory test conditions, additional work is warranted to further define potential residue disposal problems associated with refuse-processing plants.

A sound survey was conducted at the St. Louis refuse processing plant. Table 7 summarizes the equipment sound level data. OSHA limits the time workers may spend in areas with high sound levels. Equipment sound levels exceeding 90 dB on the A range, the range to which the human ear is sensitive, are given in Table 7 along with the frequencies at which maximum sound intensities were recorded. In general, the higher sound levels occur below 2000 Hz frequency. The maximum plant sound level of 110 dB at 63 Hz center band frequency was recorded inside the refuse-receiving building when refuse-packer trucks were dumping. Maximum OSHA exposure times of ½, 1½, and 2 hr corresponding to A range decibel intensities were indicated near the magnetic-belt-discharge chute, the ferrous-metal compactor, and the receiving building. Improved equipment sound-control techniques should probably be used in future plants.

3) Power Plant

A pulverized coal, tangentially fired boiler-turbine-generation unit with a nominal load rating of 125 MW was used in the St. Louis program.

Emissions from the power plant fired with coal and RDF included solids in the form of bottom ash and captured fly ash, air emissions in the form of particulates and gases, and boiler sluice water. The bottom ash accumulation rate averaged 68 kg/min for coal and RDF (at 5 to 10% RDF) in contrast to 10 kg/min for Orient 6 coal.[13] Also,

TABLE 7

Equipment Sound Levels above 90 dBA

Location	Maximum intensity (dB)	Frequency at maximum intensity[a] (Hz)	A scale intensity (dBA)	Maximum exposure times (hr)
Receiving building	110	63	100	2
Air classifier discharge chute	96	63	94	4
Magnetic belt discharge chute	103	4,000	108	½
Ferrous metal discharge chute	88	31.5	94	4
Hammermill pad	99	63	95	4
Ferrous metal compactor (shredder)	96	2,000	101	1½
Air classification fan exhaust	100	31.5	95	4

[a] Center band frequency at which maximum intensities were recorded.

elements such as lead, antimony, and tin are present in greater concentrations in fly ash collected by the electrostatic precipitator (ESP) when coal and RDF are fired together than when coal alone is used. A similar trend appears for lead and chromium in bottom ash.[13]

In contrast to emissions which result from burning Orient 6 coal alone, analysis of atmospheric emissions from the boiler fired with coal and RDF indicated that hazardous pollutants such as beryllium, cadmium, copper, lead, etc. are emitted in larger concentrations when RDF is fired with coal. Similarly, chloride emissions increase when RDF is fired with coal. Emissions of other gaseous pollutants such as CO, SO_2, NO_x, and HC were not significantly different when RDF was fired with coal.[13] One would expect the SO_2 concentration to decrease for coal and RDF, since refuse had a sulfur level of only 0.14 $g/10^6$ J in contrast to Orient 6 coal, which has a sulfur level of 0.60 $g/10^6$ J. But because only 10% of the feed constituted RDF in the study reported by Gorman et al.,[13] the difference may not have been noticeable. This interpretation is supported by another RDF/coal study in which 1:1 and 2:1 mixes (by volume) of RDF and coal were utilized.[14] Jackson indicates that the 1:1 mix had significantly lower SO_2, HC and NO_x emission levels than coal.[14] Particulate emissions were unchanged, and lead, chloride, and fluoride emissions were significantly increased with the 1:1 mix. Another important finding reported by Jackson[14] is that lead was found predominantly in the submicron-sized particle fraction. Particles in the stack effluent contained 245 times more lead than particles collected by a multicyclone.[14]

Water effluent from a coal/RDF system is limited to sluice water. A comparison was made between pollutants contained in sluice water from such a system and from a system firing coal only.[13] There was no significant difference between the two sluice water samples in potentially hazardous pollutants such as antimony, arsenic, barium, beryllium, cadmium, chromium, copper, lead, mercury, selenium, titanium, vanadium, zinc, bromine, chlorine, and fluorine. However, total dissolved solids (TDS), BOD, and COD were higher for sluice water from the coal/RDF system.

4) Ames, Iowa System

The Ames Solid Waste Recovery System is a continuously operating system that is

TABLE 8

Characteristics of Ames Municipal Power Plant Steam Generators

Unit	5	6
Manufacturer	Riley	Union Iron Works
Installation date	1951	1958
Pressure/temperature		
kPa/°C	4,895/441	4,998/441
(psi/°F)	(710/825)	(725/825)
Nominal steam output capacity		
kg/hr	43,091	56,699
(lb/hr)	(95,000)	(125,000)
Coal firing equipment	Spreader stoker	Spreader stoker
	Traveling grate	Traveling grate
Furnace pressure	Balanced draft	Balanced draft
Dust collection equipment	Western multiple	American multiple
	cyclone	cyclone
Stack height, m (ft)	61 (200)	61 (200)
Heat input at nominal capacity		
MJ/hr	154	202
(Btu × 10⁶/hr)	(146)	(191)

processing MSW for use as a supplemental fuel in the existing steam generators of the Ames Municipal Power Plant.[15] At the City of Ames Municipal Power Plant the two existing spreader-return, traveling-grate, stoker-fired boilers (Nos. 5 and 6) have been modified to burn RDF as a supplemental fuel with coal. The RDF is prepared in a nominal 136 mg/day refuse-processing plant adjacent to the power plant. The processing plant incorporates two stages of shredding, ferrous and nonferrous metal recovery, and an ADS. RDF is pneumatically conveyed from the processing plant to a 454 mg storage bin. RDF is conveyed to the boilers via a pneumatic transport system.

The characteristics of the stoker boilers are summarized in Table 8. These boilers were installed in the 1950s, and use cyclone collectors (multicyclones) for removal of particulate from the exhaust gas. Both are traveling-grate spreader stokers. Boiler No. 5 was built by Riley, and Boiler No. 6 was built by Union Iron Works. In both boilers coal is discharged into the boiler by a coal distributor. RDF is fed into the boiler by a pneumatic conveying system. The RDF entry point is adjacent to the coal distributor.

Reference 15 presents results of investigations of the environmental effects of using RDF as a supplemental fuel at the Ames facility. Both uncontrolled particulate emissions before the particulate collector and stack particulate emissions to the atmosphere did not have clear overall trends as a function of RDF heat input. Particulate emissions either increased or stayed the same with percent RDF, depending on boiler unit and boiler load.

NO$_x$ and sulfur emissions both exhibited trends of decreasing emissions with increased percent RDF. During these tests, Boiler No. 5 used Iowa coal only. Boiler No. 6 used a mixture of one half Iowa and one half Wyoming coal. Wyoming coal is lower in sulfur content than Iowa coal, and thus, sulfur emissions for Boiler No. 6 are lower and the effect of RDF is not as pronounced.[15]

Chloride emissions increased with increasing percent RDF for all boiler loads. Chloride emissions were substantially lower only for coal rather than for coal plus RDF, and these emissions appear to be a function of the chlorine in the RDF.[15]

Formaldehyde, cyanide, and phosphate emissions were quite variable, with no clear trends of emissions as a function of percent RDF. Emissions at 20% RDF were either lower, or only slightly higher than the coal only emissions. The major exception was cyanide emissions from Boiler No. 6, which showed a relatively sharper increase in emissions at 20% RDF than for the other test conditions. However, a 50% RDF, the increases and decreases from the 20% RDF test condition were variable enough to make it difficult to establish a trend based on percent RDF.[15]

No significant hydrocarbon emissions in the C_1 to C_5 range were found. Many of the heavy organic compounds in the stack emissions analyzed were below the laboratory detection level, and the majority of the organics found were in the stack gases and not in particulate form.[15]

At most boiler loads, bottom ash tended to increase somewhat, and fly ash tended to decrease with increasing percent RDF.[15]

b. Oil + RDF Systems

Power plants fired with oil and RDF will most likely emit particulates (carbon and ash), NO_x, SO_x, and hydrocarbons. Based on the St. Louis-Union Electric combined firing demonstration of coal and refuse, it is thought that gaseous emissions of CO, CO_2, NO_x, and organics will be relatively unchanged in oil/RDF systems.

Table 9 presents comparative data on the air emission characteristics from oil- and coal-fired electric generating plants. Notable differences between these systems include a smaller average particle size, a lower grain loading, and a higher carrier-gas flow rate for oil units. Evidence indicates that the size distribution of particulate from oil-fired systems is bimodal, with large, hollow carbonaceous particles and finer, condensed, spherical particulate and ash less than 1 μm.

The size distribution depends on the degree of atomization of the oil, the efficiency of mixing, the number of collisions between fly ash particles, the flame temperature, the air-fuel ratio, the design of the firebox, and the flue gas path through the boiler to the stack. The lighter particles usually contain less carbon and are smaller.

c. Coal or Oil and Wood Waste Systems

The Burlington, Vt., Electric Department recently converted a 10-MW coal unit to burn a combination of wood and oil.[16] To prepare it for burning, the wood is run through a chipper that produces 50 tons of fuel per hour. The 10-MW plant burns 8 to 9 tons/hr.

Emission data for combined firing systems using coal and wood waste and oil and wood waste were not available at the time this chapter was prepared. The use of wood waste as a supplementary fuel is not expected to markedly alter air emissions, but bottom ash generation rates will probably increase. Degradation in particulate control system performance may also occur.

3. Control Technology for Combined Firing Systems

Combined firing systems discussed here are restricted to RDF and coal and RDF and oil. No control technology information was available for systems fired with wood and coal, or with wood and oil.

a. RDF and Coal

Information on the performance of control technology is reported in References 11 through 15. Highlights are presented in the following subsections.

1) Processing Plant

The program conducted at St. Louis included investigations of control systems at both the processing and power plant.[11-13]

TABLE 9

Air Emission Comparison Data for Oil and Coal Firing in Utility Boilers[a]

Electric utility power plants	Particulate			Carrier gas	
	Particle size[b]	Outlet loading[c]	Chemical composition[d]	Carrier-gas flow rate[e]	Chemical composition
Coal-fired	Typical distribution (pulverized unit) 81 < 40, 65 < 20, 42 < 10, 25 < 5 (particle size varies with type of unit)	457—12,813 (dependent on type of unit)	Fly ash SiO_2:17—65 Fe_2O_2:2—36 Al_2O_2:9—58 CaO:0.1—22 MgO:0.1—5 Na_2O:0.2—4	1.3—16 10—18	CO_2, O_2, N_2, SO_2, SO_3, and NO_x
Oil-fired	90 < 1	23—458	Carbon, ash, NiO, V_2O_3, Al_2O_3, sulfates, and a wide variety of minor components	47—12,400 348—780	CO_2, O_2, N_2, SO_2, SO_3, and NO_x

a   All data for uncontrolled sources.
b   Particle size data are presented as weight % less or greater than a specific diameter $x > y$, $x < y$; x = weight %, y = particle size (microns).
c Mg/nm^3.
d   Weight %.
e   Flow rate data are presented in thousands of normal cubic meters per minute.

At the processing plant, a pilot-scale mobile fabric filter system was evaluated on the air classifier discharge. Uncontrolled particulate emissions from the ADS unit ranged from 14 to 18 kg/hr (0.26 to 0.36 g/dNm³). The pilot-scale mobile filter, taking a sidestream drawoff (0.05 dNm³/sec) from the air classifier discharge, achieved an overall mass efficiency of 99.95% for removal of particulate.

Samples of the particulate discharged from the air classifier system were analyzed for bacteria and were found to contain average total bacteria of 5.3×10^7 counts/g, which was about the same as that found in the shredded raw refuse. Bacteria samples taken by impingers at the inlet and outlet of the mobile filter indicated a removal efficiency of 99.6% for total bacteria and at least 99.9% for specific types of bacteria (e.g., total coliform). This result confirmed the expectation that a filter system on the air classifier discharge should be able to provide high removal efficiency for particulate and associated bacteria.[12]

The performance of a fabric filter system in controlling emissions from a rotary air classification unit at a MSW processing plant in Houston, Tex., was recently evaluated.[17] The average particulate loading in the fabric filter exhaust was found to be 0.003 g/Nm³, inlet concentrations averaged 23 g/Nm³, and the average baghouse collection efficiency was found to be 99.99%. At least 92% by weight of the inlet particulate was 10 μm or larger. No outlet size distributions were obtained because of the sampling constraints dictated by the extremely low particulate concentration.

2) Power Plant
a) St. Louis

Air emissions from the boiler used in the St. Louis study were controlled by an ESP. Particulate emission measurements showed that refuse firing did not apparently affect inlet grain loadings to the ESP.[13]

The firing of RDF did have an effect on ESP spark rate and power levels, coincident with losses in ESP collection efficiency at output loads above 100 MW.

Specific factors analyzed as having a direct bearing on ESP performance were: (1) inlet particle size data; (2) particulate resistivity data; (3) particulate reentrainment; (4) electrical operating conditions for the ESP; and (5) gas-volume flow rates. The fractional efficiency of the ESP was also studied to see if the decreased efficiency could be related to specific ranges of particle sizes.

The analysis of ESP performance led to the following observations:[13]

1. ESP efficiency decreases with increasing gas-volume flow rates, both for coal-only and coal and RDF conditions.
2. Decreases in efficiency when burning coal and RDF as compared to coal are probably not attributable to changes in inlet particle size distribution, inlet grain loading, or reentrainment problems.
3. Decreases in ESP efficiency when burning coal and RDF as compared to coal are most likely due to the 8% increased gas flow rate and to changes in the ash and gas properties that occur with the burning of RDF.
4. Changes in the fly ash properties that result from burning RDF probably cause small changes in particulate resistivity.
5. The small changes in resistivity caused by burning RDF are probably magnified in terms of their influence on ESP efficiency because measured resistivities are in a very critical range for the onset of back corona and other electrical problems.
6. The decreased overall ESP efficiency at high boiler loads primarily results from an increase in emissions of particles in the 1.0 to 10.0 μm size range.

Several control alternatives could be considered for particulate emissions from the boiler. A list of such alternatives includes: (1) adding another control device (e.g., cyclone) before or after the ESP; (2) increasing the size of the ESP (retrofit); (3) restricting power output or percent RDF; (4) modifying the ESP operation (electrical or other characteristics); (5) using additives or conditioning agents to improve collectability of the particulates (i.e., resistivity); and (6) using fuel of different characteristics (either coal or RDF).

Gaseous stack emissions were also tested. The only effects noted from the burning of refuse was a moderate increase in Cl^-.

SO_2 emissions based on grams of SO_2 per 10^6 J heat input exceeded federal regulations for new sources and several individual state regulations for both existing and new sources of the size of the Meramec boiler. The slight reduction in SO_2 stack gas concentration expected when the low sulfur RDF was substituted for the higher sulfur coal was not observed, probably because of data scatter. Burning of RDF should help reduce SO_2 emissions, but such reductions would probably not be sufficient to meet regulations.

A shift to lower sulfur coal or the installation of an SO_2 control system are the viable options for achieving compliance with SO_2 emission regulations.

Few control methods are available for specific, potentially hazardous pollutants that may be emitted from power plants in vapor form. SO_2 scrubbing systems may be effective in controlling some of these pollutants (e.g., Cl), but additional research will be needed to develop appropriate control methods.

The disposal to fly ash resulting from the combined firing of coal and RDF may present problems, especially if a poorly maintained landfill is used as a disposal site. The changes and increases in trace element concentrations in the fly ash that result when RDF is used to supplement coal may increase leaching problems in landfills, and special disposal procedures might be required.

At St. Louis, a bottom ash that results from firing coal or coal plus refuse is sluiced from the boiler into an ash pond. In this pond, the bottom ash settles out and the liquid is discharged into a nearby river. Therefore, this operation represents two pollution control problems — bottom ash residue and liquid effluent.

Disposal of bottom ash residue will require more area when burning coal and RDF because of the large increase in the quantity of bottom ash. Increased concentrations of some pollutants that result from combined firing may increase potential leaching problems in landfills.

Tests by the Union Electric Company showed that of many parameters evaluated for the refuse ash pond effluent, only three did not meet guidelines proposed by the State of Missouri. These were BOD, dissolved oxygen (DO), and total suspended solids (TSS). Twelve other parameters, for some of which there are no guidelines, are higher in the coal plus RDF ash pond effluent than in the coal ash pond effluent. These include ammonia, boron, calcium, COD, iron, manganese, and total organic solids. It is likely that treatment facilities will be necessary in future plants to control this pollution problem.[13]

Aeration of a coal/RDF ash pond might be needed to improve BOD and DO. Flocculation techniques might also be required to meet regulations on suspended solids and possible future regulations on the content of specific materials in the effluent.[13]

b) Ames, Iowa

The performance of cyclone separators (multiclones) on the stoker boilers at Ames, Iowa, was evaluated when coal and RDF were fired in the boilers. Particulate-collector efficiency initially increased with increasing percent RDF, then decreased with additional RDF input. The efficiency of multiclones is a function of factors such as particulate concentration, gas flow rate, and particle size and density. No particulate sizing was done before the particulate collector, and the reasons for the changes in collector efficiency are not completely understood.[15]

b. RDF and Oil

For combined firing of oil and refuse, it is believed that particulate levels will greatly exceed existing standards for fossil-fuel-fired boilers. Experience with the St. Louis-Union Electric combined firing demonstration of coal and refuse indicates that gaseous emissions of CO, CO_2, NO_x, and organics will be relatively unchanged. Although chlorides, mercury vapor, and trace metals will probably increase in oil-refuse firing systems, particulate control appears to be the most difficult problem. ESPs, cyclones, and scrubbers may be used as controls.

1) ESPs

The most probable units for oil-refuse combined firing tests are those with ESP control. The efficiency of an ESP for combined firing of oil and refuse is uncertain, however, because of the significantly lower sulfur content of both the oil and the refuse. When oil is fired in the boilers, the efficiency of an ESP designed for 99% efficiency for firing of pulverized coal drops to about 50%, according to tests made by the Consolidated Edison Company, New York. This disparity is believed to be due to the low sulfur content of the fuel oil and the extremely small particle size of the particulate. Other utility companies have also reported ESP efficiencies for oil firing to be around 50 to 60%. However, for combined firing with refuse, the efficiency of an ESP is expected to increase because of the increased particulate loading was well as the increased moisture content of the flue gases. The designers of an ESP for combined oil-refuse firing in a unit in Stuttgart, West Germany believe that an ESP designed for 99% efficiency with pulverized coal will result in about 95% collection efficiency for combined firing of oil and refuse.[2]

ESP control modifications may be required for oil-refuse firing. Major requirements for precipitators for stack gases from oil as compared to coal may include reduction in velocity by about 50% or longer gas treatment path, higher operating current, increased rapping intensity, etc.

2) Cyclone Control

Generally speaking, cyclone control is more effective for larger particulate than that encountered in oil firing. However, cyclones are frequently used as precleaning devices for both ESP and high efficiency scrubbers. Tests on No. 6 residual oil-fired boilers (Franklin Station, Rochester, Minn.) using Zurn TA Mechanical Collectors resulted in 85.7 and 87% collection efficiency with and without fuel additives, respectively.[2] No special operating problems were noted. A large number of cyclone installations are reported in oil-fired utility boilers in Europe. Collection efficiency is between 85 and 92% during sootblowing, and between 70 and 90% during normal operation (finer particulate).[2] Both the European and American test reports are for low excess air operation (<20% excess air), which yields an increased fraction of coarse particulate.

3) High Efficiency Scrubber

As a result of recent EPA-sponsored tests at Boston Edison's Mystic Station Unit No. 6 and TVA's Shawnee Wet Limestone Scrubbing Test Facility, a fair amount of information is available on performance of high efficiency wet scrubbers in controlling particulate from oil firing. Reported collection efficiencies at Mystic No. 6 are: particulate, 88.5 to 90.6%; SO_x, 97.6 to 99.6%. Pressure drop across the Chemico Venturi scrubber is 24.1 cm H_2O at 125 MW load, and 16.5 cm H_2O at a reduced load of 85

TABLE 10

Pyrolysis Processes[18]

Location	Rated capacity (Mg/day)	Processing steps[a]	Products
Baltimore, Md.	907	SH, MS	Steam, ferrous, glassy aggregate
San Diego County, Calif.	181	SH, AC, MS, OS, FF	Pyrolytic oil, ferrous and nonferrous, glass
Cordele, Ga.	45	Drying[b]	Char, pyrolytic oil, and gas
Seattle, Wash.	1360	UN	Ammonia, ferrous
South Charleston, W.Va.	181	SH, MS	Gas, ferrous
Riverside, Calif.	45	UN	Gas, Electricity
Westchester County, N.Y.		UN	Gas, steam

[a]   SH, shredding; AC, air classification; MS, magnetic separation; SC, screening; OS, other mechanical separation; FF, froth flotation; UN, unknown.
[b]   When wood waste is used for pyrolysis feed, the wood chips must first be dried.

MW. Fractional efficiency data obtained in smaller scale tests at the Shawnee Test Facility appear to be reasonably consistent with these test results.[2]

Lack of precise information about the particulate size distribution and other properties from combined oil-refuse firing prevents an estimate of fractional control efficiency for different control devices at this time. There are at present no direct experimental data on control of particulates and other effluents from combined oil and MSW firing.

D. Thermochemical (Pyrolysis) Processes
1. System Description

Pyrolysis can be generally defined as thermal decomposition in an oxygen-starved environment. The process is a complex one of several simultaneously occurring chemical reactions, and it is poorly understood. Products of pyrolysis can be combustible gas, liquid, or solid; therefore, pyrolysis offers an option for various types of fuels in waste-to-energy systems.

Principal characteristics of pyrolysis processes vary, and include such factors as bed type, heating method, and pyrolysis temperatures. Bed types that have been commonly used are fixed (shaft), rotary kiln, and fluidized bed, and both direct and indirect methods of supplying heat have been employed. In general, fluidized-bed processes require direct contact with a heating medium, whereas fixed-bed systems can be heated directly or indirectly. The carriers that have been utilized for direct heating are steam, air, recycled gases, sand, and metal balls. Figure 2 presents a general schematic diagram for pyrolysis systems, and Table 10 delineates some of the pyrolysis processes.

Among all the pyrolysis systems shown in Table 10, the Occidental system in San Diego, the Torrac system in New York, the Union Carbide system in West Virginia, and the Landgard system in Baltimore are the best known. The Georgia Tech system has had problems operating in the portable mode, but one unit is operating successfully 6 days/week and 24 hr/day in the stationary mode.[19] This unit is fired with wood waste. Other fuels that have been successfully used in the Georgia Tech pyrolysis reactor include cotton gin waste, MSW and tires, MSW and sewage sludge, and MSW and paper mill sludge. The Torrax system has been utilized in Europe on a commercial scale but has not yet reached that level in the U.S. The Union Carbide Purox system is close to being commercially utilized, and the process has been successfully demon-

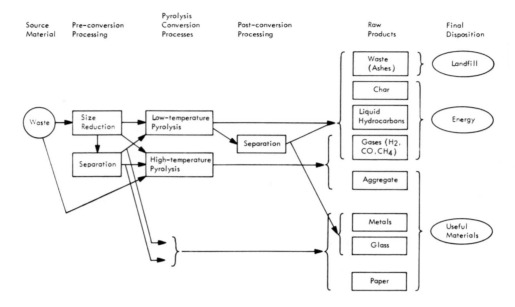

FIGURE 2.   Schematic diagram of pyrolysis of refuse.

strated on a 200 ton/day plant at Charleston, W.Va.[20] The system can use shredded MSW or shredded MSW and sludge to yield an inert slag and a fuel gas with a heating value of approximately 1.3×10^7 J/nm³. The Monsanto system is the largest of all existing pyrolysis systems (907 mg/day), but it is being plagued with severe operational problems.[21] The Occidental pyrolysis system at San Diego has successfully operated, for a few hours, producing pyrolytic oil from RDF. The system has never been operated in a continuous mode and it is presently shut down.

2. Emissions From Pyrolysis Systems

Emissions from pyrolysis systems are poorly characterized. Depending on the specific process, the major pollutant streams can be air, solid, or liquid. Air emissions can consist of particulates and gases in the form of HCl, H_2S, NO_x, and Hg. The solids can contain undesirable leachates, and wastewater from pyrolysis systems can be high in BOD, COD, alcohols, phenols, and other organic compounds.

Pyrolysis systems that require processing of waste (e.g., Purox, Occidental) generate pollutants during the processing steps. These pollutants will be characteristic of those generated in MSW processing to obtain RDF.

Pollutants generated in the pyrolysis reactor and in subsequent operations of the process include solids in the form of slag, particulate and gaseous pollutants in the gas stream, and water effluents.

In the Purox system, solids generated are slag from the reactor. The amount of slag produced is reported to be 440 lb/ton refuse.[20] An average slag analysis is shown in Table 11.[20] The slag is reported to be inert and nonleaching. The gas cleaning train consists of a scrubber and an electrostatic precipitator. Oil from the electrostatic precipitator is recycled to the pyrolysis reactor, and scrubber water goes to a liquid/solid separator before being recycled. The wastewater from the separator tank goes to a wastewater treatment facility.

Data on the wastewater pollutant concentrations are apparently not available. Union Carbide claims that their "commercial" Purox module will have the UNOX water

TABLE 11

Average Composition of Slag from Purox Reactor[20]

Constituent	%
MnO	0.3
SiO_2	59.7
CaO	10.3
Al_2O_3	10.5
TiO_2	0.6
BaO	0.2
P_2O_5	0.1
FeO	6.2
MgO	2.2
Na_2O	8.0
K_2O	1.0
CuO	0.2
Miscellaneous	0.7
Total	100.0

TABLE 12

Analyses of Typical Purox Fuel Gas[20]

Constituent	Vol %
H_2	26
CO	40
CO_2	23
CH_4	5
C_2^+	5
N_2 and A	1

Minor components: $NO_x < 1\ \mu l/\ell$

$HCl < 1\ \mu l/\ell$

H_2S: 300 to 600 $\mu l/\ell$

$COS < \mu l/\ell$

Higher heating value: 1.4×10^7 J/nm³

treatment unit available and that the pollutant potential of the treated wastewater is inconsequential.[22] However, water effluents from waste pyrolysis processes, if untreated, can pose a significant pollution problem because of the high amount of soluble organic and inorganic compounds. The water effluent from the gas scrubbing system is expected to be high in COD and BOD and is expected to contain alcohols, phenols, aldehydes, and other organic compounds. Potentially hazardous trace elements could also be present, since they are contained in RDF and sewage sludge, both of which can be used as feed materials.

The gas stream might contain particulates even after going through an electrostatic precipitator, but the particulate loading is not expected to be high. The nature of the particulate pollutants in the fuel gas is presently not documented. Table 12 presents an analysis of the typical Purox fuel gas.[20] Midwest Research Institute has recently completed a comprehensive multimedia environmental assessment of the Purox system including evaluation of the combustion of Purox gas in a steam generating boiler. The results of this program will become available in June 1978.

No major tests have been conducted on the Occidental pyrolysis system to establish its pollution potential. As with the Purox system, the liquid effluent and gas streams are probably the important ones to be tested from a pollution standpoint. Preliminary estimates indicate that SO_2 emissions are about 700 $\mu l/l$; NO_x, about 8 to 1000 $\mu l/l$; HCl, 100 $\mu l/l$; and particulates, 114 mg/nm³.[23]

The Monsanto Landgard system is also poorly characterized in terms of its pollution potential. The off gases from the pyrolysis kiln go to an afterburner, and the heat released is directed to two waste heat boilers. Waste gases from the boilers go to a wet scrubber. The scrubber has not performed satisfactorily. In addition, there have been problems involving metallic residues in the pyrolysis gas stream and excessive slagging of inerts in the solids discharge system.

The Torrax pyrolysis system and the Georgia Tech pyrolysis system have not been tested for environmental pollution either. The Torrax system is similar to the Purox system, except that air rather than oxygen is used for oxidizing the char in the bottom of the vertical reactor. A 68 mg/day Torrax demonstration system has been tested at Orchard Park, N.Y. and a 181.4 mg/day facility is in Luxembourg; but no emission test data are reported.

The Georgia Tech system now uses wood waste (sawdust and bark) as fuel and operates three shifts/day, 7 days/week. The system is a 45 mg/day demonstration plant at Cordele, Ga. and it is owned and operated by the Tech. Air Corporation. The char and pyrolytic oil produced are sold. A portion of the gas produced is used for drying the feed, and the rest is flared. Knight et al. report that an analysis of the combustion stack gases was made and that it meets all the federal standards. However, no details are provided on gas composition or the results of the analysis.[24]

3. Control Technology for Pyrolysis Systems

Control technology information on pyrolysis systems is minimal. A discussion of the Purox system follows to demonstrate what is available.

Pollutants requiring control from the Purox system are liquid effluents, air emissions, and solids in the form of slag. In addition, there will be emissions from preprocessing of MSW, which can be controlled by using techniques similar to those discussed earlier for preprocessing waste to produce RDF for combined-firing systems.

Liquid effluents from the Purox system are made up of scrubber water and the condensate water, both of which go to a quench tank for recycling and disposal. This wastewater stream is expected to have high concentrations of BOD, COD, phenols, and other organics, and it will require treatment before disposal. Union Carbide claims that their commercial Purox units will have the UNOX wastewater treatment facility available and that, therefore, this should not cause any environmental concerns.[22]

Control of air emissions from the Purox system should not pose any major difficulty, since the air stream is the product gas stream. Some trace elements may be present in the particulate, even after passing through the wet scrubber and ESP, but no data are as yet available.

The slag from the Purox system is claimed to be free of leachates and could be disposed of in landfills or as a construction material.

E. Advanced Combustion Systems

1. System Description

Since 1967, the Combustion Power Company (Menlo Park, Calif.) has been involved in developing an advanced combustion system to convert the energy in refuse to electrical power. The system uses a fluidized bed incinerator as the combustor and a gas turbine-generator to produce electrical power. At commercial scales, the system

TABLE 13

Gaseous Components in Turbine Exhaust of CPU-400 System

Gas constituent	Low-pressure test	High-pressure test
O_2	13.4%	16.1%
CO_2	5.8%	5.2%
CH_x	<30 µl/ℓ	<30 µl/ℓ
SO_2	0 µl/ℓ	2 µl/ℓ
HCl	161 µl/ℓ	63 µl/ℓ

is to be capable of converting the heating value of 544 mg/day of solid waste into 9 to 12 MW of useful electrical power while also recovering secondary materials from the waste stream. Development has progressed to a pilot-scale facility capable of converting 91 mg/day of solid waste into energy.[21]

The pilot system has two modules, one for solid waste processing and the other a power module. The waste processing module has two shredders, an air classifier, and a materials recovery system. After wastes are shredded and air classified, the light fraction is pneumatically transported to the shredded waste storage vessel. A material recovery system is used to recover steel and aluminum. A glass-rich fraction and a nonferrous-rich fraction are also separated and are available for further recovery operations.[27]

The power module consists of a vertical, cylindrical, fluidized bed combustor and its feed system, a three-stage gas cleaning system, a turbogenerator, and an automatic control system. The gas cleaning system is made up of two parallel 0.90 m cyclones, two parallel 0.80 m cyclones, and a granular filter. A four-stage, axial-flow, gas turbine is used for extracting energy from the hot gas stream to drive an air compressor and to run a 1000-kW electrical generator.[27]

2. Emissions From Advanced Systems

Processing of waste that is required to generate refuse feed to the fluidized bed combustor will result in pollutants that have been identified in an earlier section.

A high degree of particulate removal from the combustor exhaust gases is required before use in the turbine generator set. Therefore, fly ash collected upstream of the turbine can create a solid waste-disposal problem if it cannot be disposed of properly. Particulate emissions from the turbine exhaust should be of minimum concern.

The only other potential pollution problem could result from gases from the turbine exhaust. A summary of some gaseous components in the turbine exhaust is given in Table 13.

3. Control Technology for Advanced Systems

Hot combustion gases pass through a three-stage cleanup before entering the gas turbine:

1. First stage — two parallel, 0.9 m diameter cyclones
2. Second stage — two parallel, 0.8 m diameter cyclones
3. Third stage — granular filter (aluminum oxide)

The granular filter bed is continuously regenerated by slowly moving downward through a screen. It is subjected to a cleanup process and then reenters at the top of the bed. Recent information indicates that this system is currently not operating because of structural problems.[25]

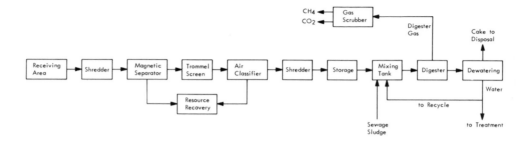

FIGURE 3.   Block diagram of the anaerobic digestion system.

Particulate (including sand from the combustion bed) collected by the three-stage separators is pneumatically conveyed to a sand bin (cyclone), which exhausts to a bag-house filter. These control options appear viable and should cause no environmental insults. Dust from the shredded waste storage bin is controlled by two small cyclones.

No water effluents are generated in the CPU-400 process except for cooling bearings.

Solids for disposal from the CPU-400 system are residue from waste shredding and subsequent recovery operations. Magnetic materials, aluminum, and glass are recovered. The residue goes to a landfill.

F. Biochemical Systems
1. System Description

Controlled anaerobic digestion is a biological process whereby organic matter decomposes in a regulated oxygen-deficient environment. Since the organic matter in municipal solid waste is predominantly cellulose, conversion of solid waste to methane by anaerobic digestion may be chemically represented as:

$$C_6H_{10}O_5 \; + \; H_2O \longrightarrow 3\,CO_2 \; + \; 3\,CH_4$$

The system for converting solid waste to methane essentially consists of feed preparation, digestion, gas treatment, and effluent disposal. Figure 3 is a conceptual flow sheet of the process.[26]

On a commercial scale, this anaerobic digestion process is being designed and developed by Waste Management, Inc., of Oak Brook, Ill., for the Department of Energy. The facility is located in Pompano Beach, Fla. The system is now ready for operation and it is scheduled for dedication ceremonies in the near future.[27] The shredding system operates at 272 mg/day but will be expanded to handle 544 to 725 mg/day.[28] The system will use mechanical mixing in the digester rather than a gas mixer, as originally proposed.

2. Emissions From Biochemical Systems

Pollutants from the anaerobic digestion process include those that result from pre-processing of solid waste, wastewater, and cake from the slurry dewatering system.

Slurry dewatering can be accomplished either by vacuum filtration or centrifugation.[29] Both processes result in filter cake solids and wastewater for disposal. Filter cake solids can be used for landfills or, preferably, they can be incinerated to generate steam. Incineration, in turn, will result in particulate pollutants and ash disposal, but techniques for particulate pollutant control from incinerators are well established and therefore should eliminate any environmental concerns. Wastewater from the slurry could be high in pollutants, and no data are presently available to characterize pollutants in this effluent stream. The Department of Energy is planning on conducting an environmental assessment of the anaerobic digestion process sometime in late 1978.[28]

The product gas from the digester (i.e., CH_4) contains CO_2 and trace quantities of H_2S. These two acid gases must be removed to upgrade the product gas to pipeline quality. Depending on the technique employed for acid gas removal, pollutants are likely to be encountered, and adequate provision should be made for their removal and/or ultimate disposal in an environmentally acceptable manner.

3. Control Technology for Biochemical Systems

Controls are required to treat wastewater from dewatering sludge. The liquid effluent can be partially recycled, and the remainder can go to a waste treatment plant for clarification and purification. If not treated, the wastewater can cause severe environmental problems.

The filter cake from the dewatering operation can either be incinerated or sent to a landfill. The latter disposal technique should be investigated further to determine if potentially hazardous bacteria or leachates are present.

Air emissions can result from upgrading digester gas to pipeline quality methane, but no information is available on these control technology aspects.

ACKNOWLEDGMENT

A portion of the work discussed in this chapter was conducted by MRI personnel under EPA Contract No. 68-02-2166. The assistance of Mr. Harry Freeman, Project Officer, is gratefully acknowledged.

REFERENCES

1. Nashville Thermal Transfer Corporation Compliance Test Report, Unit No. 3 - Incinerator, prepared by Particle Data Laboratories (PDL), Ltd., Elmhurst, Illinois, under PDL Project No. I5408, September 1976.
2. Galeski, J. B. and Schrag, M. P., Performance of Emission Control Devices on Boilers Firing Municipal Solid Waste and Oil, EPA Report No. EPA-600/2-76-209, Environmental Protection Agency, July 1976.
3. Gordon, G. E., Zoller, W. H., and Gladney, E. S., Abnormally enriched trace elements in the atmosphere, presented at the 7th Annual Conf., Trace Substances in Environmental Health, University of Missouri, Columbia, June 1973.
4. Bozeka, C. G., Nashville Incinerator Performance Tests, in Proc. Natl. Waste Processing Conf., Boston, Mass., May 1976.
5. Carotti, A. A. and Kaiser, E. R., Concentration of 20 gaseous chemical species in the flue gas of a municipal incinerator, J. Air Pollut. Control Assoc., 22(4), 1972.
6. Kaplan, L. and Franconeri, P., Determination and evaluation of stack emissions from municipal incinerators, presented at the 68th Annual Air Pollution Control Association Meeting, Boston, June 1975.
7. MacAdam, W. K. and Standrod, S. E., Jr., Design and operational considerations of a plant extracting energy from solid waste for industrial uses, presented at American Society of Mechanical Engineers Industrial Power Conf., Chicago, May 1975.
8. Chambliss, C., Paper on Nashville testing experience, presented at the Engineering Foundation Conf. on Present Status and Research Needs in Energy Recovery from Wastes, Oxford, Ohio, September 1976.

9. **Fryling, G. R., Ed.,** *Combustion Engineering,* Combustion Engineering Inc., New York, 1966.

10. **Hall, E. H., Allen, C. M., Ball, D. A., Burch, J. E., Conkle, H. N., Lawhon, W. T., Thomas, T. J., and Smithson, G. R., Jr.,** Comparison of Fossil and Wood Fuels, EPA Report No. EPA-600/2-76-056, March 1976.

11. **Fiscus, D. E., Gorman, P. G., Schrag, M. P., and Shannon, L. J.,** St. Louis Demonstration Final Report: Refuse Processing Plant Equipment, Facilities, and Environmental Evaluations, EPA Report No. EPA-600/2-77-155a, September 1977.

12. **Fiscus, D. E., Gorman, P. G., Schrag, M. P., and Shannon, L. J.,** Assessment of Bacteria and Virus Emissions at a Refuse Derived Fuel Plant and Other Waste Handling Facilities, Midwest Research Institute, EPA Contract No. 68-02-1871, Kansas City, 1977.

13. **Gorman, P. G., Shannon, L. J., Schrag, M. P., and Fiscus, D.,** St. Louis Demonstration Final Report: Power Plant Equipment Facilities and Environmental Evaluation, Vol. II, Midwest Research Institute, EPA Contract No. 68-02-1871, Kansas City, July 1976.

14. **Jackson, J. W.,** A Bioenvironmental Study of Emissions from Refuse Derived Fuel, Prof. Report No. 76M-2, Project No. AAF-520, USAF Environmental Health Laboratory, January 1976.

15. **Hall, J. L., Joensen, A. W., Shanks, H. R., and Fiscus, D. E.,** Evaluation of the Ames Solid Waste Recovery System Part III: Environmental Emissions of the Stoker Fired Steam Generators, Volume I: Results and Discussion, EPA Grant No. R803903-01-0 to the City of Ames, Iowa, ERDA Contract No. W-7405 ENG-82, 1977.

16. Utilities put the sun to work, *EPRI J.,* 3(2), 26, 1978.

17. **Golembiewski, M. A. and Ananth, K. P.,** Evaluation of fabric filter performance at Browning Ferris Industries/Raytheon Service Company Resource Recovery Plant (Draft Report), Midwest Research Institute, EPA Contract No. 68-02-2166, Kansas City, 1977.

18. **McEwen, L. B., Jr.,** Waste reduction and resource recovery activities; a nationwide survey, Environtal Protection Publication SW-142, U.S. Government Printing Office, Washington, D.C., 1977.

19. **Lohuis, D. J.,** President, Tech. Air, Chamblee, Ga., January 6, 1977, private communication.

20. **Fisher, T. F., Kasbohm, M. L., and Rivero, J. R.,** The Purox system, presented at the Natl. Waste Processing Conf., Boston, May 23 to 26, 1976.

21. **Wilson, E. M. and Freeman, H. M.,** Processing energy from wastes, *Environ. Sci. Technol.,* 10(5), 430, 1976.

22. **Moses, C.,** Union Carbide, December 3, 1976, private communication.

23. **Wilson, E. M., Leavens, J. M., Snyder, N. W., Brehany, J. J., and Whitman, R. F.,** Utilization of Wastes as Fossil Fuel Energy Substitutes, EPA Contract No. 68-02-2101 to Ralph M. Parsons Co., Draft Final Report, 1977.

24. **Knight, J. A., Bowen, M. D., and Purdy, K. R.,** Pyrolysis — a method for conversion of forestry wastes to useful fuels, presented at the Conf. on Energy and Wood Products Industry, Forest Products Research Society, Atlanta, Georgia, November 1976.

25. **Wocasek, R.,** Combustion Power Company, Menlo Park, Calif., January 20, 1977, private communication.

26. **Kispert, R. G., Sadek, S. E., and Wise, D. L.,** An evaluation of methane production from solid waste, *Res. Recovery Conserv.,* 1, 245, 1976.

27. **Walter, D.,** Department of Energy, Washington, D.C., April 18, 1978, private communication.

28. **Vardy, P.,** Waste Management, Inc., Oak Brook, Ill., January 20, 1977, private communication.

29. **Pfeffer, J. T. and Liebman, J. C.,** Energy from refuse by bioconversion, fermentation and residue disposal processes, *Res. Recovery Conserv.,* 1, 295, 1976.

INDEX

A

Acetone, A: 141
Acid drainage, A: 2, 28
Acid precipitation, A: 29
Advanced combustion system, A: 166
 emission from, A: 191
Aerobacter aerogenes, A: 141
Aerobic fermentation, A: 139—148
Aerobic process, A: 138
Aerodynamic enrichment, A: 44
Afterburner, A: 190; B: 17, 18
 type, B: 9
Agroclimatic zone, B: 183
 shift, B: 182
Air, A: 168, 176, 180; B: 122
 acid drainage, A: 28
 alkaline drainage, A: 28
 contamination by fly ash, A: 26
 energy source, impact on, A: 4, 14
 fossil fuel impact, A: 18
 geothermal system impact of, A: 84
 nuclear pollution to, A: 43, 55
 oil shale impact of, A: 78
 pollutant of, A: 2, 3, 6
 preheat, B: 122
Air classifier discharge chute, A: 180, 184
Air conditioning, A: 9
Air density separator, A: 178
Air pollution, A: 91
Air shed, A: 129
Alcohol, A: 168, 188, 189
Aldehyde, A: 189
Aldehyde emission, A: 25
Alkaline drainage, A: 28
Alpha-cellulose, A: 142
Alternate, A: 76
Altithermal, B: 183
Aluminum, A: 120, 192
 ingot, A: 112
 recovered, A: 106, 116
Ammonia, A: 168, 185
Anaerobic process, A: 138
Anthracite, see Coal
Anthropogenic emission source, A: 79
Anthropogenic energy, B: 154, 158
 consumption, B: 169
 flux density, B: 154
Anthropogenic heat, B: 166, 169
Antimony pollutant, A: 180
Aquatic life, effect of heated effluents, B: 138
Arrangement, natural, B: 125
Arsenic pollutant, A: 180
Artificial surface, B: 168
Asbestos, A: 98
Ash, A: 158, 168, 175, 182
 pond, A: 185
 quench water, A: 169, 173
Ash/sludge removal and handling, A: 168

Atlanticum, B: 183
Atmosphere, concentration of carbon, B: 152
Auger conveyor, A: 157

B

Backwash, A: 173
Bacteria, A: 184, 193
Baghouse, B: 35
Baghouse collector penetration, B: 28
Balance, B: 168
Barium pollutant, A: 180
Bark, A: 148, 173—176
Barley, A: 140
Barley straw, A: 140
Benzene, B: 18
Bernoulli equation, B: 6
Beryllium pollutant, A: 180
Biochemical system, A: 166
 control technology, A: 193
 emission from, A: 192
Biodegradable, A: 139
Biofouling, A: 103
Biological degradation, A: 138
Biomass energy, A: 10
Biosphere, A: 7
Bituminous, see Coal
Blasting, see also Noise pollution, A: 78
Blowdown, A: 58, 173
Blowout, A: 21, 31, 84
Boiler
 as afterburner, B: 17
 heat input, B: 21
 waste heat, B: 9, 17, 18
Boiler feedwater, preheat, B: 116
Boiler slag, B: 92
Boiling water reactor, A: 48
Boom town, A: 81
Boron, A: 185
Bottom ash, A: 182, B: 92
Bottom ash disposal, A: 94, 174
Brass, A: 120
Brine, A: 6
Brine, oil production, B: 105
Bromine pollutant, A: 180
Butanol, A: 141
Butylene glycol, A: 141

C

Cadmium, A: 92
 pollutant, A: 180
 sulfide, A: 91
Calciner, B: 122
Calcium, A: 185
Calefaction, B: 143
Calorific value, A: 16
Canal dredging, drainage, A: 28